A TURBULENT DECADE

A TURBULENT DECADE

The Diaries of Auberon Waugh 1976–1985

EDITED BY ANNA GALLI-PAHLAVI

William Rushton Drew the Pictures

PRIVATE EYE/ANDRÉ DEUTSCH

Published in Great Britain by Private Eye Productions Ltd,
6 Carlisle Street, London W1
In association with André Deutsch Limited,
105 Great Russell Street, London WC1

ISBN 233 97811 9

Printed in Great Britain by
Bath Press, Bath

Cover designed by James Campus
Text designed by Roger Lightfoot

INTRODUCTION

In his Introduction to the first volume of Auberon Waugh's Diaries *Four Crowded Years 1972-1976* my late father, Dr N. R. Galli, explained how he came to be editing them. He certainly never expected them to be the great commercial success they later proved, and I well remember his happiness on learning that total sales in three continents had exceeded the 1,250,000 mark. Until his tragically sudden death on New Year's Day 1985, about which so much has already been written (and so much of it ill-informed or prompted by malice rather than by any particular concern for getting to the truth) my father fully intended to edit the new volume himself. He had, in fact, made copious annotations and planned to run a critical and explanatory commentary alongside the main text.

On his death, about which quite enough has already been said, I was persuaded by my husband, Shwegar Pahlavi (who is employed, as many people know perfectly well, by the Buffo-Schneider group in Singapore) to take up the work. My husband was aware that as a member of the younger generation I would not share my father's political beliefs or social assumptions, and might easily find myself violently out of sympathy with the social and political attitudes expressed in these pages.

He encouraged me to overcome my natural distate, pointing out that many people were probably waiting for the experience of savouring again the work of a man who was once described by the late Anthony Shrimsley as 'evil' . . . I have used few of my father's notes, partly because his handwriting was always difficult and partly because, when deciphered, they seldom seemed relevant to the world he was addressing. But perhaps, in prudence, I should include the warning which Waugh himself appends from time to time to his own outpourings, that all characters in this Diary are fictitious, no resemblance is intended and everything in it is untrue.

This book is dedicated to my Husband, in some small recompense for the many months I was engaged in preparing it, often to the exclusion of himself and the accompaniment of the most appalling anger and depression. My love and apologies.

Anna Galli-Pahlavi
Singapore

1976

In the third year of Labour's reign of terror, the Prime Minister suddenly resigns for no apparent reason. The Leader of the Liberal Party continues to announce that he is not and never has been a homosexualist and suddenly resigns, too. Investigations continue into the circumstances surrounding the shooting of a dog in Somerset.

Trade Union leaders who now rule Britain welcome the great Brain Drain, and an Education Debate is launched about how best to prepare Britain for its proletarian future. Waugh joins enthusiastically in this, but is stricken with a grave illness brought about by laughing at a television programme by Jon Pilger, the left-wing thinker.

Harold Wilson's Retirement Honours List causes great merriment, but an unprecedented drought aggravated by an epidemic of rabies throughout the land produces some austere reflections. The country is bankrupt and hunger begins to bite, but the year ends happily with the wedding of Waugh's youngest brother to a young lady of grace and accomplishment.

April 16, 1976

IN THE House of Commons for the Committee stages of Robin Corbett's Sexual Offences (Amendment) Bill.

This hard-working Committee has just accepted an amendment from Mr George Cunningham which will enable a wife to bring a rape charge against her husband and send him to prison for many years.

Mr Corbett argues that marriage should not entitle the husband "to have instant sex whenever he feels like it". Mr Jack Ashley, the compassionate Labour member for Stoke-on-Trent, wisely concurs: "Instead of love, honour, and obey, a wife should in future promise to love, honour, but not obey, and I believe this to be eminently right."

Personally, I feel couples should receive a government grant for each and every time they perform the sexual act. Many British couples find it rather exhausting under present conditions. But the least the government can do is to supply us with legal forms of consent which we can keep by our beds for wives or other partners to sign as required.

Before long, I expect that those of us who really care about sexual equality and social justice will find these legal preliminaries an exciting new idea in fore-play.

April 20, 1976

IN MY first meeting with Jim Callaghan[1] since his promotion I mention that I've been invited to the private dinner party at Windsor Castle before the Queen's Birthday Ball. Noticing his look of sick rage, I explain that it is only for family and personal friends: I doubt if I shall stay for the ball itself, as I hear that all sorts of riff-raff have been asked.

I did not tell him that it was my idea that he should not be asked to the dinner party. We both agreed that it was most important he should not grow too conceited after suddenly becoming Prime Minister. That is what happened to Grocer Heath, with disastrous results for everybody.

She did not accept my alternative suggestion, that Callaghan should be asked to a separate party in the butler's pantry, where he would be given tea and sausage rolls. This might have done wonders for his image with the Labour voters, but she was frightened of upsetting her butler.

April 21, 1976

WE ARE both seriously worried about Princess Margaret.[2] Perhaps I was wrong to joke about her. The main problem appears to be that after so much discouragement of personal initiative in this country, after the attrition of incentives, comprehensive schooling etc., there may be no men left with enough heart for the job.

I suggest placing an advertisement in the Personal Columns of *Private Eye*, but the Queen feels this might cheapen the monarchy. An advertisement in any other publication would plainly be out of the question.

Then I have a brainwave. What about asking the Victoria and George Cross Association to Windsor? Surely, among their number we can find an unattached male who would not flinch from what has been described as the most gruelling job in Britain?

April 22, 1976

PETER PARKER'S appointment as Chairman of British Rail fills me with strange, unholy joy. He is quite easily the silliest man in Britain. He never opens his mouth unless it is to say something embarrassing, pseudish or fatuously maladroit. His collected wit and wisdom would fill 20 bound volumes of Pseuds Corner. The fact that he can earn £60,000 a year in British industry says all there needs to be said about British industry. When I have finished my book about Cyril Connolly,[3] I think I will write one about this man.

1 Just appointed Labour Prime Minister, to succeed Harold Wilson.
2 It had been announced that Princess Margaret was finding her single state oppressive.
3 This book remains unpublished September 1985.

May 2, 1976

TO BRISTOL, where all the leading citizens have paid £6 a head to hear me launch the Bristol Gnomefam Goldenballs Appeal[1] at a banquet in the Grand Hotel. Lord Chalfont,[2] who is chairman of the event, tells quite a funny story about his days as a Junior Minister in the Foreign Office under the late Michael Stewart[3] of evil memory.

It appears that he was called upon to attend a very grand dinner party at the British embassy in (I think) Prague. All the gentlemen wore white ties and decorations, all the ladies beautiful long dresses with tiaras and jewelled stomachers. The speeches were endless, made all the more unendurable by the fact that Chalfont had spotted a lady of peerless beauty standing alone in a long red dress by the door.

At last the orchestra struck up a gay tune and the besotted Chalfont staggered across to ask the lady if she would join him in a waltz.

The suggestion was not well received. The lady drew herself up to her full height and said: "Lord Chalfont, I will not waltz with you for three reasons. In the first place, this is not a waltz, it is the Czech national anthem. In the second place, you are drunk. My third and greatest objection is that you have made a terrible mistake. I am the Cardinal Archbishop of Prague."

May 12, 1976

PREVENTED FROM working by the Post Office whose brilliant new service means that letters put into a post box on Saturday will still be there on Monday morning, I watch television instead.

There is a film of Leon Uris's novel *QBVII*, about the famous libel action *Dering v Uris* (1964, 2QB 669) in which the plaintiff was awarded a halfpenny damages and had to pay all the costs. Oddly enough, I remember the case well, and have just been re-reading it.

Dering was a confused and broken old man who had once served as a doctor in Auschwitz, being involved in a relatively minor way and very much against his will in some of the bestial experiments carried out there. Since the war he had dedicated himself to good works and atonement. Uris, a rich and successful novelist, accused him in an almost unreadable book called *Exodus* of "having performed 17,000 'experiments' in surgery without anaesthetic". The book sold over ten million copies internationally – about 580 copies per alleged experiment – and was translated into thirty-five languages.

Obviously, Dering was ill advised to bring such a libel action, even in England whose libel laws make it a haven for every sort of crook and pervert in public life. But Uris's

1 Goldenballs Appeal – for funds to fight innumerable libel suits brought by Sir James Goldsmith, the businessman and "entrepreneur".
2 A *Times* journalist ennobled by Harold Wilson to serve as junior Foreign Office Minister.
3 Labour Foreign Secretary during the Nigerian Civil War.

repulsive film, with its second-hand vindictiveness and nauseating sentimentality, its smug use of concentration camp film sequences to illustrate a schmucky love story must remain for all time as a terrible reminder of the dangers of gloating.

Now I expect I shall receive about 4,610 letters accusing me of anti-Semitism, genocide, etc. I don't care. If I were a Jew, I would take Leon Uris by the beard, spit him in the face and call him horse. As it is, I can only go out into the garden and shoot a cat or two.

May 17, 1976

TO A dreadful Press luncheon, where the man appointed to present me with a cheque for my services to the British Press last year turns out to be none other than the Grocer[1] himself.

Poor old Grocer. It is a sad sight to see this man with his MBE scraping free meals while Wislon with his Garter and a vast fortune stashed away looks forward to a future of prosperity and acclaim as he sues British newspapers, one by one, for anything they dare to say about him.

We should try to remember the few bright patches in what was otherwise the unredeemed squalor of Grocer's rule: the fact that he chose Betjeman rather than Stephen Spender-Penny or E.J. Thribb as Laureate; the fact that he raised the Queen's income to hitherto unprecedented heights.

But I am afraid neither the Queen nor the British public will ever forgive him for his treatment of P.G. Wodehouse on that beautiful man's 90th birthday. Grocer is a national embarrassment, doomed to spend his days handing out pathetically small cheques at gruesome luncheon parties to sneering journalists who will turn and insult him afterwards.

May 22, 1976

THE NICEST story I ever heard about Gowon[2] – and indeed the nicest story about the Queen – concerns his State Visit to London shortly before the coup which ousted him.

He was rather nervous about meeting the Queen for the first time, and apparently she was rather nervous of meeting him, having heard so many lurid stories about the Nigerian Civil War – mostly, in fact, from me. They sat rather formally side by side in the State Coach to begin with, but by the time they had reached the Mall, where I turned up to scowl at them, they were laughing like lunatics together.

It was some time before I discovered the

1 Edward Heath, a disgraced politician, presented the British Press Awards for 1976. Waugh received a commendation as Critic of the Year, for his *Evening Standard* reviews.
2 General Yakubu Gowon, head of the Nigerian Federal Government during the Nigerian Civil War 1967–70.

reason for this. Apparently, as the Coach was moving off, one of the horses gave a thunderous fart. Seeing that her guest was ill at ease, the Queen leant across and said, with her beautiful Continental manners, "I'm so sorry."

Without thinking, Gowon replied: "That's perfectly all right, Your Majesty. I thought it was one of the horses."

They sat for half a minute while the implications of this appalling *gaffe* sank in. Then both, simultaneously, collapsed.

May 25, 1976

AN ANGRY rebuke to the *Daily Mail*, shortly to be awarded the Gnome Trophy for the Best Newspaper in the World, appears in this week's *New Statesman*, shortly to disappear altogether as its staff join the *Spectator*, one by one.[1]

Mr Anthony Howard, the *Statesman*'s intelligent, educated editor, points out that in an interesting article about Mrs Thorpe, the *Daily Mail* has mistakenly referred to her as "Lady Marion", as if she were the daughter of an earl, marquis, or duke. In fact, as he points out, she came from distressingly humble origins, which may explain much of what one hears.

It is good that someone is still trying to keep up standards in areas where the Press is woefully ignorant. I am sure we will find a place for Tony on the *Spectator* – or even the *Eye* – before long. By then, I hope we will have forgotten all about this repulsive politician and his controversial wife.

June 5, 1976

THROUGHOUT THE countryside we are organising ourselves into patriotic cat-shoots to counter the greatest peril our country has faced since the Rees-Mogg Ice Age.[2]

On our first day out we bag 43 cats: 15 neutered toms; nine un-neutered toms; eight females, ten neutered females and an old tabby of indeterminate sex.

The joke behind this sport is that all the talk of the Continent swarming with rabies is a pack of lies. No doubt it is put around by the politicians to take our minds off the sterling crisis, Wislon's satirical Honours List,[3] Jeremy Thorpe's Amazing Denials, etc., etc. Nobody has caught rabies in France since 1926, whereas the last person to die of it in England was last year.

Even in countries where rabies is endemic it is very seldom indeed that anybody catches it. Far more people are likely to be killed in these cat shoots. I just wish some of our old age pensioners would learn to look slightly less like pussycats.

June 11, 1976

THE ROADS of West Somerset are jammed as never before with caravans from Birmingham and the West Midlands. Their horrible occupants only come down here to search for a place where they can go to the lavatory free. Then they return to Birmingham, boasting in their hideous flat voices about how much money they have saved.

I don't suppose many of the brutes can read, but anybody who wants a good book for the holidays is recommended to try a new publication from the Church Information Office: *The Churchyard Handbook* (CIO, £2.40).

It laments the passing of that ancient literary form, the epitaph, suggesting that many of the tombstones put up nowadays dedicated to "Mum" or "Dad" or "Ginger" would be more suitable for a dog cemetery than for the resting place of Christians.

The trouble is that people can afford tombstones nowadays who have no business to be remembered at all. Few of these repulsive creatures in caravans are Christians, I imagine, but I would happily spend

1 Waugh had recently transferred a weekly column from *New Statesman* to *Spectator*.

2 *The Times* (editor, William Rees-Mogg) had discussed the probability of an imminent Ice Age. A heatwave of historic proportions followed throughout the summer of 1976. At this time, there was a rabies scare.

3 Harold Wilson, having mysteriously resigned as Prime Minister, published a controversial Resignation Honours List including a knighthood for James Goldsmith. It was thought to have been inspired by his secretary, Mrs Williams, who became Lady Falkender.

the rest of my days composing epitaphs for them in exchange for a suitable fee:

> He had a shit on Gwennap Head,
> It cost him nothing. Now he's dead.
>
> He left a turd on Porlock Hill
> As he lies here, it lies there still.

June 16, 1976

A BLACK day for Britain, with news of another vast loan to prop up the pound. The *Sun*'s headlines for tomorrow are: "Five Billion Dollar Man: Foreign Bankers bail out Healey yet again". The *Mirror*, which decorates its front page with the flags of eight countries giving Labour this loan will read: "Big Boost for Sterling: They're Backing Britain".

The political coverage of the *Daily Mirror* is a disgrace to British journalism. As much as *Pravda*, the *Daily Mirror* is now an official organ for State misinformation. No wonder that more and more of the new generation of Britons – especially those in the important 25-35 year-old age group – are now turning to *Beano*.

June 19, 1976

THE *Sunday Times* at last produces its dreaded Thalidomide Article[1] after four years of smirking and boasting how brave it was not to print it. I nearly suffocate. Five-sixths of this incredibly boring article could be cut without losing anything of value. I find myself more than ever on the side of the Distillers Company against the money-mad thalidomide parents and their slop-mongering friends in the Press.

July 20, 1976

A GOLDEN DAY, one that I am unlikely to forget for as long as I live. Today, at lunch, I meet Mr Hugh Montgomery-Massingberd, the editor of *Burke's Peerage* and one of the few men able to talk with authority and wit about the great issues of the day.

For nearly two years I have been badgering the College of Arms, even Garter himself, for a ruling on whether Lady Falkender's two children are permitted to use the courtesy title of "honourable".[2] I was awaiting an answer on this crucial point from the previous Earl Marshal, the great Duke of Norfolk, when the shattering news of his death overtook me.

July 23, 1976

AFTER AN interminable day in court[3] I take myself to the first of the great Goldenballs Appeal events. It is a Ball in the Chelsea football ground, attended by the entire *jeunesse dorée* of the land. The young women are beautiful and lithe, golden bracelets jingling on their sun-kissed limbs as they dance to the baffling music.

Once again all the youth of England are on fire. Gentlemen of England, now abed, shall think themselves accurs'd they were not here.

For my own part, I sit completely deafened and sweating like a horse, unable even to greet two junior members of the Royal Family who slink past looking strangely furtive and out of place in this happy company. I try to think of Jesus at His crucifixion. It is all in a good cause.

1 The *Sunday Times* had been involved in endless litigation over a long article it wished to print asserting that there had been negligence by the manufacturers of Thalidomide.

2 Lady Falkender, then Mrs Marcia Williams, gave birth to two children when acting as secretary to the Prime Minister, Mr Harold Wilson. The father was Mr Walter Terry, then political editor of the *Daily Mail*. The issue of whether these children, although illegitimate, are entitled to the honorific, being born out of the body of a peeress in her own right, has never been satisfactorily resolved.

3 A plea in the High Court by Sir James Goldsmith for an injunction preventing Waugh from naming him in print was rejected by Sir John Donaldson, later Master of the Rolls.

July 28, 1976

"BRAINS OF BRITAIN QUIT IN DROVES" says the front page of the *Sunday Express*. I nearly sent them a telegram of reassurance, that I'm only away for a week.[1] But they are worried about doctors and scientists and such-like.

If the *Sunday Express* hopes to panic our rulers into doing something about it, they are making a big mistake. Union bosses would be only too delighted if nobody remained in the country who had an IQ of more than 15.

Then the handful of crafty, crooked union leaders left behind could appoint each other Lords Warden of the Cinque Ports, Keepers of the Privy Purse, Knights of the Garter – while the sottish masses gape open-mouthed at them and cheer obsequiously whenever they are told to do so. I don't care. I shall stay behind and sneer at them even if it means having to eat tinned spaghetti on toast for the rest of my life.

July 29, 1976

NO *Sunday Times* arrived in Venice yesterday. Perhaps they have decided not to publish out of respect for their dead proprietor,[2] but I fear it is more likely they've had difficulty with their production and distribution workers once again.

How long will it take newspapers to realise they can manage perfectly well without these tiresome people? A journalist of average intelligence could master the simple skills required in four hours, and with 30,000 teachers unemployed there is no excuse for keeping on these picturesque "workers" whose only function is to stop anyone else from working.

They are just another of those luxurious anachronisms which we as a nation can no longer afford. They increasingly find any form of work tedious and undignified and would be much happier on the dole, watching television programmes about themselves or punching each other at football matches.

August 4, 1976

FROM DUBLIN, I hear of a Convent of Poor Clares who are praying night and day for the defeat of Goldsmith as their contribution to the Goldenballs Fund.

This seems an excellent idea. If anybody else is too poor to contribute, he might well spend a few hours every morning and evening on his knees praying.

Durham University is to hold a Goldenballs Benefit Night which I have promised to

1 Waugh was spending a short holiday in Venice with his wife and children.
2 Lord Thomson of Fleet (1894–1976) had just died.

attend on October 22nd. There will be a Grand Subscription Debate in the Union, followed by dancing in the streets etc.

I think every university in the country should follow Durham's example, while every convent, monastery or friary looks to the Poor Clares of Dublin. It is thought that the Queen Mother may be making a gracious contribution to the Goldenballs Auction in November.[1]

August 10, 1976

LORD BRADWELL, as Uncle Tom Driberg was known in his last few months, has collapsed and died at 71. He will be sadly missed at Gnome House, where his visits often left a fragrance behind which lasted the rest of the day.

He was a man who never managed to do much harm despite being an MP for 32 years. He will probably be best remembered (at any rate until his memoirs are published) as the compiler of the excellent Tiresias crossword in *Private Eye*, which several people have managed to complete in its time.

He is thought never to have been given office in the Labour government because of his bachelor and High Church habits, but I think there may have been more to it than that. Shortly before he died, he told me he could not publish his memoirs until something or other had happened to Jenny Lee (Baroness Lee of Asheridge), widow of his intimate friend Aneurin Bevan, the fun-loving Welshman.

Although several months his senior, she appears to have survived. Perhaps we shall never see his memoirs now. It is all very sad. But I think I can remember the salient points.

August 24, 1976

DENIS HOWELL, the Minister for Sport directly responsible for Britain's miserable showing in the Olympics, is a curious choice to lead the country in its battle against the worst drought to hit the world since the arrival of the Sahara Desert in the second millennium B.C.

It is some months since I gave up studying the power-maniacs and social cripples of political life, but when I was last on the scene, D. Howell was generally considered to be quite easily the stupidest minister in the Government.

No sooner is our Denis installed than he starts giving orders to the country like some demented captain of a spaceship heading straight for the nearest spiral nebula.

> "The flowers are going to have to wilt, the cars are going to have to remain dirty. Water used for bathing is also going to have to be used for flushing toilets. . . That dripping tap you have been meaning to fix for so long must be mended within the next couple of days."

He has even set up a round-the-clock telephone answering service for worried housewives to receive his ministerial ruling on whether they can flush their lavatories or not.

Of course, this buffoon has no power to grant or refuse such permission. He has no power to make us fix our dripping taps or take our baths in the lavatory. His whole demeanour shows a breathtaking contempt for the law.

If anybody is in serious doubt about whether he has the right to flush his lavatory, his best course of action during the long Law Vacation will probably be to apply to the Vacation Judge, giving full details of everything at present contained in the lavatory bowl under discussion. The Vacation Judge's telephone number at the Temple is 01-353-2411; at his home in the country, it is Harrogate 81537.

August 25, 1976

SIR JOHN BETJEMAN's 70th birthday is a glorious moment, to be compared in its grandeur with the Diamond Jubilee of Queen Victoria's reign in 1897. No wonder the whole country seems intoxicated with joy.

The only poet writing in the English language who has a genuine passion in his soul, a true anger and a true charity, he is also one of the very few who has stayed aloof from the drivelling, doomed experiments of the Modern Movement.

1 Waugh himself contributed one of his letters from the Queen Mother, which made £350.

No wonder that all the twittering, nudging, ogling Seymour-Smiths of this world dismiss him as "silly" and "coffee-table":

"One has to be crass to be a best-selling poet in these days," lisps the pathetic Smith who is not, as you will have realised, a best-selling poet. "And Betjeman is cwass."

Oh the depths of arrogance and emotional insecurity those words betray! On the contrary, Betjeman's success reveals that there are still 100,000-odd intelligent, educated and civilised people left in this country. He also reveals that it is still (just) possible for a poet of genuine passion and sensibility to break through the elaborate mine-field of pseuds, charlatans, left-wing fanatics and assorted creeps who monopolise the serious newspapers and have virtually destroyed poetry in this country as a result.

September 3, 1976

A NEW horror to come about as a result of the water shortage has been diagnosed as Weil's Disease. A miner in Yorkshire has died from it, a canoeist and water-skier are recovering from it, and an ambulance driver in Northampton is critically unwell.

I wonder if the name derives in any way from Simone Weil, the French mystic and philosopher, whom I visited shortly before her death in Ashford, Kent during the war.

She was one of the few really admirable women of our time. Starting as a socialist revolutionary, she was disillusioned after a spell in a motor-car factory convinced her that it is machinery which dehumanises workers. In 1936 she was with an Anarchist unit near Saragossa, but as her pacifism would not allow her to fight, she became the camp cook. Badly scalded by cooking oil, she retired from the Spanish Civil War, had a mystical experience and came to the conclusion that her previous social convictions had been no more than perverted religious instinct.

In the course of her tragically brief life, she had many illnesses, nearly all brought on or aggravated by refusal to eat whatever other people in other parts of the world were denied. It was not a recipe for a long life, but if this is the disease threatening to assume epidemic proportion in Britain, we can comfort ourselves it has a certain heroic quality about it.

October 3, 1976

AFTER FOUR weeks' hovering between life and death in hospital, attended by beautiful, smiling nurses, deft, self-effacing surgeons and a Ward Sister I still dream about, I find myself back in Somerset with an enormous accumulation of letters, petitions and appeals to attend to.

The crisis resulted from my foolish and intemperate laughter at one of Pilger's programmes on television, described by the grotesque Philip Norman in the *Sunday Times* as "three hard news reports on world affairs". Something about the bottomless stupidity and deviousness of Pilger's face had me in stitches even before IBA's extraordinary announcement at the end, that the views expressed had been Mr Pilger's own.

This idea, that Pilger himself thought up all those *kindergarten* left-wing opinions and attitudes, had me in such paroxysms as might easily have been mistaken for the last stages of rabies. It was at that point that someone wisely telephoned for an ambulance.

October 15, 1976

THANK HEAVENS my health does not allow me to go to Brighton for the Tory Conference this year. The spectacle of a

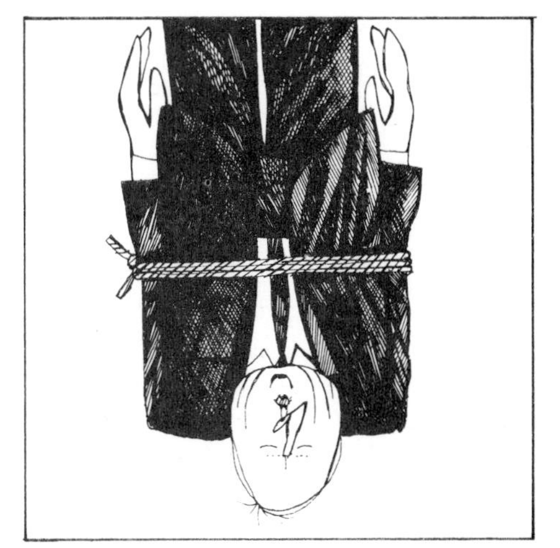

Thatcher-Heath reconciliation, wildly cheered by sobbing Conservatives, might easily have killed me.

In any civilized country, Heath would have been left hanging upside-down on a petrol pump long ago. He is the architect of nearly all our present misfortunes, with his lunatic programme of government spending and his ignominious defeat by the unions. His oily side-kick, Peter Walker, destroyed more of Britain's history in a few months by his insane redistribution of county boundaries than the Labour Party has managed in its 70 years of existence.

October 16, 1976

JUST BACK from six days' recuperation in East Africa, I learn of the Government's secret plans for bread rationing in December. Fortunately I still have 500 metric tons of wheat in my driers. It is the coming shoe shortage which will bite hardest. I suppose we will all have to get used to wearing the same pair of shoes more than once. Still, I expect it will teach the lower classes not to vote Labour next time around – if there ever is another time.

Idi Amin was the most charming and attentive of hosts. Every morning at breakfast he put out new buttonholes, sometimes a carnation, sometimes a rare orchid or a rose, and on one memorable occasion a *Magnolia Grandiflora*; he had them flown in from New Guinea. Of an evening we accompanied each other on the lute and viola, and sang *A Bird in a Gilded Cage*, *Love's Old Sweet Song*, *Wait Till The Sun Shines*, *Nelly*, and other golden oldies – he in a light tenor, I in my pleasing baritone.

The visit was only slightly spoilt by a succession of frantic telegrams from my editor in London, demanding that I ask the Field Marshal if he is really a mass murderer like Winston Churchill, Harold Wilson and so many other great leaders of the past. I refused to ask him this question, partly because I judged it a breach of the rules of hospitality.

October 19, 1976

AFTER HEARING James Callaghan call for a great national debate on education, we start one immediately. I maintain that an essential part of any English child's education is to have a working knowledge of the peerage. This should be made compulsory up to "O" Level standard and encouraged beyond.

My listeners tend to scoff at this, until I point to the terrible example of my friend Piers Paul Read, the otherwise brilliant young novelist. Read called a character in his latest novel Lord Derwent, and made him a snobbish, dissolute, incestuous would-be rapist.

Not surprisingly, the book had to be withdrawn and various publishers paid the real Lord Derwent many thousands of pounds. The Reads have disappeared from the London social scene where they once held such a glittering place, and I would not be surprised to hear that his dear wife Emily has to take in washing to make ends meet in their Yorkshire cottage.

Now Piers announces that he has joined the Labour Party. Oh dear, oh dear.

October 27, 1976

I RULED out *The Sexual Life of Jesus Christ* in the series I am planning with some friends, on the grounds that such a film would require a cast of only one and might get us into trouble with Equity.

Instead, we are working on the sexual lives of Karl Marx, Mahatma Gandhi, Queen Victoria, Sir Harold Wilson, Lord Goodman, Arianna Stassinopoulos, and many hundreds of others.

Finance is being provided by the Arts Council, The Cadbury Trust, The British Council, The Ewart-Biggs Memorial Appeal and various other philanthropic bodies. One suggestion is that we should roll them all into one glorious composite production; introducing Harold Wilson to Queen Victoria in a personal context, Stassinopoulos to Karl Marx and so on. This would be filmed in and around Wells Cathedral, in order to draw attention to the Cathedral Restoration Appeal – after Goldenballs, probably the most worthwhile cause in Britain, if not the only worthwhile one.

November 1, 1976

OF THE six novels short-listed for this year's Booker Prize, the best is Julian Rathbone's *King Fisher Lives* and the second best William Trevor's *The Children of Dynmouth*. Unfortunately, the judges include Walter Allen, the humourless old bore whose favourite novelist is C.P. Snow, and Gladys Wilson, the former *Private Eye* diarist, who will be deeply shocked by some of the dirty passages in *King Fisher*.

So the prize, unless Francis King can stop it, will probably go to David Storey for his unreadably long-winded epic of a mining village called *Saville*.

I hope that at the Booker celebration for this pompous, mediocre stuff, Storey will be aware of the ghosts of all the thousands of better British novelists who have given up writing novels until a Public Lending Right restores their livelihood.

This measure is held up at present by three evil MPs, whose names will be accursed for as long as Englishmen can read or write. Until voters get the chance to throw them out at the next election, we can only shake our fists and spit.

They are: Ian Sproat, 38, Conservative MP for Aberdeen South, a bachelor; Roger Moate, 38, Conservative MP for Faversham, married but childless; Michael English, Labour MP for Nottingham West, a bachelor of 45 who describes his recreations as "reading history and the more usual pleasures of the majority of bachelors".

Perhaps this is a reference to his bath-time, but I should be grateful for further information.

November 11, 1976

A QUIET dinner party at Wilton's for an old friend from my schooldays, Alan Whittome. Alan now works for something called the International Monetary Fund[1] and is over here to negotiate the terms of a vast new loan to keep Labour afloat and featherbed British "workers" for a little longer.

I advise strongly against doing any such thing. He seems to agree, and says that as minimum conditions he will demand an end to all further nationalisation, restoration of selective schooling, repeal of the Race Relations and Equal Opportunities Acts, devaluation of the pound to parity with the dollar and re-creation of hereditary peerages.

He rejects my suggestion that old age pensioners should be put to work, saying he doubts if they would be much good at it. This is just the sort of attitude which has brought our country to its present abject state.

November 12, 1976

ALL THIS week I have been receiving deputations from the *Observer* begging me to stop my attacks on Lorna Sage, the newspaper's half-witted novel reviewer. So long as the attacks continue, they say, they are bound to employ her, and so long as they employ her, the newspaper is doomed.

I give due consideration to this. Of course, one does not want these pleasant little chaps to lose their jobs, but we journalists cannot compromise with Truth, and so long as there is breath left in my body I shall use it to proclaim that Lorna Sage's novel reviews are an abomination.

November 17, 1976

PHILISTINES in Leeds have beaten up two artists who were planning to shoot at budgerigars with an air pistol in an attempt to extend the frontiers of art. This is the sort of thing which makes my blood boil.

Of course it is a delusion that the public can ever be educated into an appreciation of the arts. But what on earth is the Arts Council's purpose if not to protect artists from the need to ingratiate themselves with the vulgar throng?

In Somerset, we have no such difficulties. With the help of generous grants from the Somerset County Council, the Ewart-Biggs Memorial Fund etc., our budgerigar shoots are strictly private affairs. Luckily, as chief landowner in the village, I not only have *droit de seigneur* or *jus primae noctis* over the village

1 After the sterling crisis of October 1976, officials from the IMF vetted all the Labour Government's programmes.

maidens (a right seldom exercised now that their average age is 93) but have also retained full shooting rights.

This means I can order any old age pensioner I choose to bring out her budgerigars for me and my friends to shoot at. If the old dears are upset by this, I comfort them by saying: "*Ars longa, vita brevis.*" If they go on complaining, I point out how lucky they are it is only their budgerigars I have chosen to shoot.

November 22, 1976

TO THE Village Hall of Highclere in Hampshire, where Archbishop Marcel Lefebvre confirms my two older children in the Old Religion. It is a sad sight indeed to see the once mighty Catholic Church reduced in England to an ageing foreign prelate and a dozen or so strangely assorted clergymen in a draughty village hall.

The English have no tradition for fighting religious wars, unlike the French. At the time of the Reformation practically the entire hierarchy defected without a whimper. So now, they have all followed "Pope" Paul VI and his drivelling advisers into the heresies of indifferentism and modernism, denying the Papal authority of SS Pius V and X, on whose holy memory any claim to an existing authority must rely.

In church on Sunday – another draughty village hall – the preacher reminded us that the Church is bound to win through in the end, unlikely as this may now seem: one of the signs of the end of the world will be when the Jews are finally converted to the Christian religion.

When I have the good fortune to meet a Jew I often worry about the extent of my obligation to try and convert him to Christianity. Perhaps in the œcumenical spirit of the times, one can leave them in error a little longer.

November 26, 1976

IN HIGH GOOD humour all morning. An excellently written review of *Four Crowded Years: The Diaries of Auberon Waugh 1972-1976* (Deutsch/Private Eye, £2.75) has appeared in *The Times*. It is by a brilliant and beautiful man called Paul Barker:

> "Auberon Waugh is simply one of the funniest writers we have. . . the result's as refreshing as crême de menthe. . . we should all be grateful for this honesty. . . Coax someone into giving you this book for Christmas. At the price, it is no dearer than a clutch of the glossier kinds of card."

All my life I have been hoping that someone will compare me to *crême de menthe*, which is indeed the most refreshing of drinks, especially for hard afternoons of bridge. So far, *The Times* is the only newspaper which has dared review this breathtaking book.

Half way through the fourth bottle of champagne, I send a telegram to that good and worthy man Lord Shawcross, chairman of the Press Council, urging him to appoint Mr Barker Critic of the Year. It is the least a grateful nation can do.

November 30, 1976

WITH SOME misgivings I initially gave my support to proposals for a full-length statue of Clement Attlee to stand in the Lobby of the House of Commons.

From my own days as a Political Correspondent, I know how easy it is to mistake the Members' Lobby for a public lavatory. Existing statues of Churchill and Lloyd George could not but remind one of the sort of person one meets in public lavatories, especially late at night. On the various occasions when this misunderstanding arose, I always caused great offence to the Serjeant-at-Arms, then a jolly hiccuping little chap called Shandy "Gay" Gordons-Lennox.

"Gay" has since been purged, to everyone's relief, but the problem still remains. It is thought that the grim face of Attlee, who looked like a sadistic sanitary inspector, will inhibit people from opening their fly-buttons in its presence.

December 3, 1976

TODAY I LEARN by telephone that the new High Commissioner in Nigeria is to be Sir Sam Falle, a dim F.C.O. official whose recreation is swimming. Once again, my advice has been ignored.

Nigeria is one of the dozen odd countries which can ruin Britain at any moment it chooses by selling its sterling oil revenue. All the Nigerians ask is that we should send them General Gowon, a former dictator and stooge of Harold Wilson's, whom they would like to question on matters of domestic interest and then eat.

Unfortunately, Gowon is a student in this country, and it is thought improper to send him back before he has completed his studies.

However there is a man of extraordinary physical resemblance to the deposed dictator who now sits on the Opposition Front Bench in the House of Lords – the colourful "art"-dealer and self-styled poet, Lord Gowrie. By coincidence, his name is very similar to Gowon's.

I put Gowrie's name forward to Crosland[1] as the obvious choice for High Commissioner at a party of Lord Weidenfeld's. But Crosland, half paralysed by conceit and self-importance, affected not to hear me.

If we had sent this civilised but agile young African to represent us in Lagos, we might have learned whether they can really tell each other apart or whether they have the same difficulty as we do.

December 10, 1976

THE MERITS of the *New Statesman* are probably not so absolute as to call for the supreme sacrifice of actually buying it, but there is a good article in today's issue by young Martin Amis.

He is reviewing *Four Crowded Years: The Diaries of Auberon Waugh 1972–1976* (still only £2.75 and unobtainable from most booksellers) and has this to say of the Author:

> [Waugh is] prince-elect of England, grander than anyone alive, courted everywhere by the beautiful and great, while occasionally shedding his robes to mingle incognito with his subjects. . .
>
> Waugh has . . . played a part in most of the important events of our lifetimes and is even now shaping the country's destiny. . . He is also – on account of his colossal good looks – sexually ubiquitous . . . a superb lover.
>
> *The Diaries of Auberon Waugh* is by modern standards virtually free; give it, or get it for Christmas.

It is seldom you find writing of this standard in one so young. I commend Master Amis, and shall endeavour to receive his next novel more indulgently, ignoring whatever is crude or disgusting to concentrate on whatever is beautiful and true.

1 Capt. A.R. Crosland was Foreign Secretary in Callaghan's administration.

December 10, 1976

VALERIE JENKINS writes a thoughtful piece in today's *Evening Standard* about how she survives in Healey's Britain. She still manages to have meat and butter once a week, she says, but vegetables and potatoes have priced themselves beyond her reach, and for the rest of the time she makes do with fish-heads given her free by "our excellent fishmonger".

If she tells me the name of this fishmonger, I will introduce her to my lapidary in Manette Street who sells delightful pebbles of polished onyx, agate and chalcedony for holding in the mouth and sucking while the pangs of hunger last.

My family has had no meat for two months. I spend my time with a spade, searching gardens and woods around the house for any bones that dogs may have buried during 20 years of affluence, before the government of this country decided to subsidise *New Review* and suchlike projects.

For Christmas this year we are keeping aside some tins of Kit-e-Kat – very nourishing with dandelion salad. I would have preferred Kattomeat, but only the very rich can afford Kattomeat nowadays.

December 17, 1976

TO COVENTRY for Basil Spence's memorial service. The Cathedral looks suitably dingy in the sour Midlands weather, and to my delight I think I can see some mould on Graham Sutherland's garish tapestry with its unkind caricature of Spike Milligan.

There were those who complained that this ridiculous building should have been designed by a professed atheist, but I disagree. Spence was undeniably a silly man, and in many respects I think he was a bad man, but I can't believe he was an atheist. I prefer to see his entire life's work – Knightsbridge Barracks, Coventry Cathedral, the British Embassy in Rome – as a single Prayer, imploring Almighty God to send a nuclear holocaust which will knock it all down again, and put an end to our repulsive municipal civilisation. Spence may have missed the Last Curtain, but his prayer remains.

December 18, 1976

A BEAUTIFUL day for my brother Septimus's wedding in Dorchester. The bride is serene and lovely and there is an excellent sermon by Dom Philip Jebb, brother of the notorious Julian. He compares human love to a snowball which accumulates further snow as it proceeds.

Afterwards we gather in the beautiful magnolia-clad home of a Dorset farmer and writer. The guests are all distinguished for their beauty, their birth, or their artistic ability. After a luncheon of delicious food we wave off the radiant couple to their honeymoon in Cerne Abbas and repair to Taunton School for a special performance of the Messiah.

On such days as this one realises that England still survives. Beneath the notice of television or colour supplements there exists a whole world of quiet, intelligent people going about their daily lives pretty well as they have always done, untroubled by trade unionists or transistor radios or comprehensive schools. The secret is to take no interest in what people say is happening, and disbelieve everything you read in the newspapers.

December 25, 1976

A WONDERFUL surprise at Christmas luncheon. My dear, clever little wife serves roast meat, having procured it at an amazingly low price from a man she met in the bus queue. He said the beagle had fallen off the back of a lorry, poor creature.

Our four tins of Kit-e-Kat are simmered in Madeira and then flared in brandy to make a very passable crayfish sauce. The animal itself has an agreeably tangy flavour. Beagle should be marinated for 24 hours in old Burgundy with rosemary, thyme and bayleaves, then roast in a slow oven and serve with dumplings.

1977

An inconclusive year. As Labour terror continues with the imposition of a "wages policy" most public employees go on strike, including the firemen, with an impressive disregard for the safety or welfare of old people, nursing mothers and small children. Speculation continues about the reason for Mr (now Sir) Harold Wilson's resignation. A series of threatened libel actions from Mr Harold Evans, Editor of the *Sunday Times*, causes anxiety throughout many parts of the country. Observation is made of a continuing decline in the standards of the *Sunday Times*.

The Jubilee Year of Queen Elizabeth II's accession is celebrated, but nobody, not even the Queen, can pronounce it properly. She lights a bonfire to start *Private Eye*'s appeal against Evans.

The Prince of Wales continues unmarried. While Waugh spends much time abroad, England falls to pieces, but a great religious revival is noted.

January 3, 1977

IT WAS Dr Alan Watkins who first announced what many of us had long suspected, that most women in London are now either mad or under treatment with pills to prevent their madness breaking out. Men are warned not to tell their women to pull themselves together or snap out of it, as this only makes them worse. Whipping, however, sometimes produces results.

Today I receive a solicitor's letter warning of libel proceedings threatened by a woman called Ms Emma Tennant after an exceedingly kind and understanding article I wrote about her in the *Spectator*. This nonsense has got to stop. No doubt Ms Tennant is in the best of health – I was glad to see how she had put on weight at a party in the Irish Embassy last week – but this time I shall countersue.[1]

January 6, 1977

THANK HEAVEN to be British. A woman is suing Lee Marvin, the American actor, for half his wealth on the extraordinary grounds that she has been his mistress for six years. What an appalling thing if this put ideas into the heads of people.

Life is so hazardous nowadays that I can't venture to an appointment with my *masseuse* without bundles of legal documents – disclaimers, formal undertakings, *nolle prosequis* and supporting affidavits – for her to sign before she can proceed with her administrations.

January 10, 1977

THIS YEAR marks the 50th anniversary of Barbara Cartland's[2] loss of virginity. She made the Supreme Sacrifice to the late Alexander George McCorquodale in circumstances about which we can only speculate soon after her marriage in 1927. A small commemorative party is planned in the buffet bar at Sloane Square underground station later this year.

Today she writes a challenging article in the newspapers: *Why Virginity is becoming Fashionable once More:*

> "The pendulum will swing as it always does and in five to ten years time it will be fashionable to be a virgin. It is then that we will go back to high standards, noble ideals and decency."

Too late, too late. The very words are like a knell. They are, or should be, the refrain of our times, and have been adopted as the password of a Literary Movement I have founded.

The Subsequentist Movement owes its beginnings to a chance encounter between myself and the important Peruvian neo-vorticist Jrvar Puno in a Bristol tea-shop towards the end of 1965.

We now meet under conditions of great secrecy in the buffet bar at the Sloane Square underground station every Thursday evening at eight o'clock. While little Martin Amis takes notes and Paul Ableman plays his violin, some of us read each other papers on various aspects of modern life where it is now too late to do anything constructive while others discuss further ways of exposing and humiliating such people as Martin Seymour-Smith, Lorna Sage and Toni Powell.

January 12, 1977

SO MEMBERS of the National Graphical Association have suppressed today's *Times* for daring to try to suggest (quite wrongly) that the printing unions sometimes try to censor newspapers by threatening to suppress them.

How did Rees-Mogg hope to get away with it? He must know that there are whole areas of public life which can only be discussed in newspapers like *Index* which nobody reads, or *Private Eye* which nobody believes.

In fact, the NGA – many of whose members have long, rat-like tails – now process every printed word I write, often demanding that correctly spelled words be removed and illiterate phraseology substituted. The secret is to keep the brutes drunk and engage them in conversation about football.

1 Ms Tennant dropped her action.

2 Barbara Cartland, romantic novelist.

January 13, 1977

THERE IS a photograph in today's *Daily Express* of a plump, homely middle-aged woman in slacks and bedroom slippers sitting on a sofa. She is not topless or anything like that, but I find myself eyeing her appreciatively and wondering if we have not perhaps met somewhere before.

Then I look at the caption and find myself reeling back in amazement: "A relaxed Mr Heath at his home."

It says much for Jean Rook's tact – or perhaps for her shortsightedness – that she conducted the interview without apparently noticing anything different.

I suggest it is time the *Daily Express* bought Miss Rook a new pair of spectacles.

January 14, 1977

ONLY 20 days after Christmas and our guests are beginning to leave for their various employments. It has been an expensive and debilitating business keeping them drunk enough to lose when I play them at ping-pong.

The season has been marred by ugly squabbles over the Stilton cheese – between those who prefer to scoop it out and those who say that the only sane or civilised approach is to slice it like Cheddar. I have no strong feelings on the matter, but this year I've noticed a sinister dogmatism and aggressiveness on the part of the slicers. Next year we had better order two Stiltons if we are to avoid bloodshed.

Or perhaps we shall have none. God knows what the future holds at a time when the overweening truculence of the workers is met by a middle class so hideously divided.

January 26, 1977

THE APPALLING discovery that I now pay income tax at the marginal rate of 80p in the £ makes me take to my bed for a week and claim Sickness Benefit. This amounts to a paltry £27 but it is better than nothing and there is always the encouraging thought that I am making my contribution.

I resolve to do no more work. It is a great pleasure to refuse to appear on the Melvyn Barg show, to turn down three American editors and a French one in a single week.

But my most serious thoughts are about the masterpiece I have been writing for 12 months, now keenly awaited by *literati* the world over – *Cyril Connolly: The Hideous Truth*. Needless to say it will be a terrible blow to English letters if the book never appears, although a few raddled old pseuds may breathe easier.

The position is that if I send it to Lord Weidenfeld, the elegant polo-playing former friend of Princess Falkender, he will give me a second advance of £1,200, of which I keep £200 and £1,000 goes to the Government for distribution to its oafish, rat-like supporters. But if I burn *The Hideous Truth* or hide it and send Lord W. (a popular and handsome man about town) my own cheque for £1,200 to cover his earlier advance, then the oafish rat-like ones will have to *produce* £1,000 instead. Oh, I wish I could see their faces.[1]

January 29, 1977

THE ROMAN CATHOLIC Church never ceases to distress me. Now its Cardinals have given up their traditional privilege of travelling free on Italian trains, and of reserving first-class compartments for themselves.

This privilege dates from the Congress of Vienna in 1815, when politicians and priests were wiser people than they are today. They understood quite well how disagreeable it would be for private citizens to find themselves in the same carriage as a Cardinal, many of whom bear the *stigmata* and other unattractive afflictions.

But the worst development was missed by that great Non-Conformist theologian John Junor,[2] when he commented on recent proposals for the remnants of the Church of England to accept the supremacy of the Pope and kiss Pope Paul's big toe, in effigy, every Sunday.

1 Waugh sent the cheque to Weidenfeld.
2 Editor of the *Sunday Express* since 1954.

What both sides are striving for, according to their joint document, is *koinonia*. This is a new in-word, felt by the new generation of illiterate churchmen to mean some sort of clerical nose-rubbing. In fact it has a very precise meaning through large parts of classical literature (cf. Euripides *Bacchae* l. 1277; Plato *Republic* 466 C) which is sexual intercourse.

Do these nice, ignorant Church of England clergymen know what they are letting themselves in for? That after two thousand years of sexual abstinence, the mighty body of the Roman Church is about to throw itself on them and release its pent-up passions in one great paroxysm of delight?

February 4, 1977

NEWS THAT the *Sunday Times* has gone up 4p to 22p takes a great weight off my mind. Now I can cancel it forever, since the price will never come down and 4s 4½d is a ludicrous price for any newspaper, even if it is written by people of wit, refinement and good breeding like my beloved *Times*, instead of the brash, backbiting mob of union hacks one sees at the *Sunday Times*.

It means I may never again read about 'Oonter Davies's three cute little kiddies spewing and puking all over the First Class Saloon of the QE2, but one has to make these sacrifices. The plain truth is that the newspaper's political coverage is abysmal, its leaders are tripe and the books pages are a national disgrace, where semi-literate vulgarians like Larry Adler jostle for space with obscurantist charlatans like George Steiner.

Quietly, imperceptibly, the *Sunday Times* has sunk beneath the notice of intelligent, civilized Englishmen.

How sadly I remember my days on the staff. We would have top-level news conferences every morning – me, Badge, 'Oonter, Dame, Colonel Page, little Frunk Giles (whose wife's a Lady) and perhaps one or two smaller fry, like good old Mike Randall.[1] Suddenly, in the middle of an important discussion, say, on the Thalidomide Problem in Chile, Badger would interrupt:

"Dost remember, Dame, they meat and tatie pies oop Lytham way Soonday nights?"

A great sigh goes through the company. "Aye," 'Oonter starts dribbling at this point, while Frunk Giles (who went to Wellington College) cries like a baby.

February 6, 1977

NOWADAYS I often find myself brooding about the colour problem. 'Grey' Gowrie may happen to be an old friend of mine but he is also very sweet, very idealistic and genuinely enthusiastic about Modern Art. It would be

1 Ronald Hall, Hoonter Davies, Harold Evans, Colonel Bruce Page, Frank Giles, Michael Randall, all *Sunday Times* journalists.

absurd to pretend that all black men are nice – some are undoubtedly stupid, conceited and deeply boring – but I definitely think that most of them are very nice indeed.

February 11, 1977

THE *DAILY MIRROR* should be prosecuted under the Trade Descriptions Act for advertising "Marcia and Harold: The *real* story" on its hoardings.

Apart from the two participants, the real story is known only to me, to my former friend Yuri Andropov of the Soviet Department of State Security, to a man with an unpronounceable name who worked for the *Novostny* news agency, and no doubt to one or two others.

Three years ago I was visited by a member of our own Security Services, a bachelor Old Radleian, who asked me what I knew about these matters. But why should I give these degenerate bum boys a present of something which I hope will keep me in my old age? I have no doubt they would leak it all to *Gay News* or some other favoured publication.

The full story will be written by me in fictionalised form, tentatively entitled "The Lovers of Lubiayanka" as soon as I see a chink in our present tax laws, or any sign of police activity against the theft of authors' copyright by public libraries.

February 12, 1977

TO BUCKINGHAM PALACE for my weekly tea with a lady whose identity I do not propose to reveal. We laugh a lot about Marcia's theory that she was never invited to the Palace because the Queen knew she was of Royal blood.[1]

It is a little known fact that the Queen has a marvellous sense of humour, especially if one tickles the soles of her feet with an ostrich feather.

February 28, 1977

THE *EVENING STANDARD* reveals that there are 13 officials in Westminster Council with the duty of inspecting massage and sauna parlours in what is becoming the Massage Capital of the World.

This is a job I might well apply for when *Private Eye* is closed down. Massage Inspectors have the power to enter any premises where they have reason to believe that massage may be occurring, or may have recently occurred, or be about to occur.

It is important to keep standards high in this vital field. Massage and escort agencies between them now account for 27.4 per cent of all foreign earnings from tourism, according to figures released by the Central Statistics Office.

The scandals is that no government assistance is available. All state subsidy in this field has been grabbed by the resident homosexual community for its own personal pleasures.

These are English diversions, and while I am not necessarily urging an end to all buggers' subsidies, I feel it is time we started to think of our foreign guests, not to mention the resident heterosexual minority.

March 4, 1977

I HAD hoped I would be asked to be best man at Nora Beloff's wedding today, since I imagine it was I who supplied a large part of the bride's dowry. It makes me happy to think that the £3,000 I gave her in libel damages a few years ago might have helped her find such a suitable husband as Clifford Makins, the well-known journalist.

Perhaps I had better explain myself. Like Nora, I had been a political correspondent for some years, when, tantalised by the unavailability of my luscious opposite number on the *Observer* I decided to make a joke about her. At least, that was what I intended to do. As it turned out, whether from incompetence or over-excitement, I made an allegation about her personal life of such a foul and loathsome nature that even now I blush to the roots of my remaining hair when I think about it.

1 Lady Falkender had apparently been quoted to this effect.

For 56 long summers, Nora has resisted the advances of the coarser sex. Nothing will ever be the same again. Even as I write, I imagine that Clifford Makins is exploring the unimaginable delights of her body, never sweeter than when first sampled.

If I had been best man, I would have given Clifford the advice I always give bridegrooms on these occasions: *take things gently at first; there's no rush.* A new bride should be treated like a new car. Keep her steady on the straight, watch out for warning lights on the ignition and lubrication panels and when you reckon she's run in, give her all you've got.

Now I suppose I had better go and get drunk.

March 6, 1977

MY NEW YEAR'S Resolution to take a friendly interest in the *Observer*'s efforts to improve itself suffer a setback when I find myself being violently sick all over an article by Clive James. He is writing about that great philanthropist and very wonderful man Sir James Goldsmith.

Oh dear. So soon after breakfast. Peering through the remains of a fine haddock kedgeree, I see the great intellectual and very wonderful journalist Sir Clive James Goldilicks is worried that Goldsmith (sic) may have compromised his position as would-be patron of great intellectuals and very wonderful journalists by his court action against *Private Eye*'s distributors:

> "For just this reason, he might find that the intellectuals he wants to asociate with might not want to associate with him. One of the things that makes intellectuals intellectuals is that on the whole they really do put principles above expediency . . . He will build them a forum, but they will stay away. A pity, because he would have been a welcome patron."

Personally, I doubt whether Goldsmith will worry himself too much on that score. Now I must ask my poor wife to clear up the mess.

March 10, 1977

THE FIRST day of Spring brings my copy of *Journalist*, organ of the National Union of Journalists, with news of an election to the post of General Secretary. Normally, I throw it in the wastepaper basket unopened, but this time my eye is caught by the hideous faces of the candidates.

One looks more like a pig than a human being, one like a drunken stoat; one tries hard to look like Jesus blowing bubbles, another is an obvious murderer of small children.

When I first joined the NUJ 15 years ago, I was proud of my membership. I took a friendly interest in its proceedings, and often demanded strike action in the advancement of remote and unpopular causes. Now that membership has become compulsory, I regard it with shame and loathing.

Last week I heard a story that turned my passive loathing into something more militant. The union, in the hands of the tiny group of pigs, stoats, child-murderers etc who have taken control of it, has refused assistance to my friend, the great Abergavenny journalist Patrick Marnham,[1] who is faced with the possibility of a prison sentence for alleged criminal libel.

It appears that these bubble-blowing Jesus freaks are so busy with their own ideological in-fighting that they have no time to concern themselves with the Abergavenny One, as Marnham will soon be known. I would have thought that if trade unionism has a single useful function, it is to fight for members threatened with prison sentences for allegedly going about their daily business.

After some time studying the faces of the candidates I decide that the ugliest, nastiest and most obviously inane belongs to someone called Ron Knowles. He is the one I shall vote for.

March 16, 1977

AS WE approach the second anniversary of Jamie Mar's death[2] by falling from a Knightsbridge balcony, I find myself brooding more

1 Marnham had perpetrated the Goldsmith libel and was co-defendant, with Ingrams, in the criminal libel suit.

2 The 30th Earl of Mar. See *Diaries* for April 23, 1975.

and more about those early days when we kicked pigeons together around Europe.

In Siena, where Jamie and I once kicked a plump hen-bird all the way round the ancient course of the *Palio*, the Italians have now taken to guillotining their pigeons. They claim that this is to prevent them catching a disease to which pigeons are prone, but one can easily see that it is an excuse for cruelty. Like many foreigners, Italians don't know where to draw the line.

But the worst news for *aficionados* of the Kick comes from Leeds, where a television executive has been fined £25 with £60 costs for kicking his girlfriend out of bed. At the end of a two-year affair this wretched girl called Ms Jackie O'Gorman had him up for assault.

If chaps like us are no longer allowed to kick women out of our beds, we have no protection left. They can have us for rape or indecent exposure if we let them in, for assault if we turn them out. Never mind. O'Gorman is now on the secret list of Dangerous Women, a target for every red-blooded member of the Kickers' Circle. Just let her try crawling her way into my bed and find out what's waiting for her.

March 22, 1977

AN ITEM provides food for thought in my copy of today's *Socialist Worker* (most entertaining, from all good newsagents at 10p). It comes in an article by Geoff Ellen about the promised police strike, and asks: "If the police won't keep the workers down, who will?"

I don't think Geoff need worry. In Somerset we are being issued with *batons*, helmets and whistles. In the event of a police strike, the idea is that we should put the helmets on our heads and use the *batons* to thump anybody who looks as if he needs keeping down. We will use the whistles to confuse these "workers" and possibly make them urinate.

March 29, 1977

IN ST JAMES'S Street I meet a friend who tells me a nasty rumour he has heard that the dear old Duke of Portland has died at Welbeck Woodhouse.

Since the old boy must be nearly 84 it seems quite possible, but I refuse to believe it at first. This is just the sort of rumour which might be spread around by politically motivated people in order to create an atmosphere of confusion and despondency. Why has there been nothing in the Press?

April 10, 1977

JUDGE Mervyn Griffith-Jones (whom God preserve) has launched the great national debate on a question which has often exercised me: should Etonians receive lighter prison sentences or none at all for armed bank robbery and other offences?

It could be argued that in common with other public schoolboys they have already served at least a four-year sentence in advance of any offences they may choose to commit. Moreover, by paying huge fees for their education, they release other sums for the government to spend on the working classes, whether in educating them, imprisoning them or stuffing them with wonderful medicines.

In fact, many Etonians rather enjoy prison, finding it reminds them of the happiest days of their life, and this must be the decisive argument – the appalling effect that they have on the morals of other prisoners. Now Judge Griffith-Jones has made the law clear, I can't wait to go and put it into practice.

April 16, 1977

AN EXCITING invitation arrives for the 80th birthday party of my friend Douglas Woodruff, the great Catholic editor and biographer of the Tichborne Claimant, on May 8.

Guests are invited to start the celebrations with Holy Mass at 12 o'clock. This may seem a curious hour of the day to be attending Holy Mass, but I think it may prove to be *the* Party Idea for 1977.

It has two advantages. In the first place, it confirms the trend that religion is the new "in" thing for swinging party-goers. In the second place, it is a most economical entertainment for these hard times.

For my own birthday later this year, I propose to hold a Pontifical High Mass in Westminster Cathedral. This will start at 10.30 p.m. and will be followed by Terce, Vespers and Compline, re-starting with Prime, Lauds and Matins at 5 o'clock in the morning, by which time I hope most of my guests will be in a state of religious ecstasy.

April 21, 1977

IN DUBLIN to lecture the delightful undergraduates of Trinity College on the perils of socialism, I learn that a new series of writs has been received from Mr Harold Evans, the small but active editor of the *Sunday Times*.

Evans received £2,000 in an out-of-court settlement 16 months ago, although I was strongly opposed to the settlement at the time. Now he returns for a second bite at the apple, and it has been decided that there can be no question of another out-of-court settlement. The writ will be fought to the end on the point of whether it is *Private Eye*'s function to supplement the salaries of less successful Fleet Street editors by huge tax-free bonuses of this sort.

I have been appointed Director of the Dametrash Appeal which will be launched in June after we have put Goldenballs out of the way. When my Committee is formed, we hope to hold a series of concerts, poetry readings and other cultural events throughout the summer, as well as a Grand Dametrash Ball in the Royal Pavilion at Brighton.

Commemorative ashtrays, EP records and plastic effigies will be on sale, and I hope to persuade the Queen to open the Appeal by lighting a Bonfire on June 7th. Meanwhile, offers of secretarial assistance will be gratefully received.

April 28, 1977

TO LUNCH at the *Spectator* where guests include Spiro Agnew, the much-maligned former Vice President, Kingsley Amis, the humourist, and Mr Barry Humphries, the female impersonator. Also, my old friend George Hutchinson is there. What a happy occasion.

Agnew, whom I rather dreaded, turns out to be entirely charming: intelligent, funny, modest and well informed. He skilfully evades an attempt to have himself photographed in compromising circumstances with Barry Humphries disguised as Dame Edna Everage, and tells me a very funny story about his Vice Presidential trip to Thailand.

The Vice President's party was entertained to dinner by Thailand's three foot six Prime Minister, Field Marshal Thanon Kittikachorn. They were given birds' nest soup and other delicacies, and soon one of Agnew's aides, a six foot six State Department official, began to feel queasy.

When his turn came to shake hands and say goodbye at the end of the evening, the aide was violently sick all over the tiny Prime Minister. Kittikachorn behaved like a perfect

gentleman and after he had been swabbed down by Thai Secret Service men said it didn't matter in the least, he was only sad that his guest was ill.

Agnew visited the sick man in bed next day and tried to comfort him by saying that it could have been worse.

"*How* could it have been worse?" the man asked.

Agnew thought hard about this one for a long time. "Well," he said eventually. "Yesterday we had lunch with the King."

May 3, 1977

AS I never tire of pointing out, the worst problem of having the working classes in power is that like baboons in the Zoo they can't bear to be laughed at.

We saw this with Clive Jenkins's action against Paul Foot and *Socialist Worker* – it only needs a bad judge and a timid jury to make any form of humour illegal for all time. But I am afraid we shall see much more of it now that Mr Moss Evans has been elected to one of the two highest offices in the land, as General Secretary of the TGWU.

Evans's idea of press freedom is rather a curious one. He proposes not only that he and his friends [the TUC] should have a newspaper of their own, guaranteed by a National Press Finance Corporation, but that they should also have the power to correct any information about themselves in any other newspapers, and redress any "lack of balance" in reporting about their very wonderful activities.

God help us. The best thing, until we are swept away by the Evanses and Jenkinses of this world, is to keep laughing at the brutes.

May 6, 1977

GOOD NEWS for the religious revival. The clotted blood of St Januarius, the fourth-century martyr and patron saint of Naples, has liquefied again.

Even more remarkable is a discovery by doctors at King's College, Denmark Hill, London. In a project financed by the World Health Organisation, they have found that an extract from the urine of Italian nuns, called Pergonal, allows infertile women to have babies without the risk of multiple birth.

For my own part, I never doubted the miraculous property of nuns' urine. Where the nun is Portuguese, her urine may be used in place of anti-freeze in motor cars. Make friends with a German nun, and she will show you unusual ways of polishing silver.

May 10, 1977

I DO wish the Queen would learn how to pronounce the world "Jubilee". Until this shameful year, nobody put the stress on the last syllable. We expect the politicians to get it wrong, and mediamen, and ice-cream saleswomen in Blackpool, but we expect the Queen to do her homework.

May 13, 1977

I STRONGLY advised against the opening of Sandringham to the public. It is an ugly, cold and rather soulless house which won't encourage the people to work any harder. What is the point of extra overtime, if this is the ultimate reward?

Possibly the Queen suspected my advice was not entirely disinterested. It is true that her decision to open Sandringham can only increase pressure on me to open Combe Florey, which I have resisted up to now.

The question is what sort of effect an inspection of my gardens and *parterres*, drawing rooms, saloons and music rooms will have on the masses. It might elevate their minds, affording them a glimpse of the sublime which would enable them to forget, if only for a moment or two, their own crass and squalid preoccupations.

Or it might, as I fear, embitter their mean little hearts still further, poisoning them with envious hatred and rancour. In any case, I resent the assumption that they can demand entrance, as if the place was their heritage, rather than mine.

But one mustn't be upstaged. Combe Florey will be open for a one-day Dametrash Pop Festival in early July. As well as traditional Aunt Sallies and the sale of plastic effigies and chamber pots, there will be readings from successful entries to the Dametrash Poetry Competition, details to be announced later.

May 18, 1977

IN SUCH a state of excitement over the appointment of Peter Jay as ambassador to Washington that I have taken to my bed for a week.

His appointment will go down in history as the one bright thing Jim Callaghan did. Just as the bloodstained Wilson years are relieved by his knighthood of P.G. Wodehouse, even the shameful years of Grocer Heath were illuminated by the appointment of John Betjeman to be Poet Laureate before the serried ranks of pseuds and left-wing perverts ranged against him, so Callaghan has at last done something for which the civilised half of Britain will remember him kindly.

The friendship of Jay and Carter, I feel sure, will go down in history as one of the marriages of true minds which have contributed to the destiny of the world: Socrates and Plato; Hadrian and Antinous; Shakespeare and Southampton; David and Jonathan etc.

May 28, 1977

SAD NEWS indeed that my Somerset neighbour Mr William Rees-Mogg, saintly editor of *The Times*, is selling his stately home at Ston Easton and moving to an humbler heaven in the neighbourhood. Economic necessity appears to be the reason for his move.

I have been dreading that catastrophe will befall this wise and kind man ever since, in an uncharacteristic moment of hysteria, he instituted libel proceedings against Lord Gnome three years ago.

One can only hope that my mean old sod of an employer is now satisfied. William undoubtedly has the moral resources to take his adversity philosophically, but I suffer for him. Should he continue to come to the front door when calling on his neighbours, or should he go round to the back? Should he learn to address tradesmen by their Christian names?

June 8, 1977

HOW DISGUSTED and bored I am by everything to do with this Jubilee. When the Queen very kindly (as I thought) agreed to light a bonfire to start a chain of beacons all over the country launching the Dametrash Appeal, I never dreamed she would try and grab some of the publicity for herself and the tiresome Angela Rippon.

Well, the Dametrash Appeal has now been launched, but it will take a little while to get under way properly. Perhaps I should explain that its purpose is to raise funds for an extended legal battle on actions brought by the editor of the *Sunday Times*, who is called Mr Harold Evans.

As Director of the Appeal, I must sadly announce that commemorative ashtrays, statuettes and chamber pots will not be available for at least another six weeks owing to the almost unbelievable idleness of the British working class. When they arrive, the full programme of concerts, poetry readings, Miss Dametrash competitions and gala fêtes will be announced.

July 14, 1977

IN ECONE, Switzerland, for the ordination of some Christian missionaries by the saintly Archbishop Lefebvre, I learn that my friend Georgie Nabokov is far from well in his hotel at Montreux, and hasten to his bedside.

Alas, I am too late. Although he doubted the genuineness of my enthusiasm for some of his later novels, we pretended to share a passion for butterflies and often tired the sun with talking on the shores of Lac Leman as we swopped anecdotes about these delightful creatures, sipping an agreeable aperitif made from rare Alpine herbs.

In fact Georgie, or Vladimir as his foreign friends called him, was an inveterate practical joker and could scarcely tell a butterfly from a bluebottle or a grasshopper. After two excellently humorous novels – *Pnin* (1957) and *Lolita* (1958) – he wrote his supreme masterpiece of irony, *Pale Fire*, in 1962. When the American literary establishment (and a few English critics, like poor, mad Anthony Burgess) missed the joke and insisted on taking it seriously, he despaired of the human race and settled down in the land of cuckoo clocks to write gibberish.

Perhaps he derived a certain wry satisfaction from seeing all the pseuds and charlatans greet his greatest rubbish – like the preposterous novel *Ada* – as significant contributions to literature, but it was a lonely, selfish pleasure and I think I had better ask Archbishop Lefebvre to say a Mass for him.

July 22, 1977

I SUPPOSE the conviction of *Gay News* for blasphemy[1] means the end of civilisation as we have known it, but the incident does offer opportunities. One might easily launch prosecutions wherever the blasphemous Jerusalem and New English bibles are read, or wherever Montini's obscene "Feast of the People" is being celebrated.

In his summing up, Judge King-Hamilton touched only lightly on the aspect of blasphemy and seemed to regard the occasion as little more than the opportunity for a prolonged queer-bash.

I have an open mind about queer-bashing. From one point of view it seems rather cruel, although from another I can see it might be necessary on occasions. I simply don't know. But if it has to be done, it should be done properly on Wimbledon Common and not in an underhand way at the Old Bailey.

July 29, 1977

Languedoc, France[2]

DISTURBING EVIDENCE about career women reaches me from the Professor of Medicine at Cambridge University. It supports what I have frequently observed, that strain on a woman's brain is related to a change in hormone function which produces extra facial and body hair, higher sex drive, aggressiveness and a deepening voice.

Research on this subject was carried out at Addenbrooke's Hospital, Cambridge,

1 In a curious prosecution, the first for many years, *Gay News* was fined for publishing a blasphemous drawing of the Crucifixion with a poem on the same subject.

2 Waugh customarily spends the summer months on his estates in southern France, between Toulouse and Carcassonne.

where Prof. Ivor Mills has been treating hairy women for the past 14 years. He reports that many female executives in their twenties now have to shave once a day, and warns: "It is vital that women recognise their limits before it is too late."

In the part of France where I live, all the women over a certain age have moustaches and many have fine, black beards. They are thought to add dignity and even a certain grandeur to old age, when sexual anxieties are put behind.

But if a young woman in her twenties produces these signs, it is assumed that she is a witch. They may cut off her head and bury it under a heavy stone or they may shut her up in a hayloft and set light to it, but I think it fair to say that hairiness among young women is discouraged. Perhaps we have allowed the pendulum to swing too far in England.

August 4, 1977

AT LAST the *Observer* has arrived in Castelnaudary, the small market town where my dear wife buys goose fat, dried beans, pig skin and other ingredients for the *cassoulet* which is our main food in this neglected area of Southern France.

There is a curious article on MI5 investigations into the rumour I started six years ago about whether or not Sir Harold Wilson K.G. was ever a Soviet agent working under instructions from the KGB. Ever since I tipped off MI5 they have been keeping a watch on the man and burgling his various homes, but without any useful results, so far as I know. On one occasion, I intervened just in time to stop them arresting Peter Wilson, the much-loved Chairman of Sotheby's.

Sir Harold, it now appears, reacted by pretending to believe his MI5 shadows were South African agents. He persuaded Sir Charles Curran, Director-General of the BBC, to take him seriously, and in Sir Charles's presence gave these mysterious instructions to two BBC free-lancers called Penrose and Courtiour:

"Occasionally when we meet I might tell you to go to Charing Cross Road and kick a blind man sitting on the corner. That blind man may tell you something, lead you somewhere."

Obviously, Wilson is playing a very devious game in his campaign against the BBC. One can just imagine the cross-examination in Court:

Q: So why, Penrose, did you kick this blind man sitting on the corner?

A: Because I thought he might tell me something, lead me somewhere.

Q: Why did you hope he might have something to tell you, somewhere to lead you?

A: Because Sir Harold Wilson told me he might do this if I kicked him.

Judge: *Ah!* [Loud and prolonged laughter.]

But now Wilson's secret instructions have been published, no blind man can feel safe.[1]

August 6, 1977

TODAY I join the swarm of Englishmen returning to London for the Wedding of the Decade, between Old Sherburnian Nigel Dempster, 38, our greatest living Englishman, and lovely 16-year-old Lady Olga Maitland (*née* Harris), thrice-married daughter of the late Duke of Neasden.[2]

Although I have met the stunning bride on countless occasions, I never realised before that she owns the biggest pork pie factory in the western hemisphere. Possibly for this reason, I never realised how lovely she was. Damn.

Former Council refuse collection officer, mortuary attendant, *gigolo* and dental psychiatrist, Dempster looks a million pounds today in his discreetly faded Old Etonian tie. It does the heart good to see him. I have no time to warn the bride what is in store for her as I must rush back to my civic duties in the Languedoc, where I have been elected mayor of two villages, with powers of calling out the militia in cases of civil disturbance.

1 Penrose and Courtiour followed these instructions to the point of investigating allegations against Jeremy Thorpe, which resulted in *The Pencourt File* (Secker & Warburg, 1978) and Thorpe's subsequent arrest.

2 Dempster married Lady Camilla Harris (*née* Osborne), daughter of the penultimate Duke of Leeds.

August 11, 1977

Languedoc, France

THE SERMON in Church today, delivered in the thick guttural accents of the Languedoc, warns the congregation (unless I am very much mistaken) against the new sin of sperm-freezing or *semogelaio as it is called in the local patois.*

For my own part, I am greatly relieved that the fiend Montini has suppressed his fatal urge to be trendy and allowed the Vatican to come out against this disgusting new craze.

Probably it was the threat of Larry Adler's ecological time-bomb[1] which brought them to their senses.

August 15, 1977

VAST AMUSEMENT has been caused among the peasant farmers of the Lauragais by pictures of Mr Fred Mulley, Secretary of State for Defence, dozing beside the Queen at the RAF Jubilee Review. The trouble is they seem convinced he was drunk.

In vain do I explain that it is physically impossible for a British Cabinet Minister to be drunk. Overworked, possibly. Even tired and emotional. But not drunk.

The real explanation is probably that Mr Mulley was stupefied by the unaccustomed richness of the food at lunch beforehand in the Officers' Mess of RAF Finningley, near Doncaster. The incident adds weight to my argument that when Labour Defence Secretaries visit service establishments they should be invited to eat in the other ranks' canteen, for the greater happiness of all concerned.

August 19, 1977

MY ANNUAL pilgrimage to the tomb of St Thomas Aquinas in the Eglise des Jacobins, Toulouse. For luncheon we eat:

foies de canard chauds aux raisins
melon charentais
bouillabaisse (three courses)
jambon cru de pays – salade
entrecôte de bœuf sauce thymoise
fromages

At this point there is a pause, during which many of the ladies order strawberries or ices – my dear Wife chooses *profiteroles au chocolat*. But my eye is caught by a man at a neighbouring table eating pigs' trotters, so I order a couple.

This gives rise to a Great Debate about the propriety of eating pigs' trotters at such a time in the world's history. The point is put to me by a member of the decaying or "downwardly mobile" Angevin nobility who has somehow bummed her meal ticket off me on the strength of a common acquaintance.

I reply with the traditional Thomist argument that it is the consummation of a pig's existence to have its feet eaten in this way: if the good Lord did not intend us to eat pigs' trotters, He would scarcely have equipped pigs with feet in the first place, since they would fatten more easily in an immobile or sausage-like posture.

August 20, 1977

LAST NIGHT, I spent from midnight to dawn lying on my back in the Languedoc countryside staring at the sky.

This was because the *Daily Telegraph* had promised a "spectacular fireworks display" caused by meteorites streaming from a comet named Temple-Swift which has just passed near the Earth. According to a Harvard scientist quoted in the newspaper, "A person not expecting it may find it frightening."

I am determined not to be frightened and have invited a large party of local landowners, government officials and fun-loving young persons to watch the phenomenon. We watch for hours, seeing innumerable bats and a *chouette* or screech owl which frightens two young Ugandans by the side of the swimming pool. But no sign of a meteorite.

Probably it was a practical joke by the *Telegraph*'s science correspondent, Dr Adrian Berri-Berri. If so, I take my hat off to him. But if one can't believe the *Daily Telegraph* one might as well become an Existentialist.

1 Larry Adler, the left-wing mouth organist and letter-writer, announced that he had had large quantities of his sperm frozen (see *Diaries 1972–76*).

August 28, 1977

TO CHURCH in the Cathedral of Ste Cecile, Albi, built in 1282 as a massive fortress against the Cathar heretics, most of whom had already been burned at Montségur in 1244. The sermon is all about Elvis Presley – the Christ-like simplicity of his life on a diet of peanut butter and banana sandwiches with soda, the God-given beauty of his voice, his compassion for teenagers etc.

There are no relics of the Saint available – the priest has not been able to secure even a finger for us to worship – but the sarcophagus of a 16th-century bishop has been emptied and rigged up on a catafalque in the Choir. The priest instructs us to wiggle our pelvises as we file past, singing the Nunc Dimittis.

Outside the Palais de la Berbie I see an old peasant woman, prostrate with grief, being carried by her weeping sisters and thrown into the River Tarn, which meanders on its placid way towards Gaillac, birthplace of the little-known 18th-century lyric poet Gérard Foucaud d'Alzon.

September 4, 1977

OUR LAST day in France finds us in Burgundy. Tomorrow I must be in London for the Open Day at Lambeth Crematorium – a once in a lifetime opportunity. But first there is luncheon.

Since writing about this subject from Toulouse, I have been persecuted by progressive theologians claiming that I misinterpreted St Thomas Aquinas's teaching on pigs' trotters. This seems unlikely, but I suppose I had better answer these troublesome people on their own terms.

The greatest discovery of progressive theology has been that the Mass – or Eucharist – is not a Sacrifice as we were once led to believe; it is a Meal. The only way we can reconcile this disturbing idea with traditional doctrine is if we now regard Luncheon as a Sacrifice: in some mysterious way, the Christian sanctifies whatever he eats.

Certainly this new dispensation extends to Dinner and even, for those who take their religion very seriously, to Breakfast and High Tea or Television Snacks. Whether it extends to food eaten by Muslims and Jews must be decided by the next Vatican Council, but they wouldn't eat pigs' trotters in any case. By eating them on that occasion, I elevated them to a higher form of utility or divine purpose. This correspondence is now closed.

Our last Sacrifice in France is dictated also by the need to spend remaining French francs to prevent the British Government from seizing them. This is what we eat:

Une douzaine d'escargots de Bourgogne

—o—

salade — foie d'oie gras truffé

—o—

cuisses de grenouilles — truites à la crème

—o—

civet de sanglier Bourgignon

—o—

fromages — fruits — pâtisserie

—o—

AMEN

September 6, 1977

THE CULTURE SHOCK of finding oneself once again among hungry, dirty, dishonest Englishmen is immense. Many of the beggars in the streets have open, gangrenous wounds from the recent fighting; hospitals have been closed by their "ancillary workers"; many newspapers are failing to appear or appear in garbled, incomprehensible form with the new, pupil-oriented spelling. In Blackpool the Trade Union Congress deliberates its next programme of theft, chaos and destruction in the name of Workers' Power.

But the Tooting grounds of Lambeth Borough Crematorium prove an island of tranquillity. Here, for the very reasonable fee of £13.50, dead or allegedly dead workers are taken, injected with formalin in case a spark of life survives, and then burnt in a gas oven.

Then their bones, teeth etc are put into a "cremulator", or bone-crushing machine, the residue is scattered tastefully over municipal lawns and their names are recorded by hand in a "Book of Remembrance".

Where everything in Britain is breaking down, and nobody does anything properly, this operation is marked by the efficiency and quiet enthusiasm of its staff. I think I will give up everything and come to work at Lambeth Crematorium. If they have no other

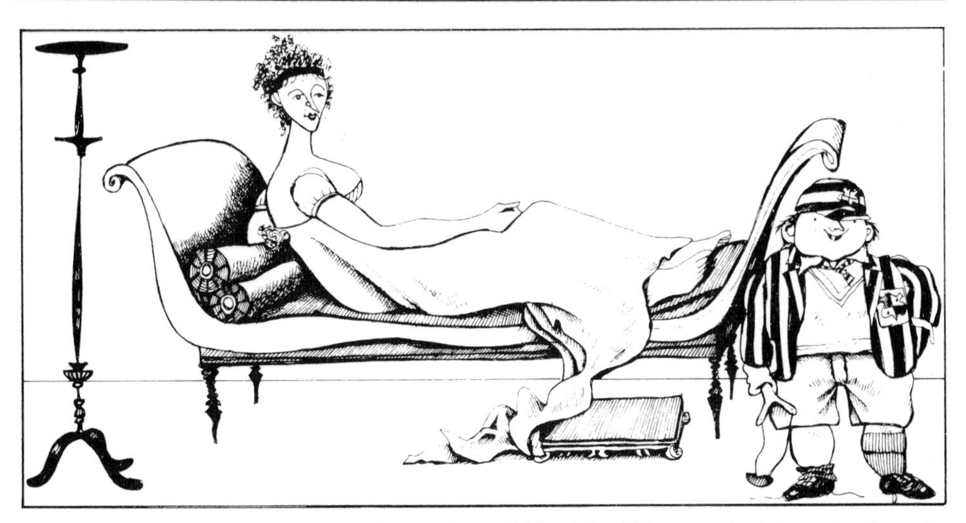

job available for me, I will set myself the task of learning all the names in the "Book of Remembrance" by heart. In that way, at least someone will remember them.

September 16, 1977

I HAVE never been much drawn towards paedophilia although I suppose one never knows what new horizons may present themselves as one grows older, and one should try to keep an open mind.

But the case of Mrs Sandra Mayhew, the teacher accused of intercourse with an 11-year-old boy, is very puzzling. I never doubted her innocence, for the simple reason that 11-year-old boys, in my experience, are seldom up to it. The whole prosecution results from a fatal and idiotic trait of the British working classes that they believe what their children tell them. As prosecuting counsel, Mr Richard Carr, said:

"If she has been made the subject of a vile accusation, a wicked, immoral and dishonest accusation by a young boy, then that is equally important to be made public."

But while Mrs Mayhew's name has been dragged through the mud, the boy's identity and the identities of his moronic parents have been kept secret. Even if Mrs Mayhew had been found guilty, the boy should be ostracised by polite society and hounded out of his clubs. Women who kiss and tell can be forgiven, eventually, on the grounds that they have nothing else to talk about, but men have no such excuse.

September 21, 1977

AFTER FIVE days of struggle I give up the attempt to review J.R.R. Tolkien's *The Silmarillion* for the *Evening Standard*. I, who have ploughed through much of Alain Robbe-Grillet and most of Proust, who have read all the bye-laws governing attendance at Taunton swimming-baths and can recite by heart the addresses of all the Special Clinics in the Greater London area, I must admit defeat. The book is completely unreadable.

Allen & Unwin, the publishers, have printed 600,000 copies of it. If they sell 10,000 I think I shall give up reviewing. It can only mean that books are bought and sold in bulk without any regard to the contents, only to the brand-name.[1]

I find it hard to believe that J.R.R. Tolkien ever wrote this rubbish. He will be remembered for the important discovery that "Wales" is the plural of "Waugh".

He did not share my indignation that this honourable name should have been requisitioned by a brutal, shifty race who have already given our language the verb "to welsh" as well as such ill-favoured things as the Welsh rarebit, Jack Jones, Moss Evans, and half the poisonous dwarves of the Labour Party.

1 The book sold over 1,200,000 copies, but Waugh has yet to give up reviewing.

September 25, 1977

I SPEND the morning in front of the mirror, rehearsing answers to questions and short, impromptu speeches for the forthcoming libel action *Harold Evans vs Pressdram & Others*.

Evans, it may be remembered, is the small but much-loved editor of a newspaper called the *Sunday Times*. Very much against my advice, he received a payment from *Private Eye* three years ago in consideration of a regrettable inaccuracy. Now, as I warned he would, he is coming back for a second bite at the apple:

> "And that is called paying the
> Dame-geld
> But we've proved it again and again.
> That if once you have paid him the
> Dame-geld
> You never get rid of the Dame."
> (*Kipling*)

September 30, 1977

AN OLD friend telephones me with some information she thinks I ought to know about Sir Eric Miller, Sir Harold Wilson and MI5. It is a rumour I started myself five days ago in the French Club, and now it comes back virtually unchanged but with several juicy bits left out. Plainly it is time for me to go back to the country.

October 1, 1977

Brighton

A TERRIBLE stench of rotting corpses hangs over the Labour Party Conference at Brighton as the national strike of undertakers and embalmers moves into its second week. Delegates pretend not to notice as they pick their way over dead bodies lying on the pavement and ogle each other with rheumy, yellow eyes.

Sometimes, in quiet moments, I wonder what I am doing at this ghastly event. Perhaps it is penance for my agreeable life at other times of the year. Perhaps I need to be reassured that such dim, ugly, spiteful people really exist. Whatever brings me here, it certainly isn't sex.

At a party given by Mr Peter Parker, Chairman of British Railways, this evening, men outnumber women by about thirty to one. It would not matter so much if the women were reasonably typical of their sex, but they are all either hunch-backed or hairy-legged or obviously lesbian.

This is the miserable truth behind all the lurid stories the delegates will tell when they get home to their sniffing, squinny-eyed wives.

October 2, 1977

AT THE annual Richard Marsh Memorial Dinner given by William Camp for all that is brightest and best in Fleet Street I meet Parker again and remonstrate with him about the terrible ugliness of the women at his party.

Parker says he's pleased I gate-crashed it but he is still smarting from my description of him last year as the silliest man in Britain. He seems a friendly, talkative soul, but when challenged to name anyone sillier, he demurs.

October 3, 1977

TODAY I must address myself seriously to the O'Driscoll Trophy for Overtired Journalist of the Year. Peter Seend of the *Daily Mirror* has allowed himself to be lifted from the floor of the gentlemen's lavatory of the Metropole Hotel by the Prime Minister, and I plainly have ground to catch up.

In the morning I drink seventeen bottles of Guinness, two of port, one and a half of champagne and half a bottle of whisky. I am not sure what happened in the afternoon.

October 4, 1977

I WAKE UP to find myself in the bedroom of a strange but delightful young lady who does not seem to know my name. I wish I could tell her. The Labour Party Conference has decided by six million votes to abolish the House of Lords, and I must get out of this madhouse, even if it means resigning from the O'Driscoll Trophy.

If they really intend to abolish the Lords, many of us will have nothing left to live for. What is the point of making pots of money, robbing widows and orphans, grinding the faces of the poor and making children cry on the way home from school if there is to be no peerage at the end of the struggle?

October 14, 1977

NEWS FROM London plunges me into a melancholy. Somebody called Mr Bernard Brook-Partridge, law-and-order supremo of the GLC, proposes to close down London's massage parlours by raising their licence fees from £2.10 to £10,000.

Does anybody know anything about this repulsive man? The only reason he gives for his decision, which will destroy London's only remaining tourist attraction at a stroke, is that he thinks many of these establishments are owned by vicious Maltese. He must realise he will simply drive the vicious Maltese to selling popcorn and soft drinks, which destroy our morals with our teeth by sending children and impressionable young people to dental parlours where they will find copies of *Punch* magazine prominently displayed.

I defy Mr Brook-Partridge to produce anything in Christian or Judaic law which is against massage. Ignorant, timid people assume that these establishments are knocking shops, but they simply aren't. I challenge Mr Brook-Partridge to accompany me to one, where he will find himself received with exquisite tenderness and consideration by some of the finest flowers of the mysterious East.

October 20, 1977

THANK HEAVEN I was not at the Church of the Apostles, Manchester, to see Holy Communion celebrated by attractive American priestess Rev. Alison Palmer, 42-32-44.

If I had been present I might easily have lost all control and committed some outrage like exposing myself over the altar rail. Attractive women should be more aware of the effect they can have on susceptible males. If poor old Tom Driberg had been there, he would almost certainly have choked on the Host.

A group of Tom's friends are getting together for a Tom Driberg Memorial Lavatory, or "cottage", as he called it, to be built on the Westminster Embankment – scene of so many romantic encounters.

Designed as a Puseyite oratory, it will provide a convenient meeting place for MPs to sharpen their social awareness and generally to practise compassion with like-minded tramps and derelicts of the neighbourhood. It will be equipped with copies of the Bible and Karl Marx and a Division Bell in every cubicle.

October 28, 1977

CORPORAL Reginald Booth is said to have seduced innumerable women by writing passionate letters to them. I wonder what his secret is. I constantly write passionate letters to strange women, but nothing ever comes of it.

Now he is accused of obtaining sex by deception – allegedly pretending he would marry the poor idiots. How many of us knew this was a crime? There used to be something called breach of promise but that was abolished years ago and it seems to me they must have invented a new offence especially for him.

Poor Corporal Booth is a victim of envy from two groups in our society – those who are no good at sex, and those who are no good at writing. Only a tiny minority is any good at either, I suspect, and this explains repressive laws against writers and sexual enthusiasts throughout the ages. It also explains the almost universal loathing for that degenerate dwarf Martin Amis, who seems to have scored more beautiful women in the past four years that I have ever had first courses.

November 5, 1977

TO NEW Scotland Yard where Jeremy Thorpe[1] has called a press conference to discuss various allegations that have been made about his sex life. I have many interesting new allegations to make, but they throw me out at the door.

When all the weeping toadies are assembled, only one of them dares ask him whether he has ever done it. Mr Keith Graves, of BBC-TV, who is hereby given the Gnome Award for News Reporter of the Year, has been vilified by every prig and pharisee in Fleet Street for asking the only worthwhile question.

Poor Jeremy. He is his own worst enemy, but with friends like these he really has no need of himself. The only remaining mystery is why the Liberal Party policy committee decided to murder Scott rather than Jeremy.

November 11, 1977

WRITTEN DURING a power cut, in the dark and biting cold. Many of the children on the estate have been found frozen stiff in their beds. The old age pensioners in my attics are dying like flies, but all the hospitals in the neighbourhood are closed – some by the Ennals Terror, others by the floorwipers union protesting about student conditions in Chile – and there is nothing to be done.

Actually that is not strictly true. We have had no power cuts at Combe Florey yet; when we do, I have two emergency generators in reserve. The local hospitals are still open, and in fact I had a general clear out of OAPs from all my attics two years ago.

But it seems to me that it is the solemn duty of everybody employed in the communications industry at the present time to promote a hatred and dread of all the brutal, moronic union leaders who, in the name of the working class, are leading the country into destitution and slavery. At such moments in history, I think a little exaggeration is justified.

November 17, 1977

TODAY is my birthday. A well-preserved 56,[2] I sit and watch the Miss World competition with a terrible question at the back of my mind: am I losing my libido?

It seems to me I have never seen so many ugly young women together since watching a hockey match at Somerville College, Oxford, nearly 40 years ago. They are all half-witted too.

For the first time I miss my old friend Charlie Vass, popular, smooth-bottomed executive of Times Newspapers, who came within a whisper of winning six years ago as Miss Costa Rica. Perhaps he thinks he is too old, but I feel sure he would have won this year. He might have been able to tell me where they found so many ugly women. Perhaps in the Battered Wives Refuge of Chiswick.

November 18, 1977

I AM GETTING fed up with seeing the great fat grinning face of Elizabeth Bagaya, self-styled "Princess of Toro", as she emerges from the High Court after yet another libel settlement. By my reckoning, it is the seventh time this large lady from the far-flung lakes and savannahs of Uganda has been rewarded for an imputation on her chastity. Her receipts to date must exceed £40,000.

Quite a price to put on one piece of tail. Since the Slander of Women Act, 1891, it is a very dangerous thing to impute unchastity in a woman, even verbally. Yet on almost every page of every newspaper I open I see such imputations freely made about autochthonous Englishwomen.

It is mainly foreigners who are getting wise to the absurdity of our English libel law. Beyond any question of doubt this Bagaya is as chaste as the lovely Nora Beloff, and a virgin to boot. For my own part, I do not care much either way, having no urgent desire to discuss the affairs of her native country with her.

1 Thorpe, leader of the Liberals, was later accused and acquitted of conspiracy to murder a male model, Norman Scott.

2 Waugh is often confused about his age. He was born on November 17, 1939.

November 21, 1977

THE QUEEN is alarmed by Prince Charles's illness, as well she might be. I point to a photograph of His Royal Highness kissing an Australian lady called Sylvia Cresnar on the lips. His eyes are tight shut.

In England, this is a sign of good manners, but in many overseas countries it is advisable to look hard at anything before you eat it. I have suffered agonies of indigestion in foreign parts from neglecting this simple rule.

November 23, 1977

FOOD MANUFACTURERS are sternly taken to task in the marketing journal *Mintel* for failing to provide special food for people with false teeth. Over 60% of adult citizens in Britain now have false teeth and the proportion is growing, but while scientists hope to be able to produce babies born with a complete set of false teeth before very long, it will all be in vain if there is nothing for them to eat.

A particular need, according to the market survey, is for an apple which old people can eat without losing their dentures; something which is soft, squashy, and round, excitingly flavoured in the various long forgotten aromas of toothpaste.

It would be easy – far too easy – to blame God for this oversight. Before Old Age Pensioners set up a picket outside St James's, Spanish Place, I think they should apply to Sir James Goldsmith, the visionary *entrepreneur*, national saviour and purveyor of disgusting food to the lower classes.

November 24, 1977

PERHAPS IT IS too late to do anything about growing squashy apples for old people. It appears they are all going to be burned to death as a result of the firemen's strike. Old people and children will be the first to burn according to the Home Secretary, whose name I failed to catch.

This may explain why the strike is so popular. At times it has seemed that I was the only person who realised how much the English hate children and old people, but nobody can doubt it now as they see striking firemen showered with gifts of money, pheasants and warm winter clothing.

My only dread is in case any of our beloved workers are burned. They are especially vulnerable living in their picturesque high-rise tower blocks where the lifts are out of order and the stairways choked with debris as the result of other strikes.

Even if it is true, as Wedgwood Benn argues, that the "workers" are now an expensive anachronism this doesn't stop us from being sentimental about them. I particularly like the way they talk with cigarettes in their mouths.

November 25, 1977

ANOTHER STRIKE which should have all our support is that of the Inland Revenue Staff Federation. Tax collectors really have had a rough deal. Their average take-home pay is £9.22p a week and few have had any food since the Easter before last. Their children's socks have so many holes in them that they are ashamed to hang them up for Father Christmas.

On top of this they and their wives are constantly reviled, sometimes assaulted, by members of the self-employed. Their children are beaten up at school and horrible, unspeakable things are left in their front gardens.

If anybody deserves to be treated as a special case, they do. On the other hand, of course, the Government must stand firm. It will be a long, bitter struggle, and I can see no possible end to it.

November 28, 1977

UP TO LONDON to buy one of these new Mormon chastity vests which are said to have such a strange effect on members of the opposite sex. On the platform of Paddington Station I am horrified to meet the wobbly, sun-tanned figure of Edward Heath at the start of his Flying Grocer tour of the country.[1]

Grocer's train should be seen as a literary equivalent of the sealed compartment which the Germans used to send Lenin, like a poisonous bacillus, into Russia during the Great War. From it, the illiterate rubbish Grocer calls his "books" will be released to poison the minds of millions in all our major cities, convincing them that literature is indistinguishable from groceries, something to be wrapped in polythene and put in the freezer.

Friends of literature must organise themselves to mock and humiliate anyone found with this absurd book in his possession. We should roll our eyes, let our tongues hang out and waddle with flapping motions of the arms around the drawing rooms of anyone displaying it.

November 30, 1977

ANTHONY BURGESS, whom I have always revered as the grandfather of British Punk, turns on his own creation in a bitter attack published in *Psychology Today*:

"British youth. . . needs a good kick up the pants and a bit of solid education. It needs also to be reminded, occasionally, how very, very dull its mouthings, shrieks and unmuscular spasms are."

But this is exactly the purpose of the Punk Movement. Has he forgotten the ideals which inspired us when we planned it together, sipping Maltese brandy in the brumous, olive-scented Mediterranean dusk of Valetta – or possibly it was Nicosia and we sipped *ouzo*, or winking beakers of *grappa* in Rome, I forget the details?

The idea was to encourage the deprived, half-witted youth of our poor country to come out of its closet and expose itself as it really is. This would serve as a reminder of our own cultural and intellectual superiority while allowing people like ourselves, of philosophical or contemplative turn of mind, to amuse ourselves by spitting at them. But I fear Burgess is in his dotage, his spittle has run dry, and I am pleased to take up the responsibilities he has abandoned.

December 11, 1977

SIR CHARLES Petrie, the historian, has died at the age of 82. I met him several times but never liked him much. Although it is always a sad thing for anyone to die (unless he is a religious maniac) I can't claim to be much surprised by the news.

Twelve or thirteen years ago – I forget which – Petrie chose to give evidence for his old crony Lord Russell of Liverpool in a libel action which Russell was bringing against *Private Eye* – the famous *Liver of Cesspool* case. As soon as I saw Petrie shuffle into the witness box I knew he was doomed. The Curse of Gnome has a long arm.

December 17, 1977

ANTHONY HOWARD has resigned from editorship of the *New Statesman* as I urged him to do long ago. There is nothing much wrong with the magazine, it is the readership which is so frightful. Tony deserves better.

Now I must write my traditional letter applying for the editorship of the *New Statesman*. I think it is my fourth application. They say I should address it to Dr Richard Hoggart, the new Chairman, who is a nasty, boring, lower-class prig without a glimmer of humour, but I think I shall write to Lord Jock-strap[2] for old times' sake.

1 Heath covered the country in a special train, signing books about sailing and music.

2 Sir Jock Campbell, later Lord Campbell of Eskan, a former Chairman of the *New Statesman*.

December 20, 1977

BACK IN Somerset, I listlessly turn on the television to watch a play called *Charades* by our shocking, abrasive new playwright Lady Magnesia Freelove.

It is about life in a Scottish castle. The laird's wife, Lady Caroline, is discovered in bed with the gardener, Hector, by her maid, Kirstie, who is secretly having it off with the laird, Sir James. The thrilling *dénouement*, which I do not altogether follow, is that Lady Caroline has to wait on her maid, Kirstie, when their roles are ingeniously reversed.

I am not quite sure I understand what Lady Magnesia is saying here, but understanding has never been essential in appreciation of the arts. For the first time, I hear a clear, honest voice describing contemporary Britain as it really is.

December 25, 1977

A WONDERFUL Christmas with no Sunday newspapers and the R.S.P.C.A. on strike for more pay. I lose no time in settling a number of old scores with various members of the animal kingdom, singing little carols of joy at the absence of Sunday newspapers.

This surely is the great Christmas message of today, that Sunday newspapers are a nonsense and an abomination. They are a paradigm of all that is futile and worthless in our society. We would do so much better to read the intelligent weeklies, like *Spectator* and *New Statesman*, or specialist publications like *Books and Bookmen*, *Christian Order*, *Socialist Worker*, *Gay News* etc.

The other Christmas message is one of hope. From my property in southern France, I hear that the Research Institute of Toulouse University has given itself over to the quest for a method of destroying the part of the goose's brain which tells it when it has had enough to eat.

If they succeed, there will be enough *foie gras* for everyone, even the relatively poor, to gorge themselves on at Christmas-time.

December 31, 1977

RUMOURS WHICH continue to reach me that there is something terribly wrong with Master Peter Phillips can only be strengthened by the Queen's decision to have him improperly christened in a drawing room at Buckingham Palace instead of publicly in Church, as his religion demands.

Perhaps the Queen feels she can no longer trust the Press to be tactful about such matters. When I think of how cringingly tactful we all were about her poor Uncle Henry (or "Bonkers" as he was affectionately known in the family)[1] I am deeply hurt.

First reports that the lad was born with five legs can surely be discounted. It is quite normal for the male organ to appear disproportionately large in new-born infants. The truth may be much more simple, that the Princess Anne Dame Anne Phillips has given birth to a centaur.

If so, it is hard to decide whether one should congratulate her on her good fortune

or commiserate with her. It happens in the best families. The best thing is surely to enter him for Eton and for Fred Winter's stable at Lambourn and decide which is more suitable nearer the time.

1 Henry, Duke of Gloucester, suffered from a distressing illness for many years before his death in 1974.

1978

Distressing frenzies of anti-Semitism are inspired by a television serial called *Holocaust*. A warrant is issued for the arrest of Lord Kagan, a friend of Sir Harold Wilson, and Jeremy Thorpe is arrested on charges of conspiracy and incitement to murder one Norman Scott, a male model. But Sir Harold Wilson remains untouched by any breath of scandal, and free to come or go as he chooses.

Callaghan's Government adds hugely to the privileges already enjoyed by trade unionists. A new Pope speaks out against sexual impropriety, but the homosexual revolution continues and Waugh observes that many of his friends are changing sex. A mysterious singer called Kate Bush occupies much of his attention; he is also worried about his friend Nigel Dempster's married life.

The *New Statesman* collapses, taken over by barbarians and bores, but the year ends happily with the closure of the *Sunday Times* during the magistrates' court hearing in Minehead at which Mr Thorpe is committed for trial in the Old Bailey.

January 4, 1978

SIR CHARLES CHAPLIN, the Communist multi-millionaire and sex maniac, has died at 88. Perhaps I am mad, but I never found him remotely funny, and I suspect he had no sense of humour whatever.

His career, even down to the Wilson knighthood, demonstrates that humourless people will accept anything as funny if they are told it is.

What little skill he once possessed in throwing custard pies and knocking people about with brooms soon vanished when he began to believe he was a great political thinker.

Still, his sexual antics were endearing, and it is for those that he should be remembered.

January 17, 1978

A SENSIBLE MAN called R.J. Rees writes to *The Times* urging that in 1978 we should all put our napkins under our chins when eating after the Continental fashion rather than on our laps in the Alan Brien[1] position.

I have always done so, but the idea has never caught on with the working class. We will probably have to negotiate any agreement with the trade unions. Some may not approve of such foreign habits. It may cost an hour off the national working week but this is a small price to pay, as it would surely help to keep their shirt fronts clean. One does not really like to be reminded of what these people eat.

January 20, 1978

"AN ACT of vandalism unequalled in the history of art," is how Graham Sutherland describes the destruction of his portrait of Winston Churchill.

Of course he is right. The dispersal of the great library of Alexandria, the sack of Rome, the burning of Moscow, the bombing of Monte Cassino, the hammer attack on Michelangelo's *Pietà* were as nothing to this outrage.

It would be hard to imagine anything worse, except perhaps a custard-pie assault on Lord Clark of Civilisation himself. But I must admit, as one who was present when this dreadful deed was done, that it was great fun at the time.

January 23, 1978

THE QUEEN was most interested in some photographs which I showed her from today's *Daily Express* – of a Saudi Arabian commoner being beheaded after his wife, a princess, had been shot for daring to marry him. But she was not in the least bit amused when I started making pointed remarks about her own son-in-law, Captain Mark Phillips and his bride, the Princess-Dame Anne Phillips.

Never mind. She has been absurdly protective of her daughter throughout the whole disgraceful episode, and somebody had to tell her. It ill becomes us to mock the Saudis when we think how much we have lost through neglect of traditional practices. But with a little pressure from my friend Faisal Alhegelan, the Saudi ambassador, all can still be put right.

January 28, 1978

A BLACK DAY for journalism. My friend George Hutchinson closes down his Saturday political column in *The Times*, so long an oasis of civilised urbanity, a symphony of agreeable noises, a *stupor mundi* of High Literature.

I am amazed by this cruel act of vandalism at *The Times* comparable, in its way, to the destruction of Graham Sutherland's portrait. I suspect the dread hand of Charles Vass,[1] smooth-bottomed, jodhpur-wearing 19½-year-old former knitting page supremo and expert on women's nightwear.

The Times without Hutchinson on Saturdays will be like St Paul's Cathedral without an organ, an echo-chamber of ugly, discordant noises. But the new brutalism triumphs everywhere. I attribute the newspaper's shame to its forced association with the

1 Alan Brien, a notoriously dirty journalist suspected of molesting women with his toes under the table.
2 Charles Douglas Home.

Sunday Times in Thomson's hideous new building in Grays Inn Road:

> *"Bad company is a disease*
> *Who lies with dogs shall rise with fleas."*
>
> (Rev. Rowland Watkyns, 1610-1664)

February 5, 1978

I NOTE that the *Sunday Times* Insight team is not having much success in solving the murder of David Holden for the Egyptian police. From a friend in Cairo, I hear a rumour that one of its members, John Barry, has caught a nasty dose of *bilharzia*, possibly from his lavatory seat at the Sheraton Hotel.

At the moment they are footling around with the theory that Holden was working for British Intelligence, but they should know that under the terms of its Charter, MI5 can employ only full-time homosexuals, and David was certainly never that.

From this distance, it is hard to know whom to accuse of the murder. But if I were investigating, I should certainly make routine enquiries about the movements of one Colonel "Bruce" Page, a former member of the Insight team who left the *Sunday Times* after accusing its Editor of murdering Jon Swain, another reporter. Swain was later found eating goat's cheeses under a cactus, having lost his way in the Eritrean desert.

February 10, 1978

SAD TO SEE the statue of Antonio de Oliveira Salazar decapitated in his birth-place of Santa Comba Dao. Of all 20th-century politicians, he is the one whose statue least deserves to be mutilated.

An ascetic by nature, he ruled Portugal rather strictly by some standards for 36 years, but it was a happy and surprisingly carefree country in his time. He controlled the press savagely, imprisoned a number of socialists and tortured a few, but seldom very severely. In 36 years he murdered only one political opponent – General Delgado – and that may have been an accident.

Perhaps it would be a good idea for public statues to be made with disposable heads that can be changed with every change of popular fashion. The same bodies could be used for Churchill, Wislon, Grocer, or whoever was the hero of the moment.

But an even better plan, and one more in keeping with modern ideas about art and democracy, would surely be to make statues without any heads at all, representing simply the idea of a good, wise politician, a brave footballer, an unusually gifted hairdresser or whatever. This is no time for elitist personality cults. I promise that if anyone puts up a statue of Charlie Chaplin I will knock its head off within three months.

February 11, 1978

GOOD NEWS that C.J. Driver, whoever he may be, is going away to teach in Hong Kong and will not be reviewing any more novels for the *Guardian*. Although the *Observer*'s Lorna Sage is undisputed as Lord Gnome Trophyholder for Most Boring Reviewer of All Time, Driver comes second with his record-breaking three-year run of picking dud novels.

I often wondered how he did it and he explains how it is done in the current issue of *New Fiction*. This is the organ of the New Fiction Society, an Arts Council "front" organisation dedicated to swamping the English novel under great waves of boredom, pseudery and self-importance:

> ". . . certainly I don't read word for word. . . I read word clusters, phrases, sentences, moving my eyes down the middle of the page. . . At times I am conscious that my eyes and mind have been working together like a high-speed camera, photographing chunks of text, assimilating syntax and image. . ."

In his two-and-a-half page article, Driver uses the word "I" one hundred and fifty-seven times, which may be a record. Even this figure gives no impression of the stupefying boredom he produces. First one must realise that C.J. Driver is almost certainly the least interesting person on earth. Then imagine 157 C.J. Drivers, all with some unoriginal or banal statement to make about themselves. There you have the perfect *New Fiction* formula.

February 13, 1978

AN UNPLEASANT postcard has arrived from a Cornish "artist" called Patrick Hughes. "I have cancelled my subscription because I can't stand that humourless prick Auberon Waugh! I just had to tell you. . . "

I know nothing about Patrick Hughes and have never heard of him before, but somebody has a theory he may be married to Molly Parkin. If so, it serves him bloody well right.

March 3, 1978

I UNCOVER a sex scandal of hideous proportions. It appears that after six months marriage, Nigel Dempster is now cohabiting with his wife.

The reason for this shocking state of affairs is that Dempster was turned out of his former residence, owned by Lord Anthony Rufus Isaacs, for allegedly writing about Lord Anthony's friends in the *Daily Mail*.

Instead of trying to lie his way out of it or taking the brute before the Fair Rents Tribunal, Dempster pathetically moved into the Cadogan Gardens apartment of his still-unravished bride, the lovely 16-year-old Lady Camilla, and is now living openly with her.

By strange coincidence, on the week Dempster moved in Lady Camilla was burgled, losing many valuable pictures and some rare old pork pies. I try selling this story to William Hickey, but the miserable hack who writes that column is too nervous of having his own sexual irregularities exposed.

March 17, 1978

LAST WEEK I went to the First Night of Simon Gray's new play *Rear Column* at the Globe Theatre, and today I hear it is coming off at the end of the month.

This is depressing, as I enjoyed it more than any play I have seen for years. Of the reviews, only two seemed reasonably intelligent – one by my cousin Benedict Nightingale, in the *Statesman*, the other by Irving Wardle in *The Times*.

Wardle is to be commended as he does not start with many advantages and I have frequently called for his sacking in the past, especially after his praise for David Mercer's miserable rubbish *Duck Soup*. This time he writes sensibly and well.

I expect the other critics were fed up with seeing Gray lionised in *New Review* and the *Sunday Times* Colour Magazine. These are two publications which serious artists should avoid.

March 18, 1976

I WARNED Mrs Thatcher not to trust Baillie Vass with House of Lords reform. Now, as "Lord" Home of the Hirsel, this babbling dotard threatens to do more harm than he ever did in all his previous manifestations.[1]

"Without doubt, few would seriously defend the hereditary principle as a basis for a seat in the legislature," he burbles, proposing that two-thirds of the Upper House should be elected.

On the contrary, few responsible commentators would nowadays defend popular election as a basis for any post more influential than Miss Kraft Cheese Beauty Queen. One has only to glance at our lamentable House of Commons to see the sort of people it attracts. Heredity is certainly a more logical method of selection than self-appointment.

A reformed House of Lords would exclude all existing first creations and "Life Peers", and also those hereditary peers who had disgraced themselves by the vulgarity of their dress or behaviour, by unsuitable marriages, by illiteracy or sloppy use of the English language, by extreme stupidity or avowed atheism.

The House of Commons might be retained as a quaint anachronism, a club or enclosure for these emotional cripples, drunken dwarves with cleft palates, crooked publicity consultants, Boy Scouts and would-be Scoutmasters. They would sit in permanent session as a Committee of Privileges, scheming how best to punish anyone found laughing at them.

1 As Earl of Home, Vass was Prime Minister 1963-4.

March 23, 1978

FOR THEIR cultural outing of the year, I take my Family to a performance of *Ruddigore* at Taunton School. It is enthusiastically performed, but Gilbert and Sullivan always make me sad, expressing as they do the whole spirit and glory of England at its most confident moment of history.

In the orchestra I see a beautiful girl playing the oboe – always a cardinal element in Sullivan's orchestration, and a most becoming instrument for young women to play.

When I come to power I shall encourage all Englishwomen to learn it by making proficiency in the oboe an essential qualification for female employment in the Civil Service, nationalised industries, government contracts in the private sector, etc.

Men will be divided into trumpeters and fiddlers according to their natural aptitudes and status in life.

March 24, 1978

AGAINST GENERAL practice, I have always seen Good Friday as marking the end of the Liturgical Year, a time for reflection and quiet brooding.

It has not been a good year for former Prime Ministers, with Mr Bhutto[1] sentenced to hang and Alberto Moro[2] imprisoned somewhere by frenzied Lefties who are no doubt haranguing the poor man about Chile, international combines and other recondite topics of that sort. The great question in all our minds is whether it could happen here.

Grocer Heath might seem to offer a tempting target. Perhaps would-be kidnappers are intimidated by the thought of being shut up with him, while would-be assassins pause to reflect on the mess he would undoubtedly make if blown up.

Perhaps he will be spared. But at a time of year when our thoughts naturally turn to crucifixion, it is surely a disgraceful provocation to expose the Archbishop of Canterbury on television. I thought I had pressured Brian Wenham to ban him on this most sensitive of days, but Trotskyites on the *Sunday Telegraph* persuaded him otherwise. Coggan's best hope now lies in the virtual unprocurability of large nails.[3]

April 7, 1978

TO THE Savoy for my annual Press Award.[4] Once again I am chagrined to hear no mention of my Campaign against the ordination of women in the Church of England – one of the longest campaigns ever to have been waged in the British press and, so far at least, one of the most successful.

Prince Charles rebukes the Press for its coverage of his activities, suggesting we give undue emphasis to his more frivolous activities like the search for a suitable bride. On the contrary, it seems to me one of the most important decisions a man can make in his entire life. It is typical of the low opinion in which women are held since they have been allowed into church pulpits that the Heir to the Throne can talk of marriage in this way.

Many women are beautiful, kind, affectionate, soft, loyal and generous. Only a tiny, unrepresentative minority wants to make an exhibition of itself in church pulpits. A good counter-measure, I understand, is to release a few mice at the beginning of every sermon.

April 12, 1978

I AM growing very upset by these photographs of Kate Bush.[5] She may be magical, beautiful, wondrous, breath-taking, but I don't suppose she is available. Many girls of that age, when one enquires, already have some pimply swain in tow; if they don't, it usually means they are heavily involved in transactional analysis or some such rubbish.

The whole idea of advertising her in this way is silly and misguided. But there are wondrous, breath-taking things to be done to her face with a marker pen in the quiet moments of the evening on London's Underground.

1 Former Prime Minister of Pakistan. Later hanged.
2 Former Prime Minister of Italy. His corpse was later discoverd in the boot of a motorcar.
3 March 1978 was a period of acute shortage in many household requirements.
4 Once again Waugh had been commended as Critic of the Year by British Press Awards.
5 A singer. Her posters were prominently displayed on London's Underground.

April 14, 1978

A FAREWELL dinner party for Tony Howard, retiring editor of the *New Statesman*, at the Gay Hussar, Greek Street. It is a very sad occasion. Whatever one may have said about him in the past, he was a good editor, and James Fenton, now lost to the world as *Grauniad* correspondent in Germany, was an excellent political commentator.

The cruellest joke about Howard was made by Peter Paterson who said he spent *New Statesman* money as if it was his own. This terrible meanness was the only flaw in an otherwise noble character. True to type, he lets "Christopher" Robin Hitchens pick up the bill for the nine of us. I hope it comes from *New Statesman* expenses.

April 17, 1978

TERRIBLE NEWS that Ms Joyce McKinney has been allowed to jump bail. Her trial for allegedly raping the Mormon missionary Kirk Anderson was the only bright spot in the entertainment fixtures for May.

I don't know whether she's guilty or not but the crime of female rape is certainly increasing. Many men are too frightened to go to the police which is why nearly 100% of these cases remain unreported. In my experience, the police are seldom very sympathetic and often ask humiliating questions aimed at suggesting we welcome these attacks.

This afternoon, under the aegis of Men Against Rape, I lead a deputation of hideous, embittered old pooves to see the Home Secretary in Whitehall and present him with our demands. Here they are:

- Any woman accused of raping a man should automatically be assumed guilty and locked up for a period of not less than the rest of her natural life.
- The identity of men complaining of rape should be protected, nor should they be required to give evidence in court. One postcard or telephone call to a police station should be sufficient to put the guilty women behind bars.

April 28, 1978

SAD TO HEAR of F.R. Leavis's death at 82. Nearly all his literary judgements strike me as being wrong, and his influence on the study of English Literature has been nothing less than disastrous, but he had a certain *panache* or showmanship which is an essential attribute of the good critic, and which is certainly lacking in most of his disciples.

He also had a fine contempt for those who disagreed with him, but his few letters to me were always models of courtesy. Although we corresponded a little and were, of course, fellow contributors to *Books & Bookmen*, we never met. For some reason, he never seemed to have been asked to the same parties or the same country house weekends. I don't know why this should have been so, but there it is.

April 29, 1978

AFTER NEARLY 20 years as a regular subscriber, I sorrowfully cancel my order for the *New Statesman* at the stationers. Amusing as it may be to wax indignant about the oafish illiteracy and ignorant, bragging conceit of the new regime, under Col. "Bruce" Pages-and-Pages, the magazine has quite simply become too boring to read.

The Lead-letter catches the new tone exactly:

> *Sir*, You have allowed an unsubstantiated statement by Christopher Hitchens in last week's issue. . . The part to which I take objection reads as follows: "Stalinist dissenters. . . who are considered moral supporters of terrorism." I know of no group. . . [*groan, bore, fart*]. I ask that you substantiate your statement or retract it, giving your answer as equal [*sic*] prominence as was given the original.
>
> RICHARD BARRABALL

But the *NS* will continue to have at least one reader in bouncy 94-year-old *castrato* Larry Adler, who comments in his pathetic *What's On In London* column:

"The *NS* makes the *Spectator* seem like a very poor relation. In fact I like the *Spec* and all who sail in her, but the paper just has no balls anymore."

One can quite see that a clapped out, vasectomized mouth-organist (although I am very fond of Larry) might need something to fill the aching gap, and might seize on Barraball or any other type of balls on offer. But the *Spectator* is a most excellent maga-

zine nowadays for those without his strange appetite, featuring all the best writers in Britain and many from savage parts.

May 6, 1978

ALL THE newspapers feature Kate Bush-style photographs of my goddaughter, Lady Helen Windsor. This alarms me, as however wondrous, magical etc she may turn out to be, she is still only 14 years old and I think she is too young to be advertised in this way.

Children of the famous need protection from their parents' efforts to cash in on them. The cover of this week's *Radio Times* is given up to a disgusting photograph of Esther Rantzen's baby, Emily Alice. Inside, the baby is interviewed by someone called David Taylor with the cringing deference which journalists usually reserve for the Shit of Persia.

From time to time, we learn, Baby "let's loose a satisfied parp". Esther, an "adoring, fascinated, first-time mother", presumably farts from time to time, too, but we are not told about that. "Baby slops and chunters along, more contented than most except when indisposed by wind. She punctuates Esther's every thought and, breast-fed, regulates the day," drools Mr Taylor.

Baby Rantzen had better watch out, or the People will take a terrible revenge when they come to power. They will shut Emily Alice in a little room with wondrous Lady Helen, jumbo-sized Caitlin Davies (13-year-old daughter of Hoonter What-a-Creep-I-am) and Jonathan, the unspeakable baby son of Peter Walker and champion all-round shitter. Then they will be sorry.

May 7, 1978

BROODING about children, I fall into a gloom. Nobody ever stops to consider what effect all this publicity about Princess Margaret Rose's malarkey with "Roddy" Llewellyn might have on her young children, the Viscount Linley aged 16, and the Lady Sarah Armstrong-Jones, who was 14 on May Day. What, indeed, about her magical great-nephew, Master Peter Phillips?

It is probably time we had a law forbidding publication of any news or comment which might embarrass the young children of those concerned. I remember how a callous remark I once made at school about Attila the Hun caused Sir Iain Moncreiffe of that Ilk (a direct descendant of Attila's) to burst into uncontrollable sobs.

In fact it would probably be better to suppress all news of any description rather than make a young child, anywhere, cry on the way home from school.

May 14, 1978

NO *OBSERVER* today because the workers refuse to print it. Under protest I allow my newsagent to substitute the *Sunday Times* which seems to be making one of its rare appearances this week.

What sort of people still read this boring filth? Many, I suspect, are seriously sick. A large – over 20 square inches – advertisement for a substance called KY Jelly carries this message:

> **Two minutes spent reading this could improve your marriage.** Nowadays most people agree that a healthy sexual relationship helps to form the basis of a happy marriage. Many women have found that intercourse can be more satisfying for them and their partners if additional lubrication is used. This is when Johnson & Johnson's KY Jelly can really help as you can use it to provide additional lubrication safely.

And so it goes on, promising to make intercourse "more fulfilling" for *Sunday Times* readers if they use this jelly.

Surely most people have no need of such substances? A further insight into the sort of people who still read the *Sunday Times* is provided by the advertiser's assumption that it will take them two minutes to read his advertisement. I read it in 22 seconds before deciding to throw the whole newspaper away.

May 20, 1978

"DIVORCE IS now increasingly regarded as a matter for commiseration rather than for criticism, unless it is accompanied by a public parade of private bitterness," writes the saintly Rees-Mogg in his wonderful newspaper.

He is writing about the Snowbum divorce, but I suspect he is thinking about Mrs Tom Litterick who has taken to burning down the flat of Ms Pat Healy, Social Services correspondent of *The Times*, in protest against her husband's Ugandan activities with the said Ms Healy.

He is certainly right when he says that such behaviour would be undignified in a Royal Princess. A much better revenge for Princess Margaret to take on her bolting midget husband would be to adopt 15 babies. Some will be paraplegic, some blackish, some merely disturbed, but all will be Thalidomide victims.

While everybody shouts "how compassionate, how caring, good old Yvonne etc.," she will invite all the leading photographers to come and take photographs of them – Patric Leischfeld, Doivid Boyley, Dame Cecil Beaton. . . all except one. Snowbum, in despair, will be forced to go and hunt lepers in French Equatorial Africa, while we all laugh at him behind his back.

May 26, 1978

TO SELFRIDGES, where I intended to buy some copies of the novel all London is talking about – Harriet Waugh's *Mother's Footsteps* (Snipcock £4.95). Imagine my horror when I find the place is taken up by Esther Rantzen's baby and its frightful mother who is signing copies of some rubbishy book she claims to have written.

The art gallery is full of very strange people waiting to find out whether Baby Rantzen will perform its celebrated trick of "letting loose a satisfied parp", or whether (as I suspect) these noises really come out of its mother.

June 3, 1978

WORRYING NEWS in today's newspaper. Under a huge photograph of Nigel Dempster on the Woman's Page of the *Daily Mail* we are told that this person who was once described as the Greatest Living Englishman now pays £8.10 for a hair-wash, cut and dry at an establishment in Beauchamp Place.

Why can't he wash his own hair and get his wife to cut it? If the beautiful Lady Camilla Dempster feels she is too well-born or too rich for this task, there can be no shortage of secretaries in the *Daily Mail* who would be willing to take her place.

I suspect the real answer is that Dempster has changed sex, and we shall soon have to start talking about the Greatest Living Englishwoman. Everybody seems to be changing sex these days. John Groser announces in *The Times* that he intends to put in for the Woman Journalist of the Year award and I notice that my friend Jan Morris seems to have changed yet again, publishing her excellent new book under the name of James Morris. I always warned her she would be discouraged by the fatuousness of women's conversation after dinner.

But the most alarming news concerns a vicar in the Blackburn diocese who has had a sex change operation and now asks his Bishop, the Rt Rev. R.A.S. Martineau, if he can continue in office.

This, I can see, is the Enemy's next move – female ordination by the back passage. My friend Dr Martineau has persuaded this person to retire on the grounds of ill-health, but we must not let our vigilance slacken for one minute.

June 4, 1978

ON THE 25th anniversary of the Coronation one's thoughts go back to that dismal occasion. I decided to boycott the whole event, having taken offence over some real or imagined slight and spent the day in Weston-Super-Mare with a boy called Green-Armitage.

All moral inhibitions and legal restraints were cast aside in Weston-Super-Mare on that day. Old people in deckchairs were throwing their false teeth around and squirting each other with Pepsi-Cola. I was caught peeing against a wall by a policeman.

"That's against the law," he said.

"No it isn't, Offisher," I wittily replied. "Itsh against the wall."

The next Coronation will be a complete shambles, of course. That is something we can all look forward to, at any rate.

June 8, 1978

NIGEL DEMPSTER's brilliant column in the *Daily Mail* informs me that my dear Wife has been awarded a First Class Combined Honours Degree in French and Italian at Exeter University. This is excellent news, and richly deserved after three years' hard work.

He also describes her as a Guinness heiress, which is puzzling as she has never mentioned this to me. Perhaps I had better return to Somerset and find out, or perhaps Guinness fortunes are things which gossip columnists award, like the CBE, for meritorious behaviour. But I suspect he is confusing her with his own wife, the lovely Lady Camilla, who is heiress to the £170 million Harris Pork Pie complex.

Nigel's delicious, petite, $17\frac{1}{2}$-year-old bride takes a keen interest in the running of her companies, I hear. She is sometimes to be seen in wellington boots, driving herds of pigs into her factories. Twenty minutes later, after a few grunts and squeals, they emerge as perfectly formed pork pies.

One reason Nigel spends so long under the hair-dryer these days may be that he has started wondering what happened to this lovely lady's previous six husbands. Personally, I have never much cared for pork pies.

June 10, 1978

FOR OVER a month now I haven't heard a squeak from any member of the Royal Family. I was beginning to wonder why they were avoiding me, but today everything is explained.

Prince Michael of Kent (whom I have not seen since he was a moderately attractive junior boy at Eton) announces his plans to marry the Catholic wife of poor old Tom Troubridge. No wonder they are trying to make themselves scarce.

They may think they have outwitted me by going behind my back with the help of a slippery Pope and a mad Archbishop of Canterbury. But they mustn't succeed, or before we know what is happening the couple will be practising contraception.

This is no occasion for slinging the old lemonade bottle at Prince Charles. It will need careful planning and attention to detail, but the wedding must be stopped. Prince Michael must choose the path of duty.

June 19, 1978

I DON'T THINK Guy the Gorilla died because he was given too many ice-creams by visitors, as London Zoo officials claim. Nor do I necessarily believe he was murdered, as the Left are trying to put around.

In fact I often used to share my lunchtime sandwiches with this amiable beast, and he always liked to round off the meal with a pistachio-and-tutti-frutti ice-cream from Bertorelli. He gave the impression that ice-cream was the only thing that kept him going.

Poor old chap:

"Still are thy pleasant voices, thy nightingales awake,
For Death, he taketh all away, but them he cannot take."

The truth is that Guy fell into a melancholy in his last months. He was upset by the Snowdon divorce, terrified of a visit from 'Oonter Davies's teenage daughter, anxious for poor Tom Troubridge's wife who is threatened with contraceptive practices by a Prince of the Blood Royal, unhappy about the *Sunday Times* and disgusted by the arrival of the oafish Australian dingo Bruce Page:

"By that dear language which I spake like thee,
Forget all feuds and shed one English tear
O'er English dust. A broken heart lies here."

June 26, 1978

THE HIGH Sheriff of Somerset (whom God preserve) and Mrs Rees-Mogg have asked me to a Garden Party on July 18th to be held at Montacute. What a shame that noble man no longer has a stately home of his own for these occasions. But the invitation fills my dear Wife and myself with the greatest excitement.

It appears that my morning coat has shrunk in the years since I wore it last, but my top hat is rescued from the acting cupboard and wiped all over with Guinness. This leaves it sodden and rather smelly, but they say it is all for the best.

I spend a happy afternoon polishing my medals. In a brief military career I qualified for only one but since then I have had the good fortune to inherit a large number of medals from various gallant forebears. Soon they are all shining like lanterns, and I hope William will be proud of me.

My dear Wife tries curtseying to a pillow representing the High Sheriff while she holds a pair of gloves, a plate of cucumber sandwiches and a cup of tea, but I fear she is rather out of practice. Perhaps I will take one of my Daughters. Oh dear, I hope I do not disgrace my friend on the big day.

June 29, 1978

DINGLE FOOT has choked to death on a sandwich in Hong Kong, which is sad. I wonder if this explains the mysterious death of Guy the Gorilla at London Zoo a few weeks ago – an incident which is still veiled behind wild accusations and irresponsible rumours.

People may rebuke me for comparing the tragedy of Sir Dingle's death with this spot of trouble at the Zoo. But it is all too easy to become worked up over things which happen in distant parts of Asia while ignoring sorrows at home. After three weeks of gross indulgence in celebration of this and that I have nothing but sympathy for any fellow creature which dies of over-eating.

June 30, 1978

THIS IS the Bishop of Winchester's new prayer to be recited after an abortion:

> *"Heavenly Father, You are the giver of Life and You share with us the care of the Life that is given. Into Your hands we commit in trust the developing life that we have cut short. Look in kindly judgement on the choice that we have made and assure us in all our uncertainty that Your love for us can never change."*

A moving sentiment. It might also work as a Grace to be said before any meal which includes roast sucking pig, milk lamb or *petits poussins à la crème*. Even as I think about this I find my mouth watering. It is an extraordinary thing that the more one eats the more one wants to eat.

July 7, 1978

A DISAPPOINTING Royal Ascot. I attend in the hope of seeing a demonstration of Mr Geoffrey Wheatcroft's celebrated Rigid Man act which has become such an agreeable feature of race meetings. Most of the other 14,000 people in the Royal Enclosure seem to have come for the same reason.

After a few drinks this celebrated Highgate-born *literatus* and disciple of Thomas Szasz has often been mistaken for a railway sleeper and was once used as a public convenience by the Royal corgis.

But Mr Wheatcroft, who on this occasion is escorting 20-year-old Rhoda Koenig, lovely Bronx-born senior editor of *New York* magazine,[1] remains upright and flaccid throughout the day, before subsiding peacefully into a natural sleep.

July 14, 1978

YET ANOTHER Soviet outrage is revealed today by Ms Nora Beloff, lovely 59-year-old *doyenne* of motoring correspondents who was held (*against her will*, if you please) for 24 hours at Chop, on the Soviet side of the Soviet/Hungarian border.

This nippy old roadster was just finishing a month's motoring tour of the Ukraine – no doubt in the company of her gifted and courageous husband Mr Clifford Makins – when she was seized by KGB agents and accused of propaganda and agitation against the Soviet Union. She behaved with great dignity. "I await Mr Gromyko's apologies," she says demurely.

But is this enough? I think we should declare war on the Soviet Union without delay. It is the only sort of language they understand.

August 5, 1978

Montmaur, Aude, France

NEWS OF Jeremy Thorpe's arrest with three others breaks like a thunderclap over the Languedoc countryside. There is dancing in the streets, ceremonial rabbits are cooked and groups of peasants with lanterns are to be found wandering the lanes far into the night, singing at the tops of their voices and beating the hedges with staves.

All these men are probably quite innocent of the vile crimes of which they stand accused. But it certainly adds to the gaiety of the nations to make them prove it. Over here, where people were understandably alarmed by Thorpe's assertion that "bunnies can and will go to France",[2] a collection is being made to provide some token of their gratitude and relief over the new development.

I suggest that this take the form of a monument to Rinka, the unfortunate Labrador. Contrary to general belief, the French are even more obsessed by dogs than the English are, and a monument subscribed by Languedoc farmers to stand at the lonely, windswept spot on Porlock Hill, Exmoor, where Rinka was so foully done to death would be poignant testimony to the neighbourly way in which Europeans share each other's sufferings and joys.

1 Miss Koenig was born in the County of Queens.
2 In an affectionate letter to Mr Norman Scott, the male model.

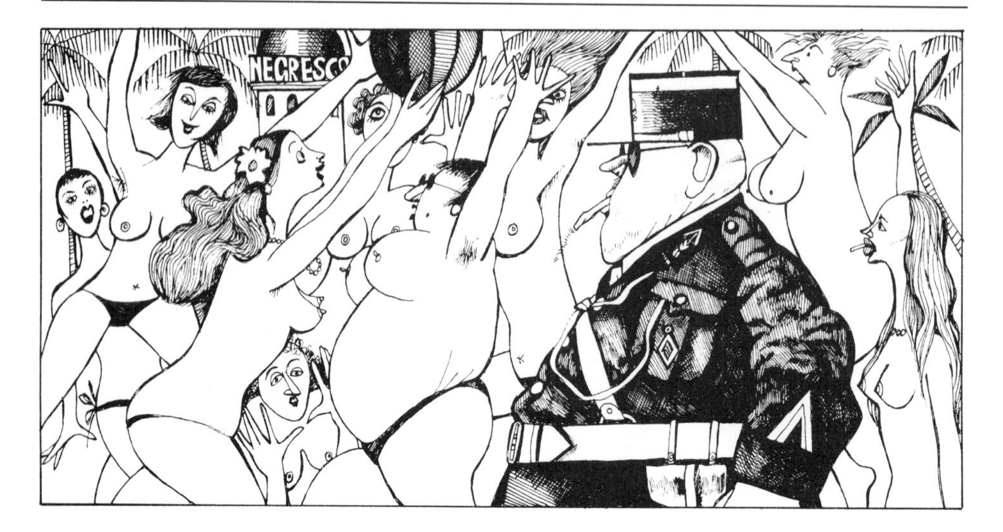

August 8, 1978

BEFORE LEAVING England I was pleased to learn of some Catholic nuns at the Monastery of Our Lady of the Passion near Daventry, Northants, who were resisting pressure from Catholic chicken-lovers to close down their battery hen unit.

I can see that some people, unfamiliar with chickens, might become uneasy about 11,000 chickens permanently locked in wire cages in artificially-lit sheds. In fact, chickens are far too stupid to notice the humiliation. The American Mother Superior, Mother Catherine, explains that the birds are quite happy – "they sit in their cages and sing all day," she says.

In the Cooperative Agricole de Lauragais, to which I belong, the battery system has been refined. We have developed a featherless chicken, which saves the labour of plucking it. It lays shell-less eggs contained in a membraneous tissue, slightly reminiscent of plastic. Many modern housewives go mad at the extra effort involved in breaking eggs. These birds are unable to stand up, which is sensible as they have nowhere to go.

The problem of persuading them to sing has been solved by a Sardinian neighbour, M. Etienne Bougainville, who served for many years in the French Legion. He puts them in an artificial draught and sprays them with cold water. This results in a strain of pleurisy or pneumonia in the birds which produces a delightful wheezing noise until they die peacefully at the end of their normal laying career, thus sparing them the horrors of slaughter as well as saving labour costs in this brutal occupation.

August 17, 1978

TO THE seaside where, in the unfashionable Mediterranean resort I have patronised for the last 15 years, slightly over half the women have suddenly decided to go topless: pubescent girls, nubile young women, mothers of four and even the occasional hairy old lesbian of 55.

I suppose I should gloat to see so many women make such fools of themselves, but it saddens me. Few women have very beautiful breasts – what made them objects of excitement and veneration was the intimacy of the circumstances in which they were revealed. Now, striding over the sands, most of the women look like chaps with silly things stuck on their chests.

Perhaps it is all a desperate attempt to revive our flagging interest in them as sex objects since they emerged as Persons. Nothing could be less calculated to succeed. Far from inviting the mind to speculate on what lies under the bottom halves of their bikinis, the sight fills me with an unfamiliar distaste for the nitty-gritty.

August 20, 1978

SAD TO hear Lord Shawcross inveighing against gossip columnists like some raddled old whore who wants to keep her liaisons secret, or crooked financier with a terror of exposure.

In fact he is a man of complete integrity in his business affairs and blameless sexual morality, so far as I know – surely *somebody* would have told me if there was anything to be told. But it is my invariable experience that those who attack gossip columns in this way, and hint darkly at further legal restriction on the Press, have something to hide.

Perhaps some misfortune has befallen Lord Shawcross's immediate family which he is anxious we should not discuss. If so, we must all sympathise, as Lord Shawcross is a blameless man usually on the side of the angels. But I wish he could find some other way to announce his problem. In my experience, the best way to stop gossip columnists printing a story is to give them a better one about somebody else.

August 22, 1978

NOTHING BUT bad news comes out of England to disturb my holiday in the sun-scorched terraces of the Languedoc. Now there has been an epidemic of botulism poisoning among Old Age Pensioners in Birmingham, all struck down after eating American tinned salmon.

A few years ago they had the same trouble with Russian tinned crab. Surely it is time the National Health Council stepped in to discourage these gastronomic experiments among the old. They should stick to their traditional diet.

In Somerset, I always feed my OAPs on Kit-e-Kat. It keeps them sleek and frisky. Eight out of ten OAP owners say their OAP prefers it. For my own part, if I didn't give my OAPs regular helpings of Kit-e-Kat they would leave home, I know they would.

September 1, 1978

MY NEWSPAPER has a photograph of Princess-Dame Anne Phillips with her interesting four-legged son "Master Peter". It is taken by Lord Snowbum, the only photographer allowed near the lad, and of course shows only the head and shoulders.

The caption describes the photograph as "charming" but it won't do, it won't do. The child should be sent to stay with his cousin, Lord Strathmore, at Glamis Castle where, I gather, an apartment is kept ready for him.

September 2, 1978

RATHER TO my surprise, as I have never met the lady, I find myself invited to a party given by Miss Olga Deterding, the elderly Dutch philanthropist, in her Piccadilly penthouse.

It is a strange scene. All the men, as one would expect, are homosexual, and all the women hideously ugly, but Miss Deterding (who is very into journalists) has supplemented them with some tailors' dummies. She also has some model sheep under which she has picturesquely scattered handfuls of raisins.

I am not entirely at home in this *milieu.* Miss Deterding herself, with her white hair *en brosse*, sits with a walking-stick looking rather like the Maharishi's grandmother and exuding a certain aura of saintliness.

But she does not look at all well, and I wonder whether she may not have picked up a spot of leprosy from her noble work with Albert Schweitzer in Gabon many years ago. When we shake hands I find several of her fingers left behind. The most alarming thing is that she does not appear to notice.

Perhaps it is another practical joke. I hope so. At any rate, I slip the fingers into my pocket and try to engage one of her dummies in a serious conversation about Mrs Thatcher's election prospects in the Spring.

September 5, 1978

LUNCH WITH Michael Joseph, my publisher, who tells me he is producing a volume of my essays collected from the *New Statesman* next week under the amusing title of *In the Lions' Den*. When I ask him how much it will cost, he replies: "£4.95," and adds that it will have a fine cover designed by Nicolas Bentley.

This is what we eat: 6 doz. large Whitstable natives (Krug '59); 4 baby lobsters, steamed with hot butter sauce (Mersault-Charmes '70); 2 grouse (Ch. Lafite '35); strawberry tart (Ch. Guiraud '47); finally we have a little Camembert with which we drink a bottle of Fonseca '45.

I refuse his offer of brandy afterwards, pointing out that it is never a good idea to drink after luncheon, at any rate for those with work to do in the afternoon. He starts to cry, saying that he did not mean to offend me. I hit him playfully over the head with a piece of celery and say it doesn't really matter.

September 15, 1978

A PATHETIC telegram from two Americans who want me to intercede on their behalf with the Queen to prove that her great-uncle, Prince Albert Victor Christian Edward, Duke of Clarence, eldest son of Edward VII, was Jack the Ripper.

In fact I have already tried to discuss this painful matter with Her Majesty on several occasions, but she is not very forthcoming. She almost gives the impression that "she does not want to know".

Another reason may be that she wishes to protect her second son, Prince Andrew Albert Christian Edward, from confusion with the earlier reprobate – especially at a time when prostitutes are being found sliced up in an amazingly similar way in the North of England.[1]

In fact, Randy Andy denies being anywhere in the Leeds area at the crucial times, and in many ways I feel it is better we should leave it like that. Jack the Ripper stopped after scoring seven prostitutes in Whitechapel, and the Son of Jack (or possibly great-great-nephew) has already scored seven. Is it too much to hope that he may now desist?

Queen Victoria handled the matter very calmly, making her grandson Duke of Clarence in 1890 after he had promised not to do any more of these dirty things, and after he had kept his word for 18 months. Of course, she had to have him disposed of at Sandringham two years later, but that is another story.

Many people feel it is time Prince Andrew was given a proper title, if only to rescue him from his unfortunate nickname. Among the Royal dukedoms Windsor, York and Connaught have been in use too recently, Kent, Gloucester, Edinburgh and Cornwall are still in use while others, like Cumberland and Albany, have gone abroad and been lost. Only Clarence survives. Perhaps it is time the Queen laid in another butt of Malmsey.

September 16, 1978

WOMAN'S OWN carries a poignant interview with "Ms" Maureen Colquhoun, 49-year-old Lesbian MP for Northampton North. She announces that she intends to fight on, but I wonder whom she intends to fight.

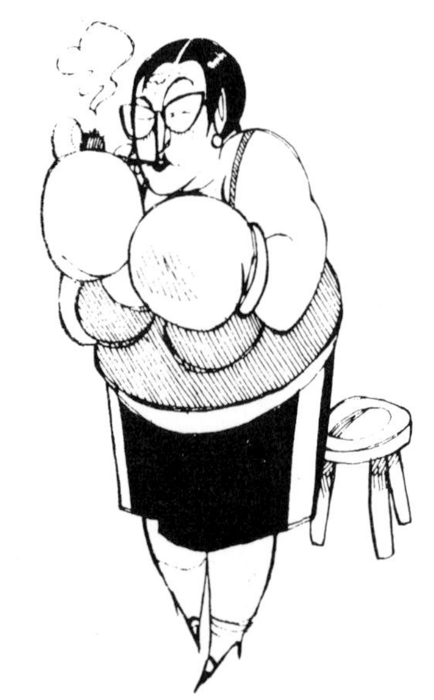

It is wrong to attack Lesbians, but if they attack first one is permitted to fight back. I always advise people on these occasions to stand at a distance and throw lumps of coal at them. Another way of retaliating is to spray them with scent, but probably nothing annoys a Lesbian so much as to be patted on the bum.

1 In the event the Yorkshire Ripper, as the murderer became known, turned out not to be Prince Andrew.

September 17, 1978

EXCITING NEWS that Mr John Sparrow is to stand for the Professorship of Poetry. Since he was appointed Warden of All Souls in 1952, this blameless and beautiful man has been a model to us all for his benign inactivity.

So far as I know, he has written no poetry since winning the Chancellor's Prize for Latin Verse in 1929. What an example to all our poets. If only the abject and ridiculous Stephen Spender-Penny had shown the same modesty he might not be held in such derision today.

After Mr Sparrow has been elected perhaps the Arts Council will take the hint and in future pay people *not* to try and write poetry. Sponsored poetry readings, at present such noisy and disagreeable occasions, will then become moments for silence and quiet meditation, for brooding over past injuries and planning suitable revenge.

September 24, 1978

THE *SUNDAY TIMES* does not reach Somerset any more – I suspect it is taken off the train at Reading and trampled underfoot by militant "workers" enraged by the way it apes their awkward mannerisms and strange habits of speech. Mysteriously, its colour magazine continues to arrive – plangent, oily, full of bad advice on how to cook food and arrange one's main reception rooms.

On the back page today it has a large photograph of Tom Baker, the actor who plays Doctor Who on television. He does not look very healthy, but I gather he once spent six years in a monastery and has been trying to catch up ever since.

He describes a day in the life of a Soho drunk and layabout, but it is the end of his day which catches my eye:

> "Then I went back to Gerry's Club for another drink and after I'd cadged some Valium from someone I went home to my padded cell. I thought about Harriet Waugh and fell asleep."

In a free country there is nothing I can do to stop Mr Baker thinking about my Sister when he is alone in bed if that is what he wants to do. No doubt he has spent many years thinking about the Four Last Things, and I can quite understand that he wouldn't want to think about Kate Bush if he has ever heard the terrible noises she makes.

But if any of my female readers would like to think about Tom Baker before they go to sleep, I provide William Rushton's impression of this thoughtful man to assist them in their meditations.

September 29, 1978

EVERYBODY IN England worth meeting is at the *Spectator* Ball given by that great and good man Henry Keswick, patron of the arts, Philosopher-King of the Far East.

For the first time I meet my heart's desire Anna Ford, more beautiful in real life even than she is on television and with a lovely nature, too.

Could I ever be worthy of such bliss? I brood bitterly on my isolated life in Somerset and yearn for London until I catch sight of Larry Adler offering his monkey's paw around.

Tomorrow I will fly to Morocco for a fortnight of eating locusts on the edge of the Sahara Desert and in the High Atlas Mountains to think about the future.

October 5, 1978

DEEP IN the Moroccan Sahara, somewhere south of Ouazarzate I pitch my tent in a sand-dune, open the last tin of locusts and sit down to contemplate eternity. Here I am free from any danger of meeting Hoonter Davies's enormous teenage daughter who has been haunting my English dreams for over a year.

A circle of eyes around the outer ring of light from the camp fire turns out to be about twenty Berber boys who have crawled like beetles out of the sand to beg for cigarettes and offer their bottoms.

I cannot understand why European pederasts come to Arabia for their pleasures. The boys are ugly, dirty and obviously diseased unlike their sisters who are beautiful, clean and proud. Probably it is a matter of habit, based on historical availability, but I should have thought that English boys were just as available in these distressing times.

October 6, 1978

ANOTHER GOOD reason for leaving England was the Westminster wedding.[1] Perhaps it is persecution mania, but I thought people were giving me mocking glances every time discussion of the young man's £500 million fortune came up.

Of course it is true that Lord Grosvenor is richer than I am, but I am richer than almost everybody else. The meanest, whingeing, blubbering Old Age Pensioner is richer than 85% of the world's population, as one soon learns in Morocco, where many people live on a diet of flies and rats' tails. We must all learn to count our blessings.

October 23, 1978

BACK IN London, I am distressed to find the mood of anti-Semitism sparked by *Holocaust* still rampant. Even the news that the television series has won 17 Oscars in the United States seems to have done little to abate it.

No doubt it will pass. Above all, I hope it does nothing to influence public opinion for or against the interesting Sir Robert Mark, who is obviously waiting in the wings to lead our country out of its present Slough of Despond into a programme of national reconstruction etc. Ignorant people may suspect, quite wrongly, that with a name like that he is of Jewish origin.

But even Sir Robert may have read the signs wrong. I am by no means sure that the country is waiting for a clapped-out old policeman with a taste for discipline. The mood seems to call for someone younger, of good family and broad acres to prove his disinterestedness. My cousin Bernard Dru has been keeping very quiet recently on his Somerset estates. Very *very* quiet. But he is still there.

October 30, 1978

ON THE THIRD anniversary of the attempt on Norman Scott's life, a small party of pilgrims climbs to the lay-by on Porlock Hill, Somerset, and stands in silence for a while in

memory of the dead Great Dane, Rinka, who gave her life to create a better world.

All those present pledge themselves anew to the struggle. Rinka's sacrifice will not be forgotten. She *will* be avenged, and a cleaner, healthier society will arise. Rinka lives on in our hearts.[2]

1 Gerald, Earl Grosvenor, heir to the fifth Duke of Westminster, married Miss Natalia Phillips.

2 Rinka belonged to the model Norman Scott, a friend of Jeremy Thorpe. The dog was mysteriously shot on Porlock Hill, the incident which led to Thorpe's arrest on a charge of incitement to murder, and to Waugh's standing as Dog Lovers Party candidate against him in North Devon in the 1979 General Election.

November 5, 1978

TODAY I LEARN an entirely new word from the *Sunday Telegraph* Colour Supplement's serialisation of Sir Keith Simpson's memoirs. Sir Keith is England's top criminal pathologist, and the word he teaches me is *adipocere*, meaning a white, foul-smelling, glutinous substance given off by dead bodies as their fatty tissues degenerate about five weeks after death.

The problem is to find some use for this excellent word. It might be employed in a literary context, to describe the "quickie" biographies which sometimes appear soon after a public person has died. Or it might refer to the general leak of revelations appearing after death, like Lord Boothby's claim that Churchill had a "cruel streak".

Boothby is certainly right, whatever one might think of his motives. On one occasion, staying at Chartwell as a boy, I saw the old brute deliberately sit down in an armchair which had a chicken in it and crush the unfortunate bird to death. There can be no excuse for this, as there were plenty of other chairs available.

November 10, 1978

IT IS SELDOM one can find anything nice to say about an MP, and almost never that one can praise an MP for courage, but Mr John Lee, Labour MP for Handsworth, surely deserves the accolade of Good, Brave Man.

He is agitating for a change in the law so that women may be charged with rape. On countless occasions, when I have gone to lay charges at the police station, I have been greeted by gales of derisive laughter.

But Mr Lee is sticking to his guns:

"There is no doubt that a woman can rape a male, particularly a youngster. Certain women can easily overpower some men and satisfy their own sexual cravings in a way which, if a man had been the predator, a charge of rape would have ensued."

Their usual technique is to threaten to scream or make a scene unless they get their way, but one of my nastiest rape experiences was with a woman (who shall remain nameless) who threatened me with a nail file and some curling tongs. I shut my eyes and thought of Thailand.

November 27, 1978

THE FIRST DAY of Jeremy Thorpe's committal proceedings in Minehead opens in a nervous mood. On the first day of Newton's[1] trial in Exeter after the dog-shooting episode Wislon announced his resignation as Prime Minister and the Snowbums announced their divorce, all by way of diversion.

When I called on the Phillipses yesterday and put it to this unattractive couple that they might be planning to make some announcement, I deduced from their grunts and screeches that they had no such plans.

In fact, the only diversions offered are a mining disaster in Yorkshire where seven men lose their lives and a massacre in Guyana where 912 religious fanatics are persuaded to drink cyanide by a man called Jones. My late Father used to warn me never to trust anyone called Jones.

We who are left in Minehead squeeze together on hard wooden benches and wait patiently for the dirty bits.

November 30, 1978

AT LAST we reach the dirty bits. Minehead Magistrates Court comes to life, and hacks who have been slumbering in a variety of unattractive postures start scribbling furiously. I watch various people in court closely to see if I can detect any signs of sexual excitement as these appalling allegations are made.

At this stage it would be most improper to speculate on whether the alleged incident ever occurred, or whether Mr Thorpe's alleged organ had the alleged effect, but it cannot be stressed too often, at a time when there is a tendency to glamourise sexual perversion of every sort, that sodomy can be an unpleasant, painful and even dangerous thing for those who indulge in it.[2]

1 Newton, the gunman, had been accused and sentenced in June 1976.
2 Scott had given a graphic account of the night he was allegedly first sodomised by Thorpe.

December 1, 1978

THIS EVENING I am invited to read a paper to the Prostitutes' Conference in London, organised by Lady Vickers. I choose as my subject *100 Different Ways of Pleasing a Man* but I am afraid the audience is not with me.

English prostitutes are the laziest, most overpaid and (with the possible exception of the Germans) the ugliest in the world. Soon they will be put out of business by the new inflatable, life-sized dolls from Taiwan. These are prettier, cheaper and twice as vivacious as the "live" English model. Now that Judge Trapnell has ruled that they are not obscene, English women had better try making a little effort again.

December 3, 1978

I HAVE asked all the church bells in West Somerset to ring throughout the morning. This is in double thanksgiving – for the Jeremy Thorpe trial and the closure of the *Sunday Times*.

As good people flock to church I content myself with reading last week's copy of the *Sunday Telegraph*, which has a wonderful 15 square inch photograph of Lord Gowrie, Mrs Thatcher's Afro-style spokesman who once published a slim volume of poems.

Unlike Spender, who has been writing poetry for sixty years without producing a single memorable line, Gowrie has immortalised himself with three lines apparently written about his Father's death in an Italian hospital during the war – "He lay in a small tub before breakfast". Here they are again:

> *"He turned the hot tap on so water ran*
> *In cataracts down his knees, floating*
> *The dark gland beneath."*

When I read these lines to Mrs Thatcher once she broke down completely.

December 10, 1978

AUDREY WHITING in the *Sunday Mirror* makes the reckless and irresponsible claim (for which there is not one tittle of evidence) that the Royal Family is watching events in Minehead very closely. This is very tiresome and I spend all morning on the phone to the Palace, discussing whether we should deny it ourselves or issue a statement through Lord Goodman.

I have told no one of my secret, secondary role in the Thorpe committal proceedings and certainly don't propose to reveal it now.

Incidentally, the Queen tells me she has a large collection of Christmas cards from Jeremy Thorpe and wonders if they are of any commercial value now. I tell her I will make enquiries in the trade.

December 14, 1978

AS SOON as I hear the news that a warrant is out for Lord Kagan[1] I organise search parties to scour the fields and woods armed with long poles and badger nets.

Later, with a party of vigilantes, I make a citizen's arrest of a suspicious-looking character in Taunton. We seize him by the throat and beat him with our walking sticks and umbrellas, crying: "Stand still, you villain. Let this teach you to allegedly export denim cloth from the UK to Belgium in a manner contrary to Section 23 (1) of the Exchange Control Act 1947."

It is an encouraging thought that we ordinary people are at last making a stand for

1 A friend of Harold Wilson, ennobled in the Resignation Honours List of June 1976.

law and order. Most of "Sir" Harold Wilson's friends have now been accounted for. Let us rejoice at least in the continued life and prosperity of "Sir" James Goldshit, the enterprising grocer and "de-bugger" by appointment to Baroness Falkender. His fine character and scrupulous business methods have never been touched by the faintest breath of scandal.

After we have held the suspect under interrogation in Taunton for a few hours, news comes that the real Kagan has been traced to Israel, so we release the cringeing imposter with a stern warning. Next time I shall instruct the Somerset constabulary to shoot first and ask questions afterwards.

December 20, 1978

AN UGLY SHOCK on opening my post to find a Christmas card from Princess Dame Anne Phillips and her frightful husband whose name escapes me for the moment but who seems to be called Milki. It shows their "son" in his pram wearing a Paul Johnson cap from Carnaby Street at what must, I suppose, be called a jaunty angle.

In the evening I listen to a brass band playing carols at Paddington Station. The players come from some London school or other and seem a shifty, unprepossessing lot. I reflect that whatever Christmas may be about – and few of the players look as if they have much idea – it certainly wasn't intended to celebrate the birth of Master Peter Phillips. He has nothing to do with it.

December 21, 1978

ANOTHER HORRIBLE shock on opening the *Daily Telegraph* to find a huge photograph of Edward Heath at the piano, grinning obscenely at a small boy in front of him, both surrounded by teddy bears.

The caption says that the toys were raised by Capitol Radio in a Christmas hospital appeal. But why on earth should hospitals be expected to send their toys to Grocer Heath?

I suppose this is the sort of picture one must expect to find in a Tory newspaper. I will have a word with my friends in SLADE.[1]

December 26, 1978

THE ONLY THING worth watching on television this Christmas was Tommy Steele's Jack Point in *Yeoman of the Guard*. The rest of the cast was indifferent apart from a tuneful Fairfax, but Tommy Steele, even more than George Grossmith, will surely go down in history as the greatest interpreter of this difficult role.

1 The Fleet Street union responsible for processing photographs had been suppressing various items recently.

His Jack Point had that strange, almost terrifying affinity with a part which I last saw in Nijinsky's Petrouchka during the unforgettable Paris summer of 1911 when Diaghileff opened at the Théâtre du Châtelet. It was on that occasion that Sarah Bernhardt murmured in my ear, "*J'ai peur, j'ai peur, car je vois l'acteur le plus grand du monde.*" She lost a leg soon afterwards, as I remember.

It seems absurd to recall how excited we were then by Stravinsky's music and the Benois setting. Now the score can be seen as a collection of borrowed tunes with a few ugly shrieks and whistles thrown in, to embellish a banal and mildly preposterous narrative.

But the genius of Gilbert and Sullivan continues to inspire generations of Englishmen with the true sentiment of the 1880s, when children did not spend their time eating chocolates in front of the television but were out in the fields and streams playing leap-frog or tickling trout. On the few days when it rained we would amuse ourselves indoors on enterprising projects like stuffing dead birds, building Mesopotamian ziggurats out of matchsticks or torturing the cat.

December 28, 1978

REMOVAL OF the Arts Council's £30,000 subsidy from the *New Review* ends the greatest public expenditure scandal since the war. Now there is no further reason for vilifying this pleasant, pseudish enterprise and one wishes it well for the future, but I think they should sack Karl Miller from the board of management now the magazine has ceased to exist. He may be a rare surviving example of the Complete 1960s Twerp but he is also a dreadful bore and will spoil the joke.

Even more money could be saved if they closed down the whole literary department of the Arts Council, as I constantly urge.[1] It should be spent where it is most needed, on keeping old people warm in the winter. I would suggest installing sauna baths in all senior citizen centres, where the old dears can sit through the disagreeable months chatting to each other about operations they have had or intend to have when the weather improves.

December 30, 1978

TO LONDON where, five days after Christmas, the holiday spirit is just catching on. Pavements are littered by groaning heaps of "workers" clutching their distended stomachs and weeping stale yellow tears from their bloodshot eyes. Many, I should judge, will never be fit enough to work again.

I have good news for them, if only they were in a condition to hear me. A friend in the Post Office tells me there will be a new issue of postage stamps in the New Year showing all the nudes, possibly including Princess Anne in the altogether and the nudest Shirley Williams.

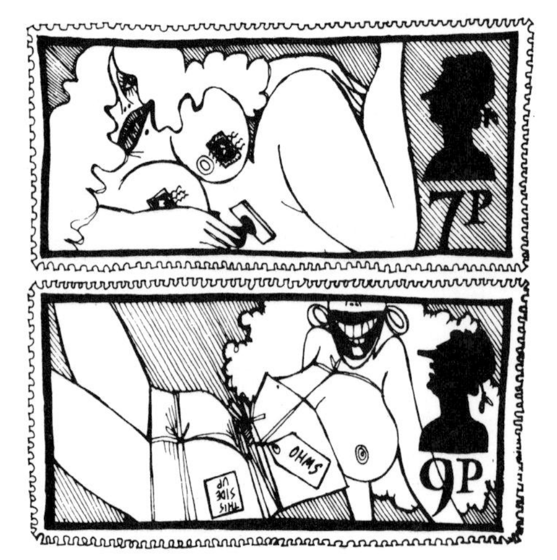

It is intended to commemorate the 50th anniversary of Barbara Cartland's losing her virginity. When I point out that Ms Cartland was first married in 1927, a Post Office spokesman replies that things often took a little while to get going in those days, and her daughter (the lovely Countess Spencer) was not born until September 1929.

December 31, 1978

NEW YEAR'S DAY tomorrow. One wonders with a sick dread what the Archbishop of Canterbury will find to say about it.

1 This necessary step was not taken until February 1985.

On Christmas morning he delivered his answer to Dr Norman's[1] criticism that religion concerns itself too much with politics, not enough with spiritual affairs. If Christmas had a meaning, he said, it was the message of a Christ "born in sordid circumstances, never afraid to dirty His hands as He grew to maturity, always willing to make Himself available at the point where He was most needed".

Never mind that Dr Coggan has got the message all wrong. The important thing is that by his moronic, gibbering trendiness he has become a scandal, a stumbling-block, an obstacle to religious faith.

Let us pray throughout the year that this foolish and unattractive old man shall not long be denied the holy Crown of Martyrdom, so that St Donald à Duckett may soon join his quacks to the celestial chorus of Thy saints who liveth and reigneth for ever and ever. Amen.

1 Dr Edward Norman, a Cambridge polemicist.

1979

The year opens with the great Winter of Discontent; most public employees are intermittently on strike. As the net closes on Jeremy Thorpe and Sir Anthony Blunt, Waugh warns Harold Wilson to fly the country.

At a general election in May the Labour Government is defeated and Britain has its first woman Prime Minister. Waugh stands in Jeremy Thorpe's North Devon constituency as Dog Lovers Candidate and Thorpe is defeated, but his trial at the Old Bailey, conducted by Mr Justice Cantley, ends with Thorpe's acquittal. Waugh writes a book about it.

Little or nothing is done about the Seal Pup Menace but the year is made considerably happier by the absence of the *Sunday Times*. It ends joyfully with news of a great moral regeneration led by Mr Bernard Levin and brought about by thinking inwardly.

January 6, 1979

IN NEW YORK for a few days to escape the horrible things happening in England. My favourite massage parlour in Lisle Street is closing down – I would have gone to my beloved Thailand but the news from Bangkok is even worse. An invading army of Brooke-Partridges from North Vietnam is poised on the Cambodian border. My mission is to alert the New York branch of International Friends of Massage to the danger.

January 10, 1979

A WONDERFUL thing about New York is the way everybody gets excited by the news. Greta Rideout has gone back to her husband, whom she falsely accused of raping her only a week ago, and Pope Ringo II[1] has opened negotiations with Archbishop Lefebvre, seeking readmission to the Catholic Church on behalf of himself and his Roman schismatics.

Personally, I find myself sceptical about both reconciliations. Now Greta has tasted the joys of publicity there is no knowing what she will accuse her poor husband of next. And while the new Pope Ringo seems a thoroughly admirable fellow with sound views about many things, he can scarcely expect Archbishop Lefebvre to recognise post-1968 ordinations in the Roman Church as valid. Few, if any, of these starry-eyed half-wits have any idea what Christianity is about, let alone what Christian civilisation stands for.

But I hear there have been complaints about my absence abroad at a time when so many British housewives are starving, old age pensioners freezing to death etc. Normally I would not worry, but I may be standing for election as Rector of Edinburgh University later this year in the footstep of the late Kenneth Allsopp, so I'd better go back and suck up to the brutes.

January 15, 1979

IS THERE no answer to the monstrous scourge of strikes, asks Paul Johnson in the *Daily Mail*, can nothing be done to stop greedy and ruthless unions from inflicting incalculable discomfort?

Yes, he thinks something can be done:

"There are, for instance, many still active pensioners who suffer in baffled anger from cruel strikes. . . they would welcome the opportunity to hit back and they often have the skills, energy and determination to do so effectively."

We *can* help ourselves, he says. "The remedy is within our own power, but we need the right kind of political leadership."

For years I have been urging that old age pensioners should be set to work. It is an excellent idea that they should be put in the front line against the "workers". But who can get the idle old buggers moving?

January 16, 1979

TODAY WE celebrate the 100th anniversary of the massacre of British troops by Zulus at Isandhlwana in Zululand. What has happened to Zulus nowadays that they have forgotten how to massacre white soldiers but sit around waiting to be massacred themselves?

Oddly enough, it was on that reeking field that I first met Olga Deterding. She was

1 Pope John-Paul II. His predecessor was named Ringo after John, Paul, George and Ringo, the four Beatles.

already rather long in the tooth and quite penniless, although she had not yet perfected her technique of getting journalists to buy her drinks by pretending that she might buy their newspapers.

Poor old Olga. More rubbish has been written about her than about any woman of our times, but at least she gave the gossip columnists something to write about. The last time I saw her she reminded me of Rider Haggard's Ayesha after one trip too many through the Fire of Eternal Life – hairless, shrivelled and black as a tinker's nutting bag. Linda Lee Potter opines that she may have died of a broken heart, but it seems more likely that she choked on a piece of meat while toasting the New Year – a reckless thing to attempt at her age. They don't make them like her any more.

January 20, 1979

TODAY I LEARN that I have been appointed Granada's Crusading Columnist of the Year but the citation from Sir Denis Foreskin does not mention which of my various crusading columns has earned the honour.

It would be nice to think it was for my *Eye* campaign to make Prince Charles marry Caitlin Davies, attractive 13-year-old daughter of Harry "Hoonter" Davies, the man of letters, but I rather fancy it is for my campaign against vasectomies in the magazine *British Medicine*, where I write a monthly column on medical matters.

Risks involved in these smaller operations are much greater than people realise. Only recently John Wayne went into hospital for a "small operation", as he thought, and woke up to discover that the surgeons had removed his entire stomach. I am tempted to use William Rushton's moving illustration for a poster in my anti-vasectomy campaign, but people have only to look at Larry Adler or Michael "Pukey" Parkinson to see what a horrible effect it can have. Mr Wayne should be allowed to grieve in private.

January 21, 1979

A HUGE LUNCH party is given at the Savoy to mark my moment of glory. All the great and good in the land are there – Alan Watkins, the late Tony Howard, Sir Alexander Chancellor, Lord Gnome himself – most of whom have conspired to set up this very good practical joke on the Prime Minister.

Callaghan plays his part like the old trouper he is, roundly declaring how much he has always admired me. In the throng I glimpse the venerable nodding head of William Rees-Mogg, saintly editor of *The Times*. He must be suffering agonies now that his prophecy of a Second Ice Age has been proved right, with no *Times*[1] to point it out.

Callaghan says how sad he is to be deprived of *The Times* and we all agree, but nobody mentions the *Sunday Times*. After much searching I find Harold Evans, its tremendously nice little editor, in a distant corner. He is still smarting from "a campaign of personal taunts and abuse" in *Private Eye* so we all make big efforts to be nice to him.

As a special treat they serve Lancashire Hot Pot after the oysters and smoked salmon. It almost makes you want to cry. Soon everybody will have forgotten his dreadful newspaper and Harold won't have to look so sorry for himself.

1 *The Times* was on strike throughout most of 1979.

January 25, 1979

I HAVE decided to go to Senegal for a few days while the snow lasts. On my way to the Hospital for Tropical Diseases for my Yellow Fever I am stopped by an advertisement. Something called the Make Children Happy Organisation is drawing attention to itself from an address in Francis Street, Westminster. It describes itself as "the new kind of organisation working for all our kids".

Seldom have I seen such a sinister advertisement. The English are growing demented about children. When I was a boy the classroom had icicles inside every window at this time of year. We were savagely beaten three times a week and made to run half-naked in the snow. But the toughest NUPE mass-murderer starts blubbing if you suggest that one little kiddie might have to queue a little longer for its din-dins as a result of NUPE's just action.

When I telephone to complain, a pert young female voice says it wouldn't like anything derogatory to appear in *Private Eye*. David Jacobs, Pete Murray, Terri Wogan and Jimmy Young are helping make children happy, it says. This seems most unlikely, but if any of them come anywhere near my children I shall send for the police. When I get back from West Africa I will devote myself to sabotaging this organisation.

January 26, 1979

PRIVATE EYE has been burgled. On arriving at Gnome House on my way to Heathrow I find an excited crowd of Knackers and Knickerettes examining a smashed door and two forced windows. Oddly enough, nothing appears to have been stolen.

Various theories are put forward. Some assume it is the South Africans, others the Liberals, others that it is MI5 acting on Lady Forkbender's orders. Members of our Vice Team suppose that the marauders were anxious to find out about a certain newly-created peer. Another suggestion is that they were sycophants of Sir James Goldsmith after material for his ridiculous new magazine.

For my own part, I suspect they came from the Make Children Happy Organisation. But one thing is certain: they left the scene of the crime in a terrible hurry; whatever they found here, it was enough to fill them with mortal terror. I suspect they may have chanced upon a pair of E.J. Thribb's old socks.[1]

February 1, 1979

IN SENEGAL, West Africa, to celebrate the second anniversary of our sister publication, the satirical magazine *Le Politicien* of Dakar. Freedom of the press has only existed in Senegal for a couple of years, and there is a general feeling that its infinitely wise President, Leopold Senghor, may be having second thoughts.

At a great banquet in the Hotel Vichy, I make a passionate speech against breast feeding, now the subject of a DHSS campaign in England. Women should not be bullied into this practice by a handful of misogynists and lesbian fanatics in the DHSS – it is disfiguring, inconvenient and in many cases cruel. If the good Lord had intended women to use their breasts in this way He would not have provided us with cows.

In Senegal many women are given to this deleterious and backward habit, but at least they do not do it in public. It is only middle class Englishwomen who insist on feeding their babies at dinner-parties. If Esther Rantzen came to Dakar she would be the laughing stock of West Africa.[2]

February 20, 1979

TONIGHT I must drag myself from my friends at Champneys to address a PEN Club dinner in Chelsea. Its president is Francis King, the distinguished novelist and reviewer whom I have never met before, possibly because he is a bachelor.

Nobody could be friendlier or more hospitable, but when I tackle him about a false statement made in one of his earlier novels to the effect that the Japanese have no

1 Eric Jarvis Thribbs, 17, resident poet of *Private Eye*.
2 It later transpired that Waugh had misunderstood his instructions. He was not invited to give a talk on "breast feeding" but on "Press freedom".

pubic hair, he behaves rather oddly. Instead of admitting his error, he maintains that he lived in Japan for many years and frequently observed how neither the men nor the women had any but the most rudimentary growth in the relevant area.

Good manners prevent me from denouncing him as a public liar. Japanese women are among the most beautiful and delightful in the world and King's vicious calumny upsets me, but what can one do? No Japanese ladies are present to prove my point, and it is boorish to go on arguing about a question of fact.

The time may be coming when everyone who honours Truth will have to carry a copy

of the famous John Lennon/Yoko Ono nude photograph everywhere to settle this argument as and when it arises. Francis King is a good writer and a pleasant man, but he must not be allowed to poison the minds of young people or to mislead an entire generation over what will almost certainly emerge as one of the great debates of our time.[1]

March 1, 1979

WEDGWOOD BENN'S resistance to the sale of Harriers to China is very interesting. These Harriers (like the Neutron Bomb, which smoked out Lord Chalfont) have become one of those issues for which the KGB send out a Three Line Whip, ordering all overseas agents to stand up and be counted. So it looks as though Wedgie may be a Soviet agent after all, although I could have sworn he wasn't.

It may just be that he thinks the Russians are going to win. This would also explain why Prince Charles has come out on the side of "workers" in the civil war, and why Enoch Powell argues that we will soon be on the side of the Russians against America and Europe.

These are difficult times, when Americans are being ritually humiliated by dusky little men in every corner of the globe, but it is no good blaming their ghastly President Jimmie 'n' Rosaleen. Unspeakable as this thing may be, sanctimonious, lying, cowardly and paralytically stupid, the truth is that nearly all Americans are like that. There is only one man in the United States with the necessary qualities and that is Billy Carter.[2]

Billy, who says he loves his repulsive brother but can't control him, is the only man in the United States big enough to fill the office of President. But are the Americans big enough to choose him?

March 5, 1979

TO THE House of Commons. Not for the first time I thank heaven I am not an MP, having no idea which way to vote on Maureen Colquhoun's Protection of Prostitutes Bill.

At first glance it might seem an obviously benevolent measure, but my doubts start in the course of Ms Colquhoun's speech when she reveals that the present laws "ensure that the incompetent prostitute, the working-class girl, is the one who gets into trouble. Successful and competent prostitutes operate very well within the law."

It is another sad fact that these incompetent or working class prostitutes, being somewhat dirtier, tend to give one the more

1 Correspondence on this delicate matter continued in *Private Eye* for many months afterwards. No consensus was reached.

2 Billy Carter, brother of the President Jimmy, was a grave embarrassment to the Presidential couple, accepting large sums of money from the Libyan government as "adviser" etc.

frightful diseases. Should prostitution (or "therapy" as it is now called) be left to properly brought-up girls of the middle class?

The older I get, the more I feel that the lower classes should be discouraged from undertaking any work at all. They don't like it, they're no good at it and it only makes them unhappy to be reminded of their own innate and unalterable inferiority.

March 8, 1979

WHEN I COME to power I am going to build a huge Temple to British Labour, like the Pantheon, with statues of British workers who have distinguished themselves in the struggle for the right not to work.

After the great Albert Thorogood[1] himself, pride of place will go to Jamie Morris, the 26-year-old NUPE organiser at Westminster Hospital. He has been paid £62 a week by Westminster Hospital as "domestic supervisor" or floor-sweeper and has managed to draw the money for two years without doing any work at all.

Some of my friends don't agree with me about Jamie Morris and think he should be named as a "legitimate target"[2] in the class war. Then he might find himself debagged and dubbined by young bloods of the Young Upper Classes Direct Retaliation Action Group in red tail coats and thrown into the Round Pond in Kensington Gardens.

Then we generally stick a fox's tail up our victim's bottom and hunt him through the streets of Kensington and Knightsbridge, blowing hunting horns. When the legitimate target is finally cornered we kill him in a manner which is too cruel and too disgusting to describe here; then his entrails are thrown to the hounds.

March 9, 1979

THE SIGHT of David Ennals[3] being pampered by delicious young nurses in the Westminster Hospital fills me with bilious hatred. The trouble is that the more Jamie Morris tries to persecute him, the sorrier these lovely creatures feel for the nasty old sod.

Jamie should not be discouraged. One way to put hounds off the scent is to carry a bag of offal – kidneys, hearts, mega-colons and pancreases. These can usually be secured from the operating theatres. No trade union leader or working class spokesman should be without such a bag while YUCDRAG is on the prowl.

March 10, 1979

IN THE GREAT Devolution Debate in the Oxford Union I catch my first glimpse of Leon Brittan, the "outstandingly able" young Member for Cleveland. The sight fills me with despair.

Why is the Conservative Party full of shits? Until this morning I was quite well disposed towards young Brittan without ever having seen him. We have several friends in common and I have always had the greatest admiration and affection for his half-brother Sam, the monetarist thinker. But now one

1 Thorogood, an earlier hero of Labour, was jailed after having refused to work for 25 years.
2 The expression "legitimate target" was used by violent pickets to describe anyone that they beat up.
3 Labour's Health Minister.

begins to understand why the Tories keep losing.

Generally speaking, the best people nowadays go into journalism, the second best into business, the rubbish goes into politics and the shits go into law. It is time the voters of Cleveland sent this odious young man with his affected, silly voice back where he belongs.

March 26, 1979

THE MIDLANDS HOTEL Manchester has many happy memories for me, not least a week of love I once spent there with a strange, squeaking Frenchwoman who later married the Duke of Bedford.[1] But for the life of me I can't think what I am doing staying alone in the Holiday Inn, Birmingham, which must be the nastiest hotel in the ugliest city in Europe.

Since there is nobody I could conceivably wish to talk to in Birmingham, I remain in my vile, freezing hotel bedroom and read the Gideon Bible – *Exodus* Chapters VII to XII: how the Jews eventually got out of Egypt after sending plagues of frogs, lice, flies, boils and locusts to annoy the Pharaoh.

It occurs to me that the odious Menachem Begin-Again could probably use similar methods to get the remaining Jews out of Russia before the Socialists start murdering them again. Now that the disgraceful frenzies of anti-Semitism inspired by *Holocaust* are beginning to abate, I think I may address myself seriously to this problem.

March 28, 1979

BEFORE LEAVING Birmingham I make a pilgrimage to the Saltley Gas Works, scene of a great working class victory when the late Sir Derrick Capper, Chief Constable of this ignoble, vile and bloody town, surrendered his force to 6,000 rioting "miners" in 1972.

Capper's cowardice – repeated by many Chief Constables since – has done more mischief than all the deliberate treason of politicians since the beginning of our island story.

The Birmingham police had no excuse. This morning we read of a Devon policeman who died of meningitis a few days after being spat in the face by a football fan in Torquay, but the lower classes had not developed this "Spit of Death" at Saltley.

We are working on counter-measures now. Camels have always been famous for their poisonous spittle – a direct hit in the eye produces tertiary syphilis within days – but this is the first time biological weapons have been deployed in the class war. Perhaps we should have police mounted on camels in the future.

Standing bareheaded before the great wire gates of Saltley Gas Works, I vow revenge. Next time I come to Birmingham I will bring rabies, botulinus toxin and Lassar Fever:

> Wild Spirit, which art moving everywhere
> Destroyer and preserver; hear, O hear!

April 4, 1979

AN EARLY morning summons to attend on Lord Gnome in person. I rush off to brush my teeth and shout at the dear Wife for not having cleaned my shoes properly. Trembling, I compose my face into the most

1 Nicole, Duchess of Bedford, claimed to have met a strange man in these circumstances. See *Diaries 1972-76*.

enthused[1] expression I can summon as I approach the Presence.

His Lordship receives me, as always, on the lavatory. He shows me a copy of the morning newspaper.

It says that Mr Thorpe has been adopted as Liberal candidate in North Devon and that the Lord Chief Justice has delayed his trial until a time more convenient to the exalted statesman. What is this to me?

Lord Gnome tells me that he has always been particularly fond of dogs. One day, he hopes to be able to own a dog for himself. Do I have any dogs? Yes, I babble, several. That is good, says Lord Gnome. Otherwise he would have to buy me some. He dismisses me with a nod.

What can this mean? Have I done something wrong?

April 5, 1979

TODAY'S NEWSPAPERS explain everything. Under huge photographs of myself, my dear Wife and my Dogs I learn that I am to stand as Dog Lovers' candidate in North Devon. As the election approaches, Lord Gnome has decided that the Liberal candidate for North Devon may not have quite the necessary qualities to appeal to the nation's dog lovers. So I am to be a Member of Parliament in his place.

Who would have thought if they had seen me during my schooldays in Lancashire – a regular scamp I was, I can tell you – that one day I would be mingling with the mightiest in the land and rubbing shoulders with television personalities like Dennis Howell[2] and Cyril Smith[3] in the Palace of Westminster?

Lord Gnome is paying all my expenses and any bribes which may be necessary, but I desperately need an agent in the constituency.

April 10, 1979

I CAN'T BELIEVE the Conservatives will present a serious challenge to me in North Devon. Mrs Thatcher hopes they will be swept to power by a general enthusiasm for hanging after nice Airey Neave's murder in the House of Commons.

She is only worried about members of the public who decide to murder a politician, of course. I wonder if she feels quite the same about politicians who go around murdering members of the public.

I am referring, of course, to poor Mr Bhutto, whose cruel hanging in Pakistan should discourage the most avid Conservative politician from this unpleasant enthusiasm.

Now I am off to Rome until April 18. Gifts of money, flowers, Pedigree Chum etc may be sent to Combe Florey, but genuine offers of help – as agent, sponsors, canvassers, envelope addressers, stewards at public meetings etc – should be sent to the Campaign Manager at Gnome House. After I am elected, a Grand Ball and Dog Show will be held in the Town Hall, Barnstaple, to which all helpers will be invited. That is my first and only election promise.

April 11, 1979

IN ROME to seek the blessing of Pope Ringo on my Parliamentary candidature in North Devon. I find difficulty in securing an audience. One explanation may be that this is Holy Week, a time when many clergymen are busier than usual, but I see something more sinister than this. I suspect the hand of Cardinal Alfredo Bougainvillea, malodorous head of the Vatican Dirty Tricks Department (the dreaded *Comitato Santo degli Squalidi Trucchi*) who is known to be my sworn enemy.

But the Pope could not be more affable. He asks if I have brought any babies for him to throw into the air, and confesses he has never tried the trick with dogs when I ask him to pose for photographs. He is anxious to do anything he can to help the Dog Lovers Party in North Devon, and offers to put the whole of England under Interdict if Thorpe is returned in my place.

This, as everyone knows, would mean that the English would be forbidden to be

1 A word used by the late Mr. A. Shrimsley, editor of *NOW!* magazine, to describe his feelings for his proprietor, Sir J. Goldsmith.

2 A particularly maladroit Labour politician, noted for aggravating natural disasters.

3 A Liberal MP, noted for corpulence.

born, marry or die, except in Church porches. I point out that with the falling birth-rate, a general disinclination to marry and the ever-present threat of a geriatric explosion, nothing should be done to discourage them from any of these things. We swear eternal friendship, and he invites me to breakfast next morning.

April 12, 1979

A SIMPLE enough meal: bortsch, green sausages, sauerkraut, cold beer and bitter black bread which tastes of conkers. The Pope says that as it is Maundy Thursday he must go to St John Lateran and wash the feet of twelve poor men. When I ask why they can't wash their own feet, he replies that the act is a symbolic one, going back to the Last Supper.

If the poor are genuinely unable to wash their own feet, then of course the Pope is doing something useful and kind. But if it is merely symbolical, I urge him to think again.

There was a time when it might have been considered a beautiful and unusual thing for the Pope to wash the feet of the poor. Nowadays, the poor expect it as a right, and many not only refuse to wash their own feet but refuse to have them washed by anyone under the rank of Air Vice Marshal or suffragan bishop.

April 15, 1979

MUSING AMONG the Bernini marbles in the Villa Borghese, I find a curious change in my attitude over the years. On previous visits I always vowed that I, too, would one day live in a home like this; such splendours seemed the normal appropriate reward for a life of honest hard work and applied intelligence.

Now I see that I was wrong. The only relevance of the Villa Borghese to our drab modern world is in the glimpse it affords of a Life Hereafter as the closest we can get to the idea of Heaven. When I come to power after the general election I shall not try to build myself a comparable palace, although I shall probably pull down Basil Spence's absurd and disgusting British Embassy in the Via XX Settembre.

The time for building is past. All we can hope to do for posterity is to tidy up some of the existing debris, and among the first to go will be the Caroline Thorpe Memorial at Codden Hill. When Thorpe put it up I wrote a moving appeal to him in the *Evening*

Standard, urging him to take it down again and restore a small corner of the countryside to its original beauty. This would be the best public memorial to his private grief, for which future generations would be grateful.

He chose to ignore my advice and must now face the consequences. When I have ousted him from Parliament and been elected on behalf of the Dog Lovers Party for North Devon I shall allow only one further public monument to be built.

This will be to Rinka, the blameless Great Dane whose death in tragic circumstances on Porlock Hill has caused anxiety among dog lovers all over the country. At this stage none of us can be certain how or why it was Rinka died, or at whose hand. All we can say for certain is that the dog is dead.

April 16, 1979

TO NAPLES for a few days, for a bracing glimpse of the poor. Neapolitans are not like other Italians. Most of them are covered by thick black hair, and many have small curly tails like Lynda Lee-Potter. I do not think I have ever seen so many dwarves and hunchbacks as I see in my first ten minutes – the only race who resemble Neapolitans in any way are the Welsh – but the two things which impress me most are the insolence of the porters and the breathtaking dishonesty of the taxi-drivers.

My ostensible reason for being here is to write a treatise on baby deaths among slum-dwellers for a magazine called *British Medicine* which is paying my expenses. It appears that babies have taken to turning red (or more often black) and dying. The English attribute this tendency to their social conditions, the Neapolitans to a strange virus which, they say, comes from England.

Preliminary fieldwork suggests a third possibility, that it may be the mussels and other shellfish from the Bay of Naples. A *zuppa di pesce* from one of the town's few *restaurants de grand confort* tastes distinctly odd.

April 20, 1979

NOBODY has invited me to the mammoth children's party in Hyde Park next month. Perhaps my friend Patric Leischfeld, the gifted photographer, will get in. He celebrates his fortieth birthday tomorrow, and plans to have a face-lift immediately afterwards. If anything goes wrong, he may even get into the next great London event, to celebrate International Breast Feeding Week at the London Hilton on June 3rd.

I will be at the Old Bailey throughout, following Mr Thorpe's trial on charges of conspiracy and incitement to murder. How sad, how sad.

April 22, 1979

MR LESLIE WOODHEAD, the Granada TV producer, has complained to the Press Council about a false report in the *Daily Mail* that he was having an "intimate relationship" with Anna Ford.

Ms Ford is not only divinely beautiful and perfectly formed, she is also clever, funny, kind and good as anybody who has watched her interviewing Margaret Thatcher will know. Any man of spirit would be honoured and delighted by such a suggestion, and so would his mousy wife and snivelling children.

How dare the worm Woodhead insult this lady by complaining? Have Anna's brothers no horse-whips?

April 24, 1979

TRY AS I WILL, I can't find tears to shed for Blair Peach, the 32-year-old Maori teacher who was beaten to death by the police during an anti-Nazi League demonstration against the National Front in Southall.

Photographs of him – he looks like nothing on earth – are now changing hands at £250 a time. If only one could think of some way of cashing in. I have some photographs of Geoffrey Wheatcroft, the celebrated Rigid Man, in a characteristic attitude of repose at the Wessex Regionalist Cave Rave in Cheddar. They are not dissimilar to pictures of the dying Blair Peach. Anybody interested may buy them from me for £50 each.

April 26, 1979

THIS EVENING I hear of an attempt in the High Court by Jeremy Thorpe to prevent my election address on behalf of the Dog Lovers Party from reaching the voters of North Devon. He claims it might prejudice his trial at the Old Bailey.

Fortunately the Lord Chief Justice, with two other High Court judges, has decided in my favour. Perhaps they saw it as a squalid political manoeuvre, dictated more by anxiety about the vote in North Devon than by anxiety about potential jurors. It would have been a strange thing for an election candidate to face the voters without an address or any sort of explanation why he was standing. Thank heavens our courts are not to be taken for a ride so easily.

Then there is another telephone call. Thorpe has gone to the Appeal Court and won.

April 27, 1979

IN COURT again, Lord Denning dismisses my Counsel's argument that there is nothing in the election address which might prejudice a reasonable juror. He says he has been reading *Private Eye*, and can see that my address is quite improper.

Papers are being sent to the Attorney General and it looks as if I and various others will end up in prison after the trial. So that is how my one attempt to come to power by legitimate means has ended. Next time I shall try less conventional methods, but I weep for the poor doggies of North Devon.

May 1, 1979

I HEAR of gigantic protests against Lord Denning with a move to have him censured being led by the Leader of the House of Commons, 86-year-old posturing ninny Michael Foot. For my own part, I urge restraint. Denning is still the best judge we have got, and the only one who dares say "boo" to the thugs of the trade union movement.

May 4, 1979

SEVENTY-NINE PEOPLE had the courage to vote for Dog Lovers despite everything.

Lady Fartwell wept with emotion when she heard. At a huge £340 luncheon party in the Epicure restaurant, Romilly Street, given by my friends in the Socialist Workers Party, I point out that Dog Lovers secured more votes in Devon than Socialist Workers in the whole country.

Tony Cliff replies between mouthfuls of lobster thermidor that if legal expenses are taken into account with deposit and printing bills, each vote cost Lord Gnome about £40. Does this qualify for the Guinness Book of Records?

May 10, 1979

FIRST DAY of the Thorpe spectacular is devoted to legal arguments which cannot be reported. Thorpe himself asks permission to wear a long black overcoat with velvet collar as he sits in the dock at the Old Bailey. This surprises the judge as it is quite warm.

But I think I understand Mr Thorpe's problem. A staircase from the dock goes down to the cells underneath, and it is the draught coming up from these cells which disturbs him.

May 13, 1979

WHY AM I sitting here in the Old Bailey day after day listening to demented allegations about Lord Goodman and others while the sun shines in Somerset, birds sing and asparagus is just beginning to show above the ground?

Is it the Money which draws me here? No. Thank heavens, I already have enough money for my simple needs. Is it a passion for Justice? I have never noticed it before.

More than anything else, I think it is a sense of what is fitting which draws me away from my pleasant acres to the dirt and ugliness of London. Number One Court at the Old Bailey is simply the best place to be at present for those of a reflective turn of mind.

May 16, 1979

MY BUM aches and a drowsy numbness pains my sense. During Mr Bessell's somewhat incoherent account of a second alleged murder attempt involving Mr Thorpe and a Dog called Hetherington, I fall asleep and dream that the next great scandal which will shake our confidence in the parliamentary system concerns my dear old friend the bachelor *parvenu* and bounder Norman "St John" Stevas.

Heaven protect us from such revelations. I must ask George Hutchinson to lunch and find out what Guinevere[1] thinks about my plan for a Royal Commission of Enquiry into the Circumstances of Mr Harold Wilson's Resignation. The general feeling is that we media folk will have to start making some pretty beefy allegations to get it off the ground.

May 26, 1979

BACK IN Somerset for the weekend I find all the roads are lined with broken-down cars and caravans caught by the petrol famine. One man offers me his wife and two daughters in exchange for five gallons of petrol; when I offer him a pint of methylated spirits for one of his daughters he bursts into tears.

Eventually, of course, these stranded holidaymakers – many of them from Birmingham, Solihull and Wolverhampton – will end up being fed to the pigs. Before their final moment of truth, they should be allowed a little glimpse of how much they are hated.

May 30, 1979

THE TRIAL of the Century staggers on. Strange pools of reticence, like quicksand, make the Crown case both difficult and hazardous to follow. Letters allegedly written by Thorpe to Norman Vater are held to be irrelevant, while long periods of argument – at goodness knows what cost to the defendants – are devoted to the question of whether the continuation of a certain line of cross-examination might result in the mentioning of Someone's name whom nobody wishes to hear mentioned.

June 1, 1979

ANDREW GINO NEWTON, a self-confessed canicide or dog-murderer, does not seem to realise how lucky he was that he killed poor Rinka with one shot. I remember some most distressing scenes from my Army days in Cyprus, on nocturnal dog-shoots with Land Rover headlights and Sten guns.

It is hard to see how this trial can end happily for everyone. Sometimes I dream, in the long sleepy afternoons, that the Defence calls a surprise last minute witness, and Rinka bounds into the courtroom, panting eagerly and wagging her tail. But even this development, happy as it would be from nearly every point of view, would leave the Director of Public Prosecutions, Sir Thomas "Tony" Hetherington, looking like the biggest fool in England.

Another dream I have is that the jury has returned. In answer to the judge's question, the foreman replies: "Not Guilty, my Lord." Mr Thorpe receives the news in silence, his face expressionless except for the faintest of smiles playing around those handsome, devil-may-care lips. Marion Thorpe faints and is carried out with loud cries – "Help me hence, ho!"; "Look to the lady." In the silence that follows a little noise is heard rising from the press benches which soon grows into a tumult, a great keening wail of lamentation.[2]

June 2, 1979

THREE NORMANS are involved in this case, in one way or another. All are or were friends of Jeremy Thorpe. As a quick reference guide, I list them here:

1) Norman Scott. Dog lover. Horse lover. No relation to the Earl of Eldon.

2) Norman Vater, called "Van". Nobody

1 Lady Tilney, wife of an MP and an influential friend of Mr Hutchinson.

2 This is more or less what occurred. See *infra* June 21, 1979.

seems to know much about him except that Thorpe once held him in "high esteem".

3) Sir Norman Skelhorn. Aged 69. Director of Public Prosecutions until 1977. *Club*: Royal Automobile.

Nobody has yet mentioned the names of either Norman Stevas (*né* Papadopoulos) the popular art expert, or Norman Balon, the Soho restaurateur, in any connection whatever.

June 5, 1979

THE HANDSOMEST QC in the case is Peter Taylor, leading counsel for the Crown. All the Glendas in the courtroom are swooning for him, saying he can *ex parte* their injunctions anytime etc. May the good Lord protect him from Lynda Lee-Potter, who still hasn't named me as the sexiest journalist of the year.

June 11, 1979

ON THE 84th day of the Thorpe trial, the judge comes into court accompanied by a stately-looking pooftah in red robes, carrying a posy of flowers.

This is Widdicombes, the ancient ceremony, re-enacted every year on St Gannex Day. In former times, the idea was that these flowers hid the terrible Newgate stench which came up from the cells under the court. They were also thought to give protection against jail-fever.

Nowadays there is no jail-fever and prisoners are deodorised, desexed and given artificial breasts shortly after capture. The only reason for carrying pretty posies now is to hide the nauseating smell of the lawyers as they toil away to milk the case for all it is worth. Today I counted 36 lawyers in court, all ticking away like taximeters, before I fainted from the smell.

June 16, 1979

SIR COLIN Coote has died at 85. He was my first Editor on the *Daily Telegraph* many years ago, in the good old days when everything was exactly the same as it is now. He always struck me as a thoroughly good egg. I should have invited him to lunch at *Private Eye* and now it is too late.

Another great sorrow is that the social workers' strike in Tower Hamlets has come to an end after six months. Everybody has been much happier in Tower Hamlets since the members of the "caring professions" ceased to care – fewer wives and babies have been bashed, fewer old age pensioners have complained of hypothermia, or fallen arches, or rabies.

From photographs one could see that most of these social workers were hideous and vile, the sort of human jetsam which can only really be employed annoying old age pensioners and teaching women to breast feed, preferably in the East End of London.

But one or two of them have pretty faces, nice figures, jaunty little bums. I feel they should be rescued from this filthy trade and given useful jobs, nursing or caring for people in massage parlours. That is where they are needed.

June 18, 1979

AN URGENT message from the Palace: Whom do I recommend as the new Royal dressmaker now that poor dear Norman Hartnell is dead?

I say I will discuss the matter with my old friend Kenneth Rose, but a cold voice at the end of the line says there must be no consulting. After a long pause while I rack my brains, I suggest they need someone completely different from the usual mould of Royal dressmakers.

I am thinking of someone small, creative, at present unemployed, heterosexual, walks with a bit of a wiggle – has she got it? Harold Evans!! There is an icy silence, a click and then the dialling tone.

June 19, 1979

THE THORPE TRIAL is over and we await the verdict. Judge Cantley's summing-up was one of the strangest judicial performances I have ever seen. Sniggering and giggling throughout he insulted the prosecution witnesses one by one, misdirected the jury about the "impeccable" character of the defendants and urged them not to believe Mr Bessell.

I decide to dedicate my book about this dingy affair to Peter Taylor QC, Chief

Counsel for the Crown, and Chief Superintendent Challes, practically the only two people who come out of it with any credit.[1]

Towards the end of his second day's closing speech Mr Carman QC said he thought there might, indeed, still be a place in public life for his client, Mr Thorpe. I think there may still be a place in public life for me, too. At the next general election I may easily find myself standing not only as a Dog Lovers' candidate, but also for Law and Order and Public Safety, against Frightening Tendencies in Public Life.

June 20, 1979

THE JURY is still out. Thorpe apparently spent the night in hospital in Brixton Prison with an upset stomach. Just occasionally, I, too, have suffered from an upset stomach and it can be quite disagreeable, although it has never occurred to me to go to hospital for it.

The other three defendants, being of lower class, spent the night locked in a single cell with two rebarbative Negroes. Although not by nature a left-winger, I feel something about this case stirs the latent Robespierre in me.

June 21, 1979

THE VERDICT. Thorpe declared not guilty, as we all knew he would be. How could it have occurred to any of us for a moment that he was anything but innocent?

Speaking for myself, I think it may have been something to do with the double-breasted waistcoats he wears. At my school, prefects were allowed to wear these absurd garments as a badge of office. So many of them were hypocrites, sodomites, and criminal psychopaths that I understandably jumped to the conclusion that Jeremy Thorpe might just possibly be one, too.

Now we know otherwise, perhaps he will consider wearing more conventional clothes in the future.

June 22, 1979

HOW AGREEABLE to be back in the country after all the filth and squalor of London. Early spring scents of narcissus and wisteria are giving way to heavy summer smells of honeysuckle, syringa and rose; blossom has broken out all over and my croquet form is miraculous.

But of all the pleasures known to man – and I have tried a thing or two in my time – I have never discovered anything to beat the simple joy of counting one's Krugerrands in one's own front parlour. My heart goes out to 22-year-old Jane Linch who, as the result of a road accident, now has an allergy which prevents her from touching gold in any form.

The judge awarded her £30,000 for this grave deprivation which restores a little of one's shaken confidence in British justice. But then one asks oneself what on earth she can spend the money on which will give her the same pleasure. Poor woman.

July 5, 1979

ONE COULD not hope for a kinder, nicer man than Trevor Macdonald to break the bitter news of Anna Ford's engagement. Trevor seems to understand exactly how I feel – the anguish and yet the joy, the terrible, over-riding fear: *has she made the right choice?*

In retrospect one can see that a clergyman's daughter like Anna might easily be dazzled by someone like "Jon" Snow, who is a son of the late Suffragan Bishop of Whitby.[2] Last Sunday was the Feast of St John the Baptist, who ate locusts and wild honey in a raiment of camel's hair and was beheaded for inveighing against the corruption of King Herod's court. But why, oh why, does the son of the Bishop of Whitby call himself "Jon" like some Neasden hairdresser of ambiguous tendencies?

1 In the event, Waugh dedicated his book: *The Last Word* (Michael Joseph, 1980), to Richard Ingrams, his employer, described as "guide, philosopher and friend".

2 The engagement was short-lived.

July 10, 1979

AT A HUGE party to celebrate the 25th Anniversary of *Playboy* magazine I begin to think that there might be some hope for the survival of heterosexuality in Britain. Mr Victor "Disgusting" Lownes, the amiable host, had the bright idea of dressing young women up as rabbits to tickle our jaded palates. The older does here, some of whom have been hopping around in this strange disguise for twenty-five years, testify to its success.

In Somerset, where the Bunny idea has not really caught on, it might be a better plan to dress them up as sheep. Anyway, it is worth trying, and there could be a fortune in it.

July 18, 1979

AT LAST I have decided on a name for the book.[1] The idea came to me in a flash of inspiration while I was reading from the works of Beatrix Potter to the outdoor servants and farm labourers. I have instituted these readings in protest against the collapse of secondary education in this country, and in rehearsal for the traditional Connolly Night celebrations later this year.

This is what I read from *The Tale of Mr Jeremy Fisher*:

> "The water was all slippy-sloppy in the larder and in the back passage. But Mr Jeremy liked getting his feet wet; nobody ever scolded him and he never caught a cold!"

Suddenly the Idea was born:

THE BACK PASSAGE

by

Auberon Waugh

Part One: The Tale of a Flopsy Bunny

Part Two: Fierce Bad Rabbit

Part Three: Mr Jeremy Escapes

Epilogue: Let Us Now Praise Famous Men

All these ideas are world copyright and anyone who plagiarises them will spend the rest of his days in a prison cell with three rebarbative Negroes suffering from upset stomachs.

July 29, 1979

PICTURES of Lord Snowdon and his new baby daughter must mean it is safe to mention this man's name in print again without danger of being sent to prison by the toothbrush-rattling Mr Justice Cantley.

Snowbum, it always seems to me, is the last of the great Welsh heroes. Born to be small and without any obvious advantages, he now enters placid middle age with an earldom – probably the last of these agreeable things to be created – *and* a pleasant, pretty wife to go with it.

His little daughter should lack for nothing which a caring family background can supply. If ever she should lose a leg or go mad, she can be certain that daddy will be at hand with his camera to catch the precious moments.

Now he can amuse himself for the rest of his days designing invalid chairs which will overturn on corners, thus adding enormously to the gaiety of the nation.

Other jokes one might try in his position are crutches and wooden legs made of india-rubber, wigs which stand on end, false teeth which glow beside you in the tumbler at night and sing the *Marseillaise* to call you in the morning. Disabled persons' lavatories should be left well alone, on the other hand. The country is not yet ready for jokes in this field.

July 30, 1979

ANOTHER half-Jewish Old Etonian Welsh dwarf who seems to be in need of congratulation is 42-year-old David Pryce-Jones, the Simon Wiesenthal of English letters. After six shots at it, he has at last written a very good novel, called *Shirley's Guild* (Popeye, Snipcock & Runne, £5.25).

"Prycey" has always been torn between two identities. There is the sad and sensitive "David", who takes high moral attitudes and is very bitter about being half-Jewish – it was this character who embarked on a strange trail of revenge against poor Unity Mitford, dead and buried these 30 years, and insulted Nick Bentley, the gentle old left-winger who illustrated this column.

1 Waugh's account of the Thorpe trial was in fact called *The Last Word* (Michael Joseph, 1980).

Then there is "Taffy" Jones, as merry and gossipy a little Welshman as ever stole telephone wire from the colliery tip at Aberfan and squabbled about the compensation afterwards.[1]

August 1, 1979

THE BEST THINGS on television this summer are the National Health Council advertisements warning parents not to overfeed their disgusting, football-like, toothless children.

Over half the population in Britain is overweight. The main reason is that it sits in front of the television all day, watching advertisements. This is the average diet of your typical toothless, spherical, 14½-year-old British child, usually of indeterminate sex:

Breakfast: 4 Crunchie bars; 3 fish-fingers; 1 pkt Coca-Cola flavour Spangles; 1 tin condensed milk; 2 btles Fanta.
Elevenses: 3 Mars bars; 2 artificial cream buns; ½pt peppermint-flavoured milk; 3 pkts Monster Munch multi-flavoured crisps.
Luncheon: 3 fish fingers; 2 Twix bars; 1 tin fruit salad; 17 tea biscuits; ½pt brown sauce; frozen peas.
Afternoon subsistence: 2lb Super-Bazooka chocolate flavour bubblegum cubes; 1 tin condensed milk; 2 small btles strawberry flavoured Lip-Gloss.
Evening meal: 7 fish fingers; ¾pt tomato ketchup; 1 tin fruit salad; 2 btles cherry flavoured Panda pop (guaranteed to taste like penicillin); 9 digestive biscuits; frozen peas.
TV snacks: 17 Mars bars; 2 pkts Birdseye cake mix; 1 pkt raspberry jelly cubes; 1 old rubber balloon; 3 cigarette ends; 2oz (approx) dog shit; 1 tube toothpaste; 1 can Pepsi-Cola; 1 elastic band.

Needless to say, there is nothing wrong with this diet, which contains everything a growing child needs. It is watching television advertisements which causes the trouble. That is what makes these NHC advertisements the only effective piece of satire which television has yet produced.

August 4, 1979

THE DEATH of Cardinal Alfredo Ottaviani in the Vatican City at a youthful 89 is a bitter blow for those of us who hoped he might eventually emerge as Pope Ringo III.

Cardinal Ottaviani's last public function was to conduct a service for the rehabilitation of Harold Evans's soul. This service, small but costly, was held in the Sistine Chapel and attended by all members of *Private Eye*'s office in Rome.

It lifted the Anathema and Solemn Curse pronounced on this man when he instituted legal proceedings against Lord Gnome some years ago. Since then, he has lost his wife, his home and his newspaper. We decided it was time to show mercy before his arms and legs started falling off.

His promotion from the pit into which he had fallen is due in part to Lord Gnome's bounteous magnanimity, in part to his own good behaviour. Now that his repulsive, illiterate newspaper has ceased to appear, we can see that he is quite a decent little chap, really, and probably on the side of the angels in most things which matter.

Evans may now travel on the bottom level of London Transport buses, if he wishes, and when travelling by train may take his seat in the ordinary Third Class compartments provided without being required to travel in the Guard's Van.

August 9, 1979

MY *Woman's World* has an exclusive interview with Anna Raeburn: "The Agony of Being Anna Raeburn". It reveals how she lost her virginity at 17 and became revoltingly fat. Then, at 19, she contracted a "very simple vaginal infection" and treated it with "a boiling water and white vinegar *douche* as well as some nice bland pessaries".

1 Theft of telephone wire at Aberfan prevented any warning of the disaster in which 100 Welsh schoolchildren died. Compensation was enormous and bitterly disputed among its beneficiaries.

As a result of this and other complications – she has exceptionally short tubes – her weight plummeted to seven stone. During her short marriage to Raeburn she was pregnant twice, once by carelessness, once by accident. When the marriage broke up, she "poured herself into her work".

In the four years between her marriages she had four "major relationships". There was also a much-advertised physical relationship with another woman, undertaken because "during my life I have attempted to question every single facet of my character. . ."

Is Anna Raeburn the most boring and hellish woman in Europe? I think so. What do you think? Write and tell me about it.

August 21, 1979

SINCE foolishly asking for readers' opinions of Anna Raeburn in the last issue, I have received slightly over 30,092 letters, 415 postcards and an uncounted number of anguished telephone calls.

It is plain that this frightful woman looms large in the nation's nightmares. Readers have blamed her for the collapse of their libidos, their inability to concentrate on the simplest matters, a mysterious, recurrent pain in their fundaments, and many other sorrows.

Quite possibly she constitutes a serious threat to our industrial efficiency, but I don't care. This has got to stop. We should reflect that Jesus had a heavier Cross to bear, remember Dunkirk and generally stiffen our upper lips. What can the rest of the world think of a nation which spends all its time blubbing about Anna Raeburn?

August 24, 1979

THE NEWS that there are to be no charges after police investigations into the affairs of the National Liberal Club breaks like a thunderclap over London's clubland. Rumours freely circulating include allegations of homosexual rape, sodomy, indecent assault, theft, improper conversion and fraud. Can any old gentleman snoozing in his leather armchair after luncheon feel safe while the present Director of Public Prosecutions is at large?

August 27, 1979

A LONG heart-to-heart conversation with Prince Charles on the subject of marriage. His problem, he says, is that his bride must at any rate appear to be a virgin.

It would never do, as he puts it, if Martin Amis or Jonathan Aitken, or some enterprising merchant banker in the City were able to go around boasting that he had screwed the Queen of England. The trouble, he claims, is that the only virgins left are Roman Catholics, and he is prevented from marrying a Roman Catholic by the Royal Marriages Act.

Must he remain celibate all his life, amusing himself with divorcées and such-like rough trade? I put it to him that if he advertises his problem there are many sporting girls who will play for the high stakes and keep themselves *virgines intactae* on the off-chance.

One or two television appearances along these lines and he will have achieved more than Mary Whitehouse and Barbara Cartland in eighty years of campaigning.

August 28, 1979

"DID FULHAM win on Saturday?" These words – the first spoken by 52-year-old football fan Keith Castle after his £70,000 heart transplant – will reverberate around the world, says Glenda Slag, the First Lady of Greek Street.

But one can't help asking oneself, if that is the limit of Keith Castle's intellectual curiosity, whether it was really worth the trouble to keep him alive. He must have heard the results of plenty of matches in his time. Was it really worth £70,000 of public money to let this sickly, retired gentleman learn one more football result?

August 30, 1979

TOMORROW I am off for a month to the sunny clime of Libya where I will finish my book on the Thorpe case, so my Diary will not appear for the next two issues.

People will accuse me of running away from Anna Raeburn's England like the proverbial rat from a sinking ship; but I have been assured there is a mass of hitherto unpublished material on the Thorpe case waiting for me in Tripoli, which will put me streets ahead of my rivals.

October 1, 1979

ON MY last day in Tripoli I make the round of my new Libyan friends to wish them *umshallahgany jibout 'halaam impha'a*. Although I cannot claim Colonel Gaddafi, the Libyan leader, as a close friend, he is often misunderstood and sometimes, I feel, deliberately misrepresented. He is a clean, straightforward person, more interested in politics than in personalities, perhaps a tiny bit boring at times – more like our own Tony Benn than anyone else. In any case, I have many reasons to feel grateful to him.

When I arrive to make my farewells I find he is closeted with his Imperial Highness the Emperor Jean Bedel Bokassa, who looks shocked and miserable at the news from home. There is always something poignant in the spectacle of a deposed Emperor and when Colonel Gaddafi asks if I would like to take Bokassa home with me to Somerset I am almost tempted to agree.

I tell him that, alas, he would not be happy in Somerset. There are few schoolchildren[1] and such as there are would offer him no sport, being toothless and pumpkin-like in appearance, unworthy of His Excellency's attention and almost certainly unable to fit into the Empress's school uniform.

My real reason is that I am not sure my dear Wife would take to him, or to his silly, untruthful stories about what might have happened one night in Paris when I was probably feeling rather tired after the funeral of a very great man.[2]

October 2, 1979

AS MY PLANE takes off, I breathe a sigh of relief. Not only is my book on the Thorpe trial finished, but I can now speak freely about Libya and its workers' democracy.

Groups of workers hold their little councils daily, deciding what they should do and how they should do it. The councils determine the whole nature of Libyan society, from its penal code to its laws on drink, drugs, sex, food, and what – if anything – should appear in the newspapers.

The laws are unbelievably repressive and punishment for any infringement so savage that I hesitate to describe them. But that is obviously what the workers want. They always treat each other like this when they are put in charge – that is what workers' control means. And Libya isn't even particularly corrupt, so far as I can see.

I think that when I get home I will tell everyone I saw pieces of human flesh in Colonel Gaddafi's deep-freeze.

1 Bokassa was thought to have a taste for murdering schoolchildren who refused to wear the school uniform designed for them (and sold) by his wife.

2 Waugh claims to have met him at the funeral of President Pompidou in Paris (see *Diaries 1972–76*).

October 6, 1979

THE LABOUR PARTY Conference is too dull to visit this year. Tony Benn has decided it should be about politics rather than personalities and as he knows perfectly well, nobody in Britain is interested in politics except for a handful of power maniacs like himself.

I often wonder why young Wedgie is so shy of discussing personalities, and what sort of personality disorder he is trying to hide. The key to his own strange character, I believe, is that like his father he was born a younger son. Until his elder brother died in the war, he had every reason to believe that the family title would pass him by.

As he told Parkinson on television recently, he was very much attached to his father, old Wedgie Stansgate, who died in 1960. This may prove the least worrying explanation for the presence of rather odd pieces of meat which visitors have noticed in his deep-freeze.

October 7, 1979

FOR SEVEN YEARS now I have been warning readers of *Private Eye* that English women are growing more masculine: their waists and wrists are thickening, their breasts are getting smaller, their voices harsher, their opinions sillier, their behaviour more aggressive and unstable. Now an underwear manufacturer called Berlei has confirmed what I say about women's shapes.

Men, in my observation, are getting weaker and more feminine, too. Many of them have started to grow breasts. By the time the fashion for bottomless male bathing arrives, they will have nothing left to show.

Various explanations have been offered. For my own part I simply do not know whether there is any connection between this distressing state of affairs and the fact that nearly a hundred times more Marmite[1] is consumed per head of the population in Great Britain than in any other country in the world.

October 8, 1979

DISGUSTED BY England, and worried by Paul Johnson's unholy alliance with "Sir" James Goldsmith in the Publishing Flop of the Century, I am off on a pilgrimage to Mauritius, home of the Dodo, with Claudie Worsthorne, intelligent wife of Britain's foremost thinker. Perhaps she will be able to explain what is happening.

October 13, 1979

ON MY WAY back from Mauritius with lovely Claudie Worsthorne. All the Dodos had already been shot, which was a disappointment, but I learned many interesting things, some of them about Britain's foremost thinker.

Personally I do not see anything absurd or unmanly in the idea of sleeping in a hairnet. The entire Polish army slept in hairnets during the last war. This may explain the clear thinking and wonderful powers of concentration of our greatest living philosopher. Mrs Worsthorne also told me that her husband never eats Marmite, and in fact positively detests the stuff.

How long must we wait before Mrs Thatcher gives Peregrine Worsthorne[2] the knighthood he so richly deserves?

1 Sir James Goldsmith owned Marmite.
2 Waugh's unsuccessful campaign to secure an honour for his friend Peregrine Worsthorne ran for the next five years.

Unless she moves fast, she may suffer the fate of Edward Heath, whose obstinate refusal to honour P.G. Wodehouse on his 90th birthday in 1971 has ensured that not a single kind word has appeared in print about him since then, nor ever will again, and no civilised Englishman mentions the Grocer's foul name without spitting.

October 14, 1979

PRINCESS MARGARET is the heroine of the hour after wittily calling the Irish "pigs" at dinner with the Irish-American mayoress-person of Chicago. All over the country people are raising their glasses to toast the Bonnie Princess.

This makes me rather angry. For the last fifty-six years this woman has been flouncing around embarrassing everybody with her rudeness, self-importance and general air of peevish boredom. Now it looks as if everything will be forgiven for the sake of one *bon mot*.

When asked to enlarge on her remark, she did not even take the opportunity to suggest she was particularly referring to Irish-Americans, who are, indeed, the most hellish people. Instead it is put around that in discussing the murder and funeral of Lord Mountbatten she might have talked about "Irish jigs".

Many people seem to feel that Lord Mountbatten was her uncle, which would explain her strong feelings about the Irish jigs. This is not true, although I believe that the old sailor was at one time very close indeed to her Uncle David, when he was Prince of Wales.

I last saw Lord Mountbatten at the Berkeley Square Ball on the night of July 11th and spoke to him briefly, saying: "Hello, you here, eh what?" or words to that effect. If only I had known what lay in store for him I would have spent more time with him.[1]

November 1, 1979

BACK FROM Bangkok and Hong Kong, I learn that *The Times* is to be saved after all. No doubt we should rejoice, but most of my pleasure at the news is destroyed by the terms of the settlement.

For my own part I'll never to able to read Mr Rees-Mogg's beautifully argued and highly principled leaders without reflecting that some loutish member of the Graphical & Allied Trades is being paid £50 an hour before he'll begin to print it. There's tomato ketchup on those pages.

November 4, 1979

MY OLD FRIEND Frank Norman is feeling sorry for himself. He tells me his latest thriller *Too Many Crooks Spoil the Caper* has gone to a rotten publisher, Macdonald & Janes, who refuse to promote it beyond a tiny library edition.

In my experience there is only one way for a writer to revenge himself on a bad publisher. He must find out which restaurant the publisher uses for his gargantuan four-hour lunch break and get himself employed as a waiter there.

For the first course he merely stands in

1 The first Earl Mountbatten of Burma was blown up by Irish terrorists shortly afterwards.

front of the publisher's table, staring at him in a mute, accusing sort of way and making small slurping noises when anything goes into the publisher's mouth.

Then, with the most abject apologies, he starts spilling things. Generally speaking, wine should go on the trousers, soup down the shirt front and anything treacly into the hair, but *bœuf bourgignonne, coq au vin* and certain jammy trifles are usually best emptied into the lap of your publisher's beautiful, quivering female guest.

November 8, 1979

MY SO-CALLED rival, the cold and increasingly potato-like Nigel Dempster, has got it all wrong about Prince Charles. He is currently romancing with Caitlin, fun-loving, 14½-year-old daughter of Hoonter ("Biggs") Davies, the North London *littérateur.*

Caitlin, whose name has been romantically linked with Harry Belafonte, Eddie Cantor, Dai Llewellyn, "Lord" Laurence Olivier of Mountebank, Blessed Arnold Goodman and Mickie ("Babs") O'Hanrahan, the North London *garagiste,* tells me she is saying nothing at present. Sensible gal. But I suspect her heart really belongs to Georgy-"Porgy" Weidenfeld, 76-year-old *bon vivant* and *raconteur,* and she is playing Wales off against this tubby publisher. Watch this space.

November 11, 1979

They shall not grow old as we that are left grow old
Age shall not weary them, nor the years condemn
At the going down of the sun and in the morning
We shall remember them.

On this Remembrance Sunday, as I stand to attention in the biting cold at the head of my detachment of the British Legion, my thoughts inevitably turn to the great sadness which has fallen on our nation with the retirement of Reginald Bosanquet from Independent Television News.

As I approach my sixtieth birthday[1] on Saturday, I find myself wishing that I had died in the mud of Flanders rather than live for this moment. Reggie and Anna were the only people holding the country together for its headlong plunge into mediocrity. Only they made the news of every fresh humiliation bearable. Only they held up a kindly light in the encircling gloom.

If I were a younger man I would march to ITN headquarters in Wells Street and string David Nicholas[2] up from the flag-post. But the new generation of Englishmen is permanently terrified, permanently masturbating, permanently wet.

Ô rage, ô désespoir, ô vieillesse ennemie
N'ai-je donc tant vécu que pour cette infamie?
Et ne suis-je blanchi dans les travaux guerriers
Que pour voir en un jour flétrir tant de lauriers?

Was it for this that my generation fought two World Wars and bombed Leipzig into a sticky black paste?

Ô cruel souvenir de ma gloire passée!
Œuvre de tant de jours en un jour effacée!

Goodbye, Reginald, Good luck, old bean. We won't forget.

1 Waugh is often confused about his age. He was born on November 17, 1939. His fortieth birthday was imminent.
2 Editor of ITN.

November 15, 1979

AT A SMALL birthday party for Prince Charles in North London the talk is all of a strange article in today's *Daily Star* about Princess Margaret's friend John Bindon, the excitable actor.

The proprietor of this lower class "family" newspaper, Mr Victor Matthews,[1] has always been a fanatical supporter of the Royal Family, which may be why he prints these ludicrous claims about Bindon:

"He used to boast that when he had an erection he could balance five half-pint beer mugs on it. There was a little queer fella in the bed next to Bindon called Dizzy and his eyes used to water at the sight of it."

Sources close to Princess Margaret (N. Dempster) say this is totally inaccurate. When Bindon was staying with Princess Margaret in Mustique, he never managed to balance more than one small sherry schooner in this way. The *Daily Star*, which heads this preposterous story: **"Big John! Secret Of A Hard Man's Party Trick!"** – and illustrates it with five beer mugs, should be reported to the Press Council. Many of its younger, more impressionable readers will be tempted to painful experiments, in some cases involving serious damage.

November 16, 1979

TERRIBLE NEWS from the Law Courts. Jack Hayward, the eccentric millionaire who is in the habit of giving Jeremy Thorpe mysterious presents of £10,000, has been awarded £50,000 damages plus £60,000 costs against the *Sunday Telegraph* for allegedly alleging he was the paymaster of the dog-murdering conspiracy.

Since the *Sunday Telegraph* is appealing, I had better make no comment except to say that I hope Hayward loses. People often ask me what has happened to Thorpe. The simple answer is I don't know, but I think I will be scrutinising the Father Christmases at Harrods more closely than usual this year.

November 17, 1979

I AM TELLING nobody about my birthday today. Many friends think I could pass for 50, or at any rate 55. In any case I am too busy for frivolity.[2]

Two great campaigns remain to be fought. One is against the insane scheme to build a public lavatory in Coleridge's village of Nether Stowey for the convenience of passing motorists, many of whom are probably disabled.

My other great campaign, having won the fight to prevent the ordination of women in the Church of England, is to have them excluded from the General Synod. Last week the reverend gathering had to listen to a lengthy harangue from Mrs Alison Adcock (sic) on the virtues of masturbation.

"Masturbation requires no apparatus," she proclaimed, ". . . in fact a masturbator is more harmlessly and less anti-socially occupied than a smoker, a toper or a compulsive consumer of confectionery."

Foolish woman. People in England – and especially young people – need no encouragement to masturbate. The difficulty is to persuade them to make the effort to try anything else.

November 20, 1979

THE ATMOSPHERE in Curzon Street[3] is strangely formal. J. tells me he is anxious to refute a Soviet-inspired campaign of denigration against Sir Maurice Oldfield, former head of the rival firm MI6. He asks me to make absolutely plain to all *Private Eye* readers that Sir Maurice is none of the following:

1) a homosexual;
2) a Jew;
3) a Soviet agent;
4) a friend of Sir Harold Wilson.

I happily agree to this, most particularly since I know Sir Maurice well and can personally vouch for the fact that he is none of these things. But I find the request puzzling in the light of previous briefings,

1 Later "Lord" Maffews of Kilimanjaro (*vide infra*).
2 See Nov. 11, 1979 n.
3 Headquarters of MI5.

when J. and his colleagues used to make tasteless jokes about Sir Boris Oddfish, "Sir" Morrie Sodfield etc. None of this brings us any closer to discovering the identity of "Horace".[1]

Sir Harold Wilson, the much acclaimed former Prime Minister, is $63\frac{3}{4}$.

December 1, 1979

NEWS OF Mervyn Stockwood's sudden resignation as Bishop of Southwark at the early age of 66 comes as a severe shock. These seem to be bad days for Cambridge-educated bachelors.

Author of *I Went To Moscow* (1955) Dr Stockwood will be sadly missed in left-wing bachelor circles. Although I never met him, being neither Cambridge educated nor a bachelor, I feel I know him well, having heard so many amusing stories about him from poor old Tom Driberg.

Needless to say, I never believed a word of them.

December 9, 1979

IN CHURCH in Taunton I reflect that nobody will believe me if I tell them I saw Arthur Askey in 10 Downing Street last week, so I might as well not tell them. I never really believed that he existed. Goodness knows what he was doing there. Perhaps Mrs Thatcher thinks he is the sort of person she ought to know. I certainly won't be going again.

The priest uses the word "community" 24 times in his sermon; the word "God" twice. The only way to survive these gruesome events is to shut one's ears, grasp a Rosary and contemplate the Sorrowful Mysteries. I don't suppose I'll be going to church again, either.

December 20, 1979

TO THE Institute of Journalists dinner where I see our wonderful old Master of the Rolls, Lord Denning, present plucky, legless

1 Pseudonym used for a fourth traitor in the Burgess-Maclean case. Mrs Thatcher later announced that "Horace" was Sir Anthony Blunt (d. 1984), Keeper of the Queen's Pictures.

little Harold Evans with the Institute's Gold Medal for Bravery in the campaign against thalidomide babies.

Describing him as "the most distinguished editor of all time", Lord Denning paid tribute to his "courage, initiative and perseverance" in providing more money for the legal profession – both as defendant and as plaintiff, no doubt – than any other editor around.

The award couldn't have gone to a nicer chap. There were times in the campaign where I lay cowering in my slit-trench as screaming hordes of thalidomide victims hurled themselves in waves against the fragile barbed-wire defences which were all that stood between us and disaster. But Harry never flinched. Harry never faltered.

December 22, 1979

SHOOTING AT Orchardleigh with my old friend Alexander Chancellor, the immensely distinguished Old Etonian editor of the *Spectator*. All the birds seem to be flying backwards, which is strange. An old boy called Major Chamberlayne makes a gallant attempt to engage Chancellor in conversation over lunch: "Have you left school yet?"

December 23, 1979

ALL DAY LONG my telephone has been ringing. Reporters in London have somehow got it into their heads that I am the prominent man in public life mentioned at the trial of three police officers as having once had an affair with Soraya Khashoggi.

It is true that Mrs Khashoggi was briefly my neighbour in Somerset, but we never met. So many people are coming to Somerset nowadays that we make it a rule to wait until they have been here five years before asking them to tea.

Which leaves the identity of Mrs Khashoggi's lover an open question. Jonathan Aitken might have had his leg over once or twice in his bachelor days, but nobody could conceivably describe him as a prominent politician. Nor could my other Oxford contemporary Winston Churchill be described as a prominent politician, since Mrs Thatcher hasn't given him a job and doesn't look as if she intends to, either.[1]

December 24, 1979

IN LONDON for some last-minute shopping, I find that hatred of Christmas is reaching fever pitch. In one Islington store, eight women drop everything they are carrying, one after the other, and fall to the ground with a high-pitched scream.

This may demonstrate nothing more than the growing insanity of women who live in London, first observed by my friend Dr Alan Watneys[2] some six years ago. But I would like to think they are demonstrating against the new form of "service" in the Roman Catholic and Anglican Churches, which are an insult to God and a mockery of the religious impulse in man.

December 25, 1979

THE STEEL strike is definitely on-going, which is very good news. We must all hope the strikers can be persuaded to stay out for the rest of their natural lives, which seems the most useful thing for them to do under the circumstances.

My own most useful Christmas present will probably turn out to be a volume of kitchen recipes re-issued by Scolar Press: *A Plain Cookery Book for the Working Classes* by Charles Elme Francatelli, late Maître d'Hotel and Chief Cook to Her Majesty the Queen.

First published in 1852, it gives numerous hints for dishes to prepare if ever, in the new spirit of amity, we ask the Harold Evanses or Frank Gileses to dinner: Potato Pie, Yorkshire Pudding, Baked Cods' Heads, Chillblains, a Cure for, etc. etc. But its most useful passages may be those on How to Prepare a Large Quantity of Good Soup for the Poor, using sheep's heads, plucks, shanks, scrag-ends and all those other parts we might have tended to throw away.

1 Churchill later claimed to have been Mrs Khashoggi's lover.
2 Alan Watkins, the contemporary historian.

1980

The year opens well with a national steel strike which eventually closed much of Britain's uneconomic steel industry, notably the vast Consett plant between Durham and Newcastle. Ronald Reagan takes his place as President, seeming to herald a new vision of strength, benignity and justice in the world. But Britain, to her eternal shame, is unable to persuade her athletes to boycott the tainted Olympic Games in Moscow, and the Soviet Union, encouraged by the general acceptance of the Afghanistan invasion, seems poised to re-invade Poland where Lech Walesa's Solidarity movement was causing trouble in the shipyards.

The Seal Pup menace continues and Mr Michael Foot is elected leader of the Labour Party in opposition, but Prince Charles seems about to announce his engagement to Lady Diana Spencer, a beautiful English virgin. Waugh leaves the *Evening Standard* after seven years, under protest, and joins the *Daily Mail* as its chief book reviewer.

January 1, 1980

AMONG THE 30-odd guests staying at my house over Christmas I had hoped to include the exiled Shah of Iran and his family, but it seems that he is unwell. This is sad, as there are a few things I wish to discuss urgently with him.

It appears that the madman Khomeini has somehow acquired lists of all the larger payments made by the Shah to prominent European statesmen and opinion-formers. Before it is too late, I would like the Shah to put a statement in writing to the effect that any sums he may have given me from time to time were either in the nature of gambling debts, or in payment for second-hand review copies of books, etc.

It may seem unimportant, but one likes to get these things right.

January 10, 1980

TO BROADLANDS, for a meeting of the Trustees to decide who should have the ticklish job of writing Dickie Mountbatten's biography.

Many names are put forward: Kenneth Rose, Lord Longford, Doris Lessing – but the family objects to them all. My own suggestion of Spike Milligan is received in icy silence.

No doubt the job will go to some remote and ineffectual don. This is not what the Old Sailor would have preferred. Before he died, he told me that his greatest ambition was to be celebrated in a "Focus on Fact" strip in *Private Eye*.

When I told him that nobody ever read the "Focus on Fact" series, or understood what the strips were about, he leant forward and winked at me with one bright blue eye.[1]

January 12, 1980

I NEVER knew it was a criminal offence to exaggerate the circulation figures for a magazine, yet a strange group of businessmen, accountants and others are up before the Crown Court in Nottingham accused of having produced bogus circulation figures for the old *Tatler and Bystander*. This publication is not, of course, to be confused with *Tatler!*,

1 Waugh had a theory that Mountbatten was a homosexualist and Soviet agent. The eventual biographer, Mr Philip Ziegler, tends to discount the former theory.

the brilliant new publication edited by winsome, doe-eyed Tina Brown.

By coincidence, I could not help noticing that the Christmas edition of *NOW!* magazine, Sir James Goldsmith's publishing failure of last year, contains the strange claim to a "total weekly readership [not circulation] of 1,040,000 in Great Britain".

Later, the even more extraordinary claim is made that on December 11th "total sales that week were well in excess of 250,000 copies".

I just hope Goldsmith's figures are right. It would be a terrible thing if this frenzied Grocer's attempts to show what a large organ he has landed him in prison.

January 14, 1980

EVER SINCE I published my suggested menu for the average British school kiddie the debate has raged about what, if anything, this unattractive object should be given to eat. A left-wing nutritionist, Ms Caroline Walker, criticises the Government's policy of giving local authorities the option of axing school meals on the ground that it will mean they eat more sweets.

I should not have thought it physically possible for the average British school kiddie to eat more sweets than it already does. But now Dr Magnus Pyke, probably the greatest nutritionist in the world, has weighed in to suggest that sweets, crisps, ice creams and chocolate biscuits provide the best possible diet.

But Dr Pyke gives no ruling about dog-shit, which is the most controversial ingredient of every town kid's diet. There are those who blame dog-shit eating for much that has gone wrong with London life – for the madness of the women, the pusillanimity of the men, for the fact that nobody on the *Sunday Times* can write English, for the terrible appearance of Mr Tony "Toady" Shrimsley, London's most upright journalist.[1]

Dog-shit has the additional advantage for many under-privileged children of being fairly soft in texture, and presenting no problems for those in a gums-only situation.

January 18, 1980

SUDDENLY, for no apparent reason, I find myself deluged with invitations and offers: will I write for *The Times*, the *Telegraph*, the *Sunday Times*, *Over 21* magazine? Will I be Guest of Honour at the Law Society's Annual Dinner?

The answer to the *Sunday Times* is of course "no" – or, as they would put it, "no way" – on grounds of class prejudice. But the truth is that I work much too hard already and have decided to go to Egypt at the end of this month.

When in Cairo, I hope to meet President Sadat, although he is much occupied by his negotiations with Menachem Begin, the enterprising Israeli. Sadat is a simple, honourable man, and I feel I ought to warn him about these things called "shell" companies.[2]

January 22, 1980

AFTER 15 years I have decided to resign my membership of the Dennis the Menace Fan Club. It brought me no benefits worth mentioning.

What sounds much more fun is this thing called the *Militant Tendency*. We all wear Blair Peach Joke Club badges, and they give you a little book of Secret Signs to make at fellow members. I can't reveal them, I am afraid, until you have paid your 55p membership and received your pack of instructions. For further information, ring 01-822 3365.

January 30, 1980

FULL OF excitement on my way to a first sight of the Pyramids. The great mystery of how they were built may have been solved, I gather, by the British Grains Chemical Company. Their answer is contained in a single word: ginseng.

All last week the *Mirror* was trying out this ancient Eastern preparation on typical British "workers" to see if it might be the answer to the great problem of, well – you know – getting them to work. First results are disappointing. As investigator Stuart

1 Shrimsley, who died in 1984, was Goldsmith's first and only editor of *NOW!* magazine.
2 *British Medicine* for which Waugh wrote medical columns, had recently folded, owing him money. It transpired to belong to a "shell" company owned by Israelites.

Reid reported, their responses varied from "Yuck" to "Ugh".

The answer, I feel, is to slip it into the "workers' " meals, heavily disguised as fish-fingers and tomato ketchup, chocolate 'n' vinegar potato crisps and jumbo-sized garden peas.

But first, I feel, I must try it out on the Egyptians. It is high time they woke up to the dangers of so-called *détente* and invaded Israel again – if only to take our minds off these filthy Olympic Games.[1]

February 3, 1980

CRUISING DOWN the Nile, past palm trees, temples and palaces in the hot bright sunshine of the Egyptian winter, I find myself wondering why anyone stays in England at this time of year.

Perhaps they are mad, like St Simeon Stylites who sat on a 50-foot-high column in the Western Desert for 30 years, preaching about the dual nature of Christ to anyone who came near him. Or perhaps they are like the desert Arabs who actually choose to live where there is no food, no water, no shade and nothing whatever to do out of some perverse, atavistic sense of propriety.

Our party is composed of such nice, sensible Englishmen and women as one only meets nowadays on a Nile cruise – a West Country baronet and his eccentric wife, two professors of medicine, a retired radiologist and some elderly managing directors. Their views about everything are eminently sound.

As servants scamper around with drinks, or to beg the favour of being allowed to polish our shoes, we decide that what has gone wrong with England is the Welfare State. The modern Englishman has lost his sense of service, and the only sensible thing to do is to ignore him.

February 4, 1980

AT THE Graeco-Roman temple of Edfu, south of Luxor, our party catches up with a group of modern Englishmen – bearded, dirty and looking for a fight with the natives. The bone of contention appears to be that they had asked for some postage stamps for England and are furious to be given Egyptian stamps which, they say, are not acceptable to the GPO.

Perhaps they are right. Now the working classes are in power one must expect this sort of confusion. The only sad thing is that they should still have enough money to inflict their vile manners, stupidity, ignorance and conceit on the Third World instead of saving them for football matches and union meetings at home.

The Egyptians seem to be a kind, friendly and cheerful race. The better classes look back nostalgically to the days of the *ancien*

1 Held in Moscow despite an unsuccessful government-inspired campaign to boycott them in protest against the invasion of Afghanistan.

régime under Good King Farouk, who regularly used to eat 14 boiled eggs for breakfast. He died an exile in Rome at the tragically early age of 45. R.I.P.

February 5, 1980

THERE WERE more modern Englishmen in the bar of the Winter Palace Hotel, Luxor – bearded, foul-mouthed, dirty and drunk. I pretended to be a German professor of Egyptology.

Today, in Aswan, I hear of the ruined 6th-century monastery of St Simeon, less than an hour's camel ride across the desert, and wonder whether this was the spot where the saint sat on his column for 30 years. The more I see of the English working class, the more I understand his behaviour.

I find a small party to go with me, but there is no sign of a column in the ruined monastery, which has been systematically looted and desecrated by Bedouins for the past 800 years. Belatedly, I remember that St Simeon Stylites lived in Syria, near Aleppo, and not in Upper Egypt.

On the return journey my camel bolts for no apparent reason and throws me off – a ridiculous and very painful incident. But I still think that St Simeon may have had the right answer to our exciting new proletarian culture. When I come to power I shall make him the Patron Saint of England in place of St George, who probably never existed.

February 15, 1980

AS A result of my terrible injuries in the Western Desert I am having to shorten a proposed tour of the country to publicise my book: *The Last Word: An Eye-Witness Account of the Thorpe Trial,* published today by Michael Joseph at the extremely reasonable price of £6.50.

My publishers had planned to hire a special train which would stop at every station in England. I would sit in a gilded coach specially designed by Cecil Beaton to resemble the *grand salon* of the Empress Catherine in St Petersburg, signing copies of the book with the assistance of 12 graceful young secretaries.

As it is, people will have to queue for copies of the masterpiece at their local bookshop in the usual way. In addition to being, as John Mortimer succinctly described it in the *Sunday Times*, "probably the best book ever written on any subject", it is widely rumoured to have the miraculous property of curing varicose veins, piles, impetigo, skin-rash and many social diseases.

February 18, 1980

A MYSTERIOUS letter arrives from the *Sunday Times*. Normally the sight of that cheap, unattractive letter-heading fills me with gloom, and I prepared to throw the thing away unread, imagining it to be a complaint from the newspaper's nice but sensitive Editor about some trifling inaccuracy in my world news service.

Then I notice the signature on the bottom of the page. It is from Susan Raven, the newspaper's pleasant, well-spoken Senior Creative Executive Assistant Managing Editor (Forward Projects). She wants me to describe, for the benefit of her readers, a day in my life, or, as she quaintly puts it, a Life in my Day.

It seems an odd request, but I resolve to answer politely because Susan, as I remember, is a sister of the late Duke of Norfolk. She does not use her title in Grays Inn Road. Who can blame her? It would cause the most appalling confusion ever. I will never reveal her secret to a living soul. But I know it is true because the dear old Duke told me so, many years ago in Italy.

But what on earth can I tell her readers about my daily life which will make them feel happy and secure in their wretched existences, which will not fill them with jealous hatred and unease?

February 19, 1980

A LIFE in my Day. I get up and clean my teeth very thoroughly, using tooth powder which should be massaged into the gums with the fore-finger. Then I strip down to my briefs and wash in front of the sink in the wife's laundry room, paying special attention to those crevices which we don't often talk about but where germs can collect if insufficient attention is paid to personal hygiene.

Then, after the toilet – this is most important, whatever fashionable doctors like to say – I put on my new tracksuit in drip-dry green Tomalin (a present from my Kids for my 60th birthday) and go out for my six-mile jog.

On the way I meet Hunter Davies, who is quite well-known as a writer. This is not to indulge in name-dropping, but he happens to be a friend of mine, and we have a grand time reminiscing about the old days when we all wore clogs and ate scrumptious Yorkshire Pudding with gravy and mashed butties for dinner on Sundays.

We are talking about the problem of having teenage daughters when who should we meet jogging towards us in the opposite direction but Prince Charles? You could knock me down with a feather, as His Royal Highness is the last person I would expect to find jogging in North London.

The Prince looks almost as surprised to see us and tells Hunter he is looking for Anthony Holden.[1] Hunter says, "I think he is working for the *Observer* now", and Charles says: "Oh, is he? Thank you very much, Sir", and jogs off the way we have come.

February 23, 1980

THE REST of my mail these days comes from women who seem to expect to be raped. In my role as *Private Eye*'s Marje Proops, I advise them of a new American idea whereby women carry around a canister of skunk oil which they spray over any man they suspect of eyeing them lasciviously or harbouring impure thoughts about them.

This is thought to discourage the men, but I don't really see why it should. Far more sensible, I would have thought, for any woman who genuinely and sincerely does not want to attract the opposite sex, to spray herself with skunk oil. She might even carry a skunk around with her, as silly, rich women sometimes carry gryphons or chihuahuas.

February 29, 1980

AN EXCITING tour of the provinces to publicise my new book about the Thorpe trial ends in the Midlands Hotel, Manchester, where I have many pleasant memories.

In the course of these literary lunches and other public events I meet a whole string of exciting new females, including Fay Weldon, the gifted gynaecologist, and Elaine Stritch, the actress. I also see some wonderful women's hats. But the climax comes at Granada, where I share a programme with Irma Kurtz, whom I have never met before and never really expected to meet.

Irma tells me she decided to bear a love child, Mark – now a bonny seven-year-old – because she felt "compulsions of the plumbing". As soon as she had bought a washing-machine she knew she was going to get pregnant.

A strange woman. One of the most corrupting things about television is the way one finds oneself liking one's fellow-performers. Shelley Rhodes, the lady presenting the programme, kindly recommends a book to me called *Love and Sex after Sixty* by M. Bugner and Myrna Lewis. Irma tells me she knows many alternative forms of lovemaking for sexy geriatrics. Thank Heaven the programme is not being shown in Somerset.

1 The Prince of Wales's favourite journalist.

March 7, 1980

BACK IN the Marie Celeste Ward, Westminster Hospital for general repairs after the assassination attempt by a demented camel in Upper Egypt, I learn that most of the hospital and the entire medical school face closure under the Thatcher cuts.

Civil servants in every department, asked to propose expenditure cuts, are suggesting whatever will save least money and cause maximum public outcry. But the Government has not woken up to this yet and poor little Patrick Jenkin, innocent wide-eyed Health Minister, is solemnly preparing to paralyse the hospital service in Greater London.

Soon, London's sick will have to be left out in black plastic bags for collection and disposal by the Department of Sanitation. But I weep for all those pretty, idealistic nurses who will be forced into prostitution by the Jenkin measures.

Actually, the beautiful Sister on Marie Celeste has been replaced by a male Charge Nurse. Nothing wrong with that, of course, as my friend Henry Root would say. Good for him! But I do not think I shall be staying quite as long as usual on this visit.

March 14, 1980

I HAD to leave hospital yesterday for the Debate of the Decade at Central Hall, Westminster: What Future for the Left?

All the comrades were there. I was given a rousing cheer by the punk anarchists for my short speech about the virtues of an organically produced marmite substitute, homemade from recycled sheep-droppings. But mine was about the only fresh idea to be heard all evening.

It is time the Left regrouped itself under my banner. "Eat more sheep shit" will be the cry of the future. A few Lesbian militants may prefer goats' turds and Benn will never look at anything which hasn't come out of a lettuce-fed rabbit, but some day, somehow, we *must* agree on a common platform.

March 19, 1980

AT LAST a real story of young love breaks through. Two students have been found in bed together at the Warwickshire Agricultural College.

All the presses in Fleet Street are stopped, television programmes are interrupted. It is the greatest news since three American morons put their smelly feet on the moon. Tom Fox, 19, and Gill Perkins, 20 – two names that will go down in history from the new wet-look generation of the '80s – have actually made it together. What does Anna Raeburn think? Over to Irma Kurtz. Were they properly equipped for this experience? Had they consulted Marje Proops before taking the step? What does Mary Whitehouse think, Mary Quant, Cardinal Basil Vass?

March 20, 1980

THE NATIONAL Association for Mental Health has asked me to support its campaign to secure voting rights for mentally handicapped hospital patients. I do so with all my heart, and would like to see the campaign carried much further.

Mentally handicapped people should be encouraged to sit on juries, drive aeroplanes, write for *Toady!*[1] magazine and generally integrate themselves much more into a society which seems in many respects especially tailored for them.

Almost everyone in Britain nowadays is mentally handicapped in one way or another. Practically nobody can think straight, and of those who can, most are usually drunk.

March 24, 1980

TO SIR CECIL Beaton's Memorial Service at St Martin's-in-the-Fields hoping to meet many old friends, but practically nobody is here. Perhaps the darling old Queen Mother is a little frail for these beanos, but I do feel the Prince of Wales might have come. Nobody would ever have heard of him if Beaton had not put his name on the map with some typically brilliant snaps of the young Prince in his pram.

It is a gloomy occasion. The address is given by a dreary old pooftah with a name that sounds like Buggle, but I find nobody to exchange glances with.

Later, I learn that Princess Alexandra was represented by Miss Mona Mitchell. I don't think I have ever met Miss Mitchell, but if she had made herself known to me, I would happily have bought her lunch and we could have exchanged reminiscences about Beaton.

Oh dear. When a bachelor dies, I always think of a cheese *soufflé*. Eat it, and it is gone.

April 1, 1980

THE PRINCE of Wales's refusal to join the Freemasons has encouraged speculation in Francis Street that he is about to come out of his closet and announce himself a Roman Catholic.

His real reason is quite different, but my lips are sealed. Prince Charles's problem is of a more personal nature. Several weeks ago he asked me whether it was true that initiates into the Ancient Craft were required to expose their persons to a Committee of very senior Masons so that there could be no doubt about their sex.

When I replied that this was indeed the case he visibly blanched. Of course I understood his difficulty. Nearly two years ago in a romantic mood he had tattooed the name of a certain Young Person indelibly on a certain organ of his body which shall be Nameless.

So shall the Young Person. Wild horses will never drag the secret from me.[2] When I suggest that a skilful tattooist might be able to alter the inscription to GAITLINE or CATTLING – a curious message for a young man to carry on his Person, perhaps, but at least it would spare a young lady's blushes – Prince Charles sets his jaw and stares straight ahead.

April 5, 1980

NED SHERRIN comes out of an entirely different closet to reveal in this week's *Gay News* (a most entertaining publication) that he is a friend of the former Liberal MP for North Devon, the unblemished Jeremy Thorpe. That is something I would never have guessed.

On the general subject of homosexual tendencies, Ned has this to say:

"As far as I am concerned it only concerns you and the people you do it with. . . and the people who want to do it with one seem to get fewer as the years go by."

The poignancy of these words from a surely-still-youthful-looking balletomane is almost unbearable. If any of *Private Eye*'s kinder readers would like to get in touch (as it were) with one they will find one at the Round House, Chalk Farm, NW1 where one's song and dance routine *Only in America* has just opened.

1 *NOW!* magazine, edited by the late Mr Anthony ("Tony") Shrimsley (ob. 1984).
2 Earlier, Waugh had given it as his opinion that the Prince of Wales had the word CAITLIN tattooed on his *membrum virilis*.

April 11, 1980

A FRIEND telephones to say that Christopher "Robin" Hitchens has written in the *New Statesman*'s "London Diary" proposing "something we have long wanted, which is a solution to the Auberon Waugh problem".

In a state of great excitement I rush out to the nearest dirty bookshop in Old Compton Street and buy a copy, but Christopher evades the issue: "If we could all agree to behave as if the man did not even exist, that might be the answer."

Typically, when confronted with an issue of real importance in all our lives, the Left chooses to bury its head in the sand.

April 12, 1980

EARLY TO BED, after witnessing terrible scenes in David Attenborough's film about iguanas. They crawl over each other without tenderness, consideration or the slightest sign of erotic awareness, like football fans after a grandstand collapse. I do not really think this film should have been shown.

Awoken in the small hours by a messenger from the village with the news that Sartre has died. A sleepless old age pensioner has just picked up the news on her wireless set, and thought we should be told. It takes several minutes to get everybody in the house awake and assembled for a conference. The following observations are made:

"I definitely feel a sense of personal loss." (Lady T. Waugh)

"Oh dear. I thought he died years ago." (Mrs Septimus Waugh, 25)

"Somebody has got to die every day. Why should it not be Sartre? People live by dying." (Mr James d'Abreu, 11)

"It was good of him to oppose the Moscow Olympics otherwise he was just a pseud." (Miss Daisy Waugh, 13)

"I just feel deeply, deeply sorry for Simone." (Mr Alexander Waugh, 16)[1]

April 13, 1980

IN LONDON I give a little lunch party for all the gossip columnists of Fleet Street (except Compton Miller of the *Evening News* whose appearance was not thought appropriate) to introduce them to a young cousin from Oxford who is writing an article in *Isis*.

The party is a great success. From the lovely, fragrant Lady Olga Maitland and the dishy Nigel Dempster (who arrives late after receiving some mysterious injections) to the sinister moustached Peter Tory of William Hickey, Grovel himself and an abandoned young man from the *Evening Standard* Diary, these are the only people in London worth meeting.

As W.H. Auden once said (he is quoted in the current *Books & Bookmen*):

> "Gossip is creative. All art is based on gossip – that is to say, on observing and telling. . . Gossip is the art form of the man and woman in the street, and the proper subject of gossip, as for all art, is the behaviour of mankind."

These are the only artists left in our stricken civilisation.

April 14, 1980

I SEEM to be the only person of any distinction in Britain who is not mentioned in Cecil Beaton's Will. Where can I have gone wrong? One would have thought that he might have left me a little lace handkerchief to clutch.

Greta Garbo once said of Beaton: "He was the only man I ever allowed to touch my vertebrae." I once touched them without her consent when I was posing as a vascular dermatologist in New York City. Her secret is that she is really a female iguana.

Although I never revealed this she has never forgiven me for discovering it. I feel like a murderer.

April 23, 1980

NEARLY ALL my friends seem to be going to Moscow to sneer at the sweaty louts who

1 These observers are, respectively, Waugh's wife, a sister-in-law, the stepson of another brother, his younger daughter and elder son.

claim to be representing Britain at the Olympic Games, but I have no curiosity to see that accursed country or meet its unpleasant, lying inhabitants. We can perfectly well persecute the half-witted "British" athletes on their return; for the present we must just hope they all have heart attacks or foul themselves publicly in the stadium.

Possibly my friends hope to be seduced by beautiful KGB agents, but I could tell them that these Russian girls are hideously self-conscious in bed – no doubt because they know they are being photographed from the moment they remove their *mifjiks*. I think I will go to Jugoslavia to celebrate the death of Tito.[1]

With a bit of luck, by waving a Press Card, I will be able to get myself into the death chamber and settle for all time the mystery of whether this odious tyrant was, in fact, a woman all along. My late Father claimed to have seen her once during the war breast-feeding a seal pup on the Island of Vis. "There's nowt so queer as folks," he remarked in his broad Lancashire accent.

April 30, 1980

ON READING that fags are to be abolished at Eton, I decide to hold my tongue. Certain things are best left unsaid. But I wish everybody had as much sense as I do.

Poor, garrulous half-witted Sir Alec Douglas-Home, who is now completely forgotten but was the last Prime Minister but four, rushes to tell the *Daily Telegraph* what he thinks about it:

"I suppose it is one of the trends, but I quite enjoyed it as long as one had a good fagmaster. It certainly did me no harm."

We can all understand how Sir Alec enjoyed fagging, but I do not see how he can possibly believe it did him no harm, when he looks at the wreck of a human being he has become.

Quite apart from his disastrous record as Prime Minister for six months, there is a strange episode from his days at Eton which nobody ever mentions and has never been explained. I have never yet opened my files on the Great Eton OTC Camp Cricket Bat Murder which shocked a generation already punch-drunk from the excesses of the First World War. One more squeak out of this sickly old brute, and I shall be sorely tempted to do so.

May 9, 1980

AN INTRIGUING letter from J.L. Hutchinson, the Walsall genealogist, advances the theory that President Tito and Queen Juliana of the Netherlands are one and the same man, or woman, as the case may be. He points out that the recent amputation of his/her left leg may make it impossible to keep up the deception much longer, which would explain why one of them is being phased out.

If she is *not* President Tito, he asks, can critics explain why the two of them have never been photographed together? Since her abdication, there have been no close-up shots of her left leg; in fact, nothing has been shown below the waist.

If the Yugoslav authorities refuse to allow me into the death chamber, we can only draw our own conclusions. But for my own part, I have grown bored of waiting for the "death" and am off to Tokyo to pursue some vital enquiries into the controversial question of Japanese body hair, which has been worrying *Private Eye* readers for many months.

Perhaps Tito will still be alive when I get back, but I am nervous of inspecting his corpse, remembering the terrible story of Rasputin. After Rasputin had been given enough cyanide to kill forty men and shot once or twice for good measure, his murderers – led by Prince Felix Youssoupoff – decided to inspect his private parts which were rumoured to be the biggest in Russia.

When they were bending over his body to see, it came to life again and started throttling Youssoupoff, who had to shoot him another six times to make him let go. Perhaps I don't really care what sex Tito is.

1 Marshal Tito, Communist dictator of Jugoslavia since 1945, had started his long process of dying.

May 11, 1980

ON THE first night of my assignment in Japan as Lord Gnome's special emissary to discover whether or not the Japanese have pubic hair, I find myself in a bar with Mr Murray Sayle, the Oriental photographer and sage. He argues that the question cannot be approached empirically but must be studied within the context of Japanese social conditions and economic history.

The best person for me to consult, he says, would be the Emperor of Japan, who has been around in Tokyo longer than anyone else and has probably seen a thing or two in his time.

There are four of us in the bar – myself, Sayle, his beautiful young English wife and their gifted son, Alexander. We have one glass of beer each – possibly, Alexander has a second – and the bill is 36,000 Yen, or about £72.

Luckily, Lord Gnome has guaranteed my expenses, so I pay up merrily. I think I'm really on the track of my enquiry now. What old bandylegs does not know about the Japanese simply isn't worth knowing.

May 12, 1980

A BUSY morning on the telephone trying to arrange my meeting with Hirohito. I tell a delightful secretary at the Imperial Palace that I wish to discuss the current Japanese situation in the context of social conditions and economic history; also that I am a noted expert on Gilbert and Sullivan and can, if His Highness wishes, whistle several arias from *The Mikado*, including "A Wandering Minstrel, I" and "Tit-Willow!" Anyone would think I was asking to marry his sister.

The bedside table of my room in the new Otani Hotel is like the cockpit of a Concorde airliner with innumerable buttons, dials and flashing lights. Eventually a flashing light on the control panel informs me of a message from the Imperial Palace, that the Emperor will be pleased to receive me to tea on Thursday afternoon.

Suddenly, I'm struck by an appalling thought. Perhaps any sparseness of body hair among the adult Japanese – it was first reported by Francis King, the Brighton novelist, a few years ago – is something to do with the two atom bombs, dropped on Hiroshima and Nagasaki on August 6th and 9th, 1945. If so, it would be dreadfully tactless to ask the Emperor to explain the phenomenon.

Tomorrow I will go to Nagasaki and make enquiries.

May 15, 1980

MY TEA-PARTY with the Emperor Hirohito gets off to a sticky start. I have been told he's interested in marine biology, so try a little bright conversation about some of the unusual raw fish I have eaten since my arrival in Japan. He replies: "Ah so?"

After a terrible silence, he asks after the health of the late Sir Winston Churchill. I have to reply that Sir Winston is far from well. He chuckles quietly to himself about this, pointing out how Churchill was kicked out in disgrace at the end of the war, while he has remained Emperor ever since.

Still nervous about whether or not any reported hairlessness among the Japanese might be the result of atom bombing, I ask him what he thinks about the changes in contemporary Japanese society. He replies that he has not noticed any changes.

Eventually, I work round to my real reason for being in Japan. Once again he says, "Ah so?", and the subject seems to be dropped. But after the Empress has withdrawn, when I am leaving after one of the smallest cups of tea I have ever been given, he leans toward me: "In Japan velly funny saying good wine needs no bush hee hee hee." Terrible gusts of raw fish overwhelm me, but I laugh politely. Dirty old brute. What on earth can he mean?

May 20, 1980

ON MY last day in Japan I discover the complete answer to the question of whether or not the Japanese have that nether covering which we all take for granted. It is a question which is crucial to any understanding of Japan's position in the world, and its ramifications were certainly instrumental in bringing about today's collapse of Mr Masayoshi Ohira's Liberal Democratic government after nearly three decades – an event in which I may, unwittingly, have had a part.

But until Lord Gnome agrees to pay my expenses in full, I'm afraid my lips must remain sealed. For as long as two visits to a hostess bar and a further two to a geisha house (£742.50 in all) remain outstanding, this Diary will remain in what can only be described as an industrial dispute situation. Perhaps I shall tell all in a forthcoming issue of *Books & Bookmen* or Tina Brown's brilliant new **TATLER!**

May 30, 1980

AN extraordinarily dirty correspondence reaches its climax in the *Daily Telegraph* today with a letter from Leyland, Lancs. It is called "The trouble with shorts".

> Sir – I wear long trousers at school because everybody else does, but I always change into shorts when I get home because I prefer them. Shorts are much better for playing around in and are much cooler in the summer.
>
> A lot of boys would rather wear shorts but won't admit it. The only problem is that my sisters sometimes write on my legs with felt-tip pens and I can't do it to them because they wear jeans!!
>
> MARK DAVIDSON (aged 13)

I don't know what has happened to Bill Deedes, who will be 67 on Sunday. But if he can no longer keep this sort of filth out of the *Telegraph* he should go and edit *Penthouse*.

June 2, 1980

A BEAUTIFUL, fresh young voice from one of our glossy magazines asks me if I will fly to Pisa to interview a female novelist. Alas, I must spend the weekend at Gnome Towers, so I suggest she asks David Pryce-Jones instead. I even suggest that David might like to take Lord Snowbum with him as photographer, since Snowbum is the only other half-Jewish old Etonian Welsh dwarf of my acquaintance, and one likes to keep people grouped.

My last visit to Pisa was on a pigeon-kicking expedition with poor old Jamie Mar, who fell from a London balcony in 1975. I am afraid we might have kicked little "Pricey" and Snowbum if we had seen them strutting around Pisa's famous Cathedral Square. Jamie was the last of the great pigeon-kicking earls. How I miss him. His daughter, the 31st Countess in her own right, works as a telephone sales representative in Worcestershire.

June 6, 1980

AN EXHAUSTING weekend lies ahead at Gnome Towers. His Lordship – or Marmaduke as I have to call him now – is plainly not used to dealing with industrial disputes among his staff, and seems to think that he has to sit up with me all night, eating sandwiches and drinking beer.

After the third glass of Watney's Red Barrel I can take no more of this torture and tell him all I know about the Japanese pubic hair situation. The sad and disreputable truth is that I decided I would never find the answer to the great question perplexing the world's artists, anthropologists and statesmen unless I married a Japanese lady. Accordingly, on my last day in Japan, I proposed to a delightful young computer systems operator (who shall be nameless) in Hakata and was rapturously accepted.

Everything is expensive in Japan but nothing is more expensive than a wedding. The bill for my marriage feast with 200 guests would have bought two Japanese prime ministers, six senior executives of British Steel, and the entire Dutch royal family. Later that evening I discovered the answer to the great question, made my excuses and left.

I tell Marmaduke privately under the seal of the Confessional, which way the wind blows in Japan. But nothing will ever persuade me to betray in public what that sweet, trusting young computer systems operator revealed to me in Fukuoka Province, Kyushu.

June 8, 1980

SOMERSET is enthralled by reports in the *Daily Telegraph* of a blackmail trial at Exeter Crown Court involving well-known Taunton personalities. One of them died of a heart attack when his former lady-love allegedly demanded £8,000 for some letters. Only the *Daily Telegraph* reveals the true nature of his fancy, which was for knicker-sniffing.

The man concerned, who was a popular lecturer at the Taunton Polytechnic, retired policeman and fairly well-known author of legal textbooks, is referred to as Mr X. It is a strangely appropriate name, under the circumstances, because he could be anyone. Nearly all the Old Age Pensioners of West Somerset, as I happen to know, indulge in this harmless but controversial pastime.

The saddest aspect is how ashamed they are when found out. If the Church of England is too timid to speak out, Cardinal Vass should announce that any elderly person or "old dear" who has a loving, stable and joyous relationship with any particular article of underwear is welcome to bring it to the weekly People's Community Service and Love Feast, where Father O'Bubblegum will bless their relationship with all proper solemnity.

June 9, 1980

TO REDDISH House, Broadchalke, Wiltshire for the sale of Cecil Beaton's effects. Nothing is much good and everything is over-priced but I secure a job-lot of four pairs of rare and interesting knickers in damask lacework for £40 in the face of heavy competition from a lady who looks like the Duchess of Argyll. Cecil would not have liked to think of her or any other woman wearing his most intimate garments. It is an expensive way of observing his last wishes, but I suppose they will come in useful for charades and family pantomimes.

June 10, 1980

PRINCESS ANNE has caused a stir in Paris by arriving there with a black eye. Several French friends telephone to enquire urgently how she got her *œil au beurre noir.*

The answer is that she has had a black eye for some years now, but people in England no longer notice it, just as people who live at the bottom of Niagara Falls never seem to hear its tumult.

There is nothing very dramatic about how she got it. A Clarence House spokesman explains that it dates from the time of her courtship, when she was trying to eat a banana and Captain Mark Phillips gave her a jocular nudge, allegedly in the ribs. The Princess interpreted this as a proposal of marriage, with results which we can all see.

June 12, 1980

A SUMPTUOUS and magnificent banquet at the Dorchester marks the 25th anniversary of *Books & Bookmen*, Britain's only worthwhile literary magazine. It is given by Miss Christina Foyle, lovely 25-year-old proprietor of Britain's best-loved bookshop, for whom the Bishop of London appears to take a violent fancy.

Addressing all the assembled duchesses, earls, baronets and knights of literary Britain, the aged bishop dwells on Miss Foyle's charms in the most embarrassing detail and very considerable length.

At last, when even Prince Philip is beginning to blush, the venerable prelate reveals that what he takes to bed with him every night is a copy of *Books & Bookmen.* "It may be naughty, but I have to confess I like it," he says.

There is an audible sigh of relief when at long last Sir Iain Moncreiffe of that Ilk calls the toast of Sweet Sally Emerson. Everybody who is worth knowing in this diminished country of ours, from the nobility, intelligentsia and literary establishments rises to his feet and drinks to the magazine's delicious, 15-year-old Editor.

June 14, 1980

TODAY is Arthur Askey's 80th birthday. What a grand little chap he is, to be sure. I send him a collection of old cigarette cards, two bottles of stout and a monkey skin with a message of congratulations and thanks that he has not decided to come and spend his retirement in the West Country, like so many great-hearted little old people from the North.

For the Queen Mother's 80th birthday later this year we are sending her a parcel of Good Boys, the doggie sweets to which she has apparently taken a fancy. They are much healthier than Kit-e-Kat, which can be bad for the breath.

June 26, 1980

ONCE AGAIN I lie awake in the small hours, tormented by my social conscience. Sometimes it is the blacks, sometimes single mothers, the lower classes or disadvantaged Highland sheep-farmers but today it is the homeless. Something *must* be done for these people, many of whom are being forced by Mrs Thatcher's cuts to sleep in odd lengths of piping, badger setts and hollow trees.

As a temporary expedient they should be given the addresses of all the 3,000 sports enthusiasts planning to visit Moscow for the Soviet Victory Parade. These lists are held by David Dryer Sports Travel of John Princes Street, W1.

Squatters' organisations should have no difficulty in getting hold of them. Many visitors to the Soviet Union will probably decide to stay there permanently when they discover how delightful it is, and that their British passports have been cancelled. The important thing is to get people out of the badger setts before they infect the badgers with strange and horrible new diseases.

June 28, 1980

THE BEST way to get into Wimbledon without a ticket is to make friends with one of the policemen at the gate. The least publicised aspect of their duties is to remove anything up to seven clergymen every day after complaints from parents that the Reverends have been absent-mindedly exposing themselves. Their seats are then given away by the police.

I find myself sitting between two weeping clergymen's wives, brooding resentfully about the reptilian Bjorn Borg. Obviously the Wimbledon selectors can't be too choosy, but Borg does not look like a human being at all and is quite plainly some sort of iguana, possibly one of the rare tennis-playing *iguanidae* from the Maldive and Co-Co Islands.

Only one commentator has spotted this, the *Observer*'s pseudish David Hunn, who compares the monster to Greta Garbo. I wonder if he knows what I know about Garbo, although my lips are sealed. It was told to me on his deathbed by poor dear Cecil Beaton. Cecil was the only man whom she ever allowed to touch her vertebrae, and he never got over the shock.

July 1, 1980

DOGS ARE being outnumbered by cats in better-off homes according to alarming new information from the pet food trade. The world has always been divided between those who like cats, Angela Rippon and Dan Maskell, and those who like dogs, Anna Ford and Ilie Nastase. This shift to cats probably reflects the greater shift in national preferences towards homosexualism.

As a general rule, homosexualists prefer cats, although two notable exceptions to this are J.R. Ackerley and C.R.R.F. Cruttwell, the fiendish dean of Hertford College, Oxford in the 1920s. No dog was safe from

Cruttwell's loathsome attentions. Lord Mountbatten's real attitude to dogs remains to be elucidated, and Norman Scott was never a homosexualist. C.R.R.F. Cruttwell died unmarried and insane in 1945.

July 2, 1980

THIS MORNING is spent sitting for my portrait by Gerald Scarfe, the cartoonist. This may seem a curious thing to do, but I am persuaded that it is one's duty to give posterity such a memorial, showing warts and all.

Scarfe's problem is one which has confronted all the caricaturists who have ever faced the task of making something ugly or grotesque out of my bland, symmetrical features: there are simply no warts to show. Many have been driven to suicide, and Mark Boxer, sent by the small but resourceful Dame Harold Evans to mock me, had to be led away after quietly, inanely, swallowing mothballs for a week.

As I watch Scarfe wrestling with the problem of finding ugliness where there is only refinement, stupidity out of high intelligence, spite out of good humour, affectation out of manliness, a strange transformation comes over him.

First, I notice a wild, frustrated look in his eyes, then his lip begins to curl like a cabbage leaf, ending up as a sort of jam-and-chocolate swiss roll; next his tongue elongates like a snake until it lies ten feet long, red and glistening on my carpet. His eyes pop out on curious antennae and his penis. . . but then, perhaps I had better not say what happens to his penis, as this is a family magazine read by many impressionable young people.

July 5, 1980

"YOUR average stink-bomb will not be affected," says a terrible man called Mr John Henley, managing director of Mad Hatter Novelty Distributors of Boreham Wood, Hants, when I telephone to enquire about the Government's new prohibition on Super Stink Bombs.

What this foolish man does not realise is that the smaller stink-bomb is ineffective out of doors. It may be perfectly all right for teenage snogging parties, editorial conferences and progressive church meetings, but it is perfectly useless at somewhere like Wimbledon.

The Government claims that at close quarters the Pong Bomb may have an adverse effect on Old Age Pensioners or some such rubbish, but almost anything has an adverse effect on Old Age Pensioners at close quarters. It looks as if another traditional British freedom will be taken away without a whimper of dissent from the cowed masses.

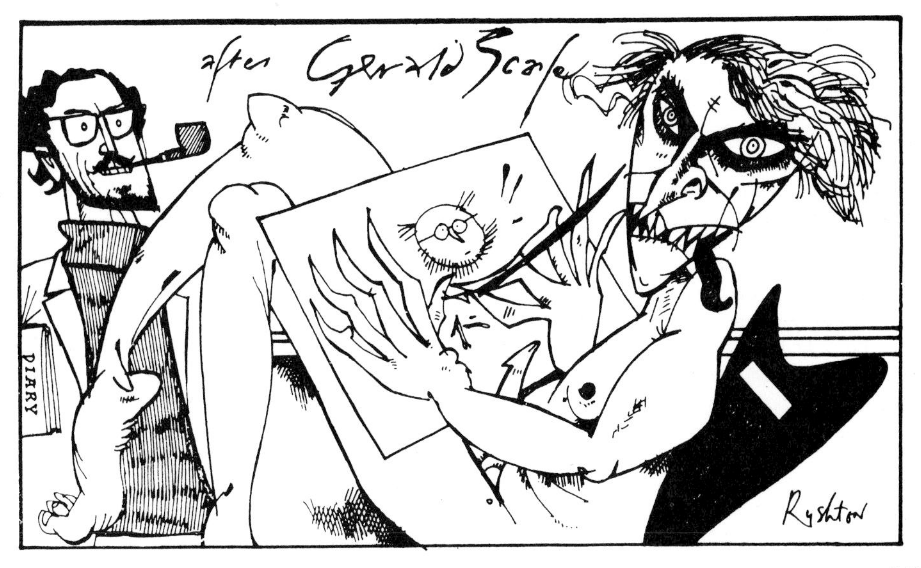

July 8, 1980

I CUT short an enjoyable break in Gstaad, where I have been investigating some rumours about Peter Sellers, when I hear of a geriatric uprising in West Somerset.

Before leaving for Switzerland I gave instructions that all OAPs in the neighbourhood should be bombarded with superstink or "pong" bombs to see if it did them any harm, as the Government has claimed in trying to ban these amusing toys. When they complained about this experiment, I was able to point out that pong-bombs were still completely legal.

Now some troublemakers have circulated details of a Rochford court case where a man was fined for terrifying one of his budgerigars. They are not worried about themselves, claim these slimy hypocrites, but about their budgerigars.

With a certain position to keep up in the County I cannot afford to be on the wrong side of the law, so I am forced to issue all their budgerigars with special gas-masks. Has there ever been anything so absurd?

July 10, 1980

ANNA FORD'S outburst against "body fascism" must give us all pause for thought, but I think she does us an injustice. It is not only for her beautiful face and undoubtedly fine (although hitherto unrevealed) body that we love her. It is also for the beauty in her soul.

Ugly women, in my experience, are seldom to be trusted. They have an inner bitterness, a hatred of the human race, which may take the form of religious activism, political fanaticism or lesbian terrorism, but there is usually a defect in their characters to match the physical flaw.

Similarly, otherwise beautiful women who have vile characters soon become physically repulsive. It is almost as if God instituted ugliness as a warning that certain women should be avoided. Left to themselves, they will probably become nuns or prison wardresses or join the "caring" professions. The idea that they should be encouraged to read the News to us is an absurdity.

July 16, 1980

SO FAR there has been a statement from the Northern Irish Secretary, another from Buckingham Palace, a leader in *The Times* and a debate in the House of Commons all denying that the Prince of Wales has any intention of marrying Princess Marie-Astrid of Luxembourg.

If Charles is forced by popular clamour to marry her it will be entirely the work of my old friend Nigel Dempster, who thought it up one day when he was short of copy. Soon we may see the collapse of the British Constitution, revolution in Northern Ireland and direct rule by Randy Andy. Bully for Nige.

My own candidate, lovely 15½-year-old Caitlin Davies, has failed to catch on as I had hoped. Her problem is that she is not a Roman Catholic, but I am sure that this could be overcome. Then we might paint her black, vaseline her hair into spikes and stick a bone through her nose. If Prince Charles still shows no interest, he *must* be a pooftah.

July 18, 1980

IT SEEMS years since I've been in Manchester, fairest of all our great provincial cities, and one which holds the warmest memories for me. On this occasion my companion – for a Granada chat show called *Live From Two* – is none other than Bubbles Rothermere, fun-loving wife of Mere Vere.

Although I read she has just come from a health establishment she is not yet the slimmest of the various women with whom I have explored the delights of Manchester. But on television, she is magnificent.

Bubbles is a born star, Queen of the Screen. I can't think why she has been wasting her talents all these years as wife of the booby Rothermere. If he persists in his idiotic schemes for a Sunday newspaper, he will almost certainly end up as a penniless booby, as well.[1]

1 Rothermere planned to launch the *Mail on Sunday*, employing Waugh's old enemy, Bernard Shrimsley, as its editor.

July 24, 1980

OF ALL my contemporaries at Oxford Raymond Asquith was always thought certain to go a long way. He excelled in every manly pursuit, and sometimes even beat me at fencing, swimming and Latin prosody, although I could generally hold my own at croquet, boxing and Greek composition. Alas, he died, with so many of the brightest and best, on the Somme in September 1916.

Raymond is now enjoying something of an apotheosis since his grandson, a young man called Jolliffe, decided there might be a bob or two in editing his letters, including some "love" letters to Diana Manners, better known as Lady Diana Cooper, widow of the fiendish Conservative politician who persecuted Wodehouse.

Nothing wrong with that, of course. Good to see the younger generation showing a little enterprise for once. I even reviewed the book most cordially (as I thought) in that estimable newspaper, the *Sunday Telegraph*. Now I hear that young Jolliffe has been crying his eyes out all over London because of my piece.

This is not the sort of spirit which won the Great War. What on earth will this pathetic new generation do when it is really attacked? Young Jolliffe missed his National Service through ill-health, but it is precisely the sickies and wetties who will be most needed to man the front lines in the approaching war.

August 1, 1980

AFTER ANOTHER five hours' work on my opening address for the Defence in the historic "libel" action brought against this Diary by Mr Bernard Shrimsley, a former editor of the *News of the World*, I retire to bed exhausted.

Throughout these nights I am constantly visited by further passages for the opening or closing address, ingenious new questions to put to the Plaintiff in cross-examination.

When I sleep, I dream I am wandering alone in the East End of London past ruined Methodist chapels and synagogues converted into sex-shops. The gutters open and among the swarm of rats a slimy thing with legs crawls out, its hideous face peering aggrieved and self-righteous through all the dripping copies of newspapers and used condoms attaching to it. Should one feel pity or disgust? I am off to France for the rest of the summer and doubt whether I shall write any more for a time.

August 16, 1980

Languedoc, France

MY ANNUAL pilgrimage to the tomb of St Thomas Aquinas, at Les Jacobins, Toulouse has the additional purpose this year of seeking guidance on how best to end the unfortunate involvement between Caroline de Monaco and her disreputable playboy Philippe Junot.

At the time of their "marriage" two years ago I expressed my disapproval in the strongest terms, and even went so far as to boycott the ceremony. But the Dominican Vicar General in Toulouse is of the opinion that my having boycotted the ceremony does not, of itself, constitute sufficient grounds for an annulment.

Much depends on the methods they employed to avoid impregnating the young lady during their brief period of infatuation. If Junot always wore a condom, or *lettera francese*, there should be no problem, as the "marriage" was never, technically, consummated. If, on the other hand, they used biorhythms, douches or inert gelatinous foam there may be greater problems, since people's intentions are seldom clear when they employ these methods.

A huge photograph in today's *Daily Mail* of the two making love while on honeymoon in the South Seas may provide some clues, but it is not explicit enough, in my view, to establish what means of contraception they are using to the satisfaction of the Ecclesiastical Supreme Court. Anybody with further evidence on this delicate matter should write to Cardinal Alfredo Bougainvillaea at the Vatican's Sacred Congregation on Sexual Congress, using invisible ink.

August 23, 1980

A LETTER from my London solicitors causes mixed feelings. It appears that Bernard Shrimsley, the slimy, rat-like former editor (until he was sacked) of Britain's dirtiest newspaper,[1] has dropped his ludicrous "libel" action against me, grabbed a token sum paid into court and run squeaking for cover. So ends the first and only court action brought against this Diary in the history of the world.

August 26, 1980

ALL THE NEWS from England is sad. Now a 17-year-old youth in Ramsgate has hanged himself in mourning for Sid Vicious, the former Sex Pistol.

No doubt many young people in Britain find it hard to get over Sid's untimely death, but just when they need help most the Society for the Right to Die with Dignity has been prevented from publishing its useful handbook *Five Ways to Commit Suicide* through fear of prosecution under the Suicide Act 1961.

I can't claim to be an expert, but here are my suggestions:

1) Swallow forty whole dead mice;
2) Put your head in a 4-gallon tin of Mansion Wax Polish and keep it there;
3) Hide yourself in a crate of herrings on its way to the Walls Ice Cream factory;
4) Stitch a tail on your trousers (or skirt) and pretend to be a dog until you are taken to Battersea Dogs' Home. If you are unclaimed after a few days they will have you put down;
5) Buttonhole Lord Goodman between dinner engagements and tell him you know his secret.

September 6, 1980

IN ALL the fuss about Penny Arnot's party in Jeddah[2] nobody has thought to ask me if I was there. Possibly they imagine it was not the sort of place where I would normally be found and in this they are absolutely right, but the truth is there is very little social life in Jeddah and one can't afford to be choosy.

It was a hellish party and if I am asked who was there I can honestly say that absolutely nobody was – at any rate nobody I knew or had ever heard of. Neither Lord Snowdon nor his ex-wife Princess Margaret was present, or if they were I did not see them. Admittedly, they are both rather small and the place was full of ill-mannered Germans and frankly lower-class English.

Possibly they all worked for MI6 – you find very odd people in the Foreign Service nowadays – but I saw no obvious homosexualists, and suspect this is just another wild rumour.

There was a time when no party was complete without a death. I remember boat parties on the Thames with people splashing overboard and Lady Diana Cooper screaming; a most successful dance in Ireland where two bastard sisters of Oscar Wilde were burnt to death; even a lunch party at the French Embassy in Vienna where Count Coudenhove-Kallergi passed on with the asparagus still in his mouth – although it is true that we never managed to drown poor Cecil Beaton at the Wilton frolic in 1927.

But it was never a good party idea, and certainly not one that should be revived. On reflection, I am glad I left early before the "fun" started.

September 10, 1980

EVERYBODY should read the *Daily Star*, if only to cultivate that agreeable feeling of superiority which is the one remaining benefit of an expensive education. Its main news item of the day is that 18-year-old Lord Linley (son of Snowbum) has attended a topless bathing party in Florida.

Far be it from me to criticise the pleasures or pastimes of the great, but I can't see the joy of looking at girls' breasts when they are publicly exposed. To my way of thinking, it spoils much of the feeling of achievement and all the fun of discovery when they are eventually revealed in more intimate circumstances. But I have already written on this subject at great length and am in danger of becoming a bore.

I just hope little Lord Linley knows what

1 *News of the World*.
2 A nurse, Helen Smith, was found dead after it, having apparently fallen from the roof.

he is doing. How can he be sure, if they only reveal their top halves, that they are not men with things stuck on their chests? Friends tell me that false bosoms are plentiful and cheap in America.

There is also something distinctly odd about today's *Daily Star*bird on an inside page – almost as if the hideous young woman is in pain. I hope these things don't hurt. I was thinking of wearing a pair to Lord Weidenfeld's lunch party later this week. They might cause a few bulging eyes, at the very least.[1]

September 11, 1980

WATCHING television in the hellish discomfort of the Kensington Hilton, I see "Sir" Peter Parker, Chairman of British Rail, appear on *Call My Bluff*. Perhaps it is time somebody did call his bluff and expose him as the madman and sadist he undoubtedly is.

Nothing else can explain his decision to deny day-return tickets from Taunton to Paddington except for those travelling up by the late morning train. At one stroke he has buggered up the entire economy of the West Country. It also means I must spend large parts of the week in London, risking diseases.

The great question we must ask ourselves is how we can reconcile a lifelong opposition to hanging, or any other death penalty, with the continued activity of vicious simpletons like Parker. I do not even suppose he is a very happy man. But the joy of not being a politician is that one can leave decisions of that sort to Mrs Thatcher.

September 12, 1980

TO MY Lord Weidenfeld at Chelsea Embankment. His Lordship is in amiable mood, his eyes twinkling and well secured. He is making enormous sums of money by publishing some private letters written by my late Father at the extraordinary price of £14.95 a time. As I may make a little money from the same source, I decide not to mention my fears about the Curse of Gnome.[2]

Conversation turns to the unbelievable boredom of the reviews. Has Anthony Powell had a stroke or was he always like that? I tend to the latter view, His Lordship to the former.

1 It had been rumoured that Lord Weidenfeld's eyes were liable to fall out in the act of sexual intercourse. Hence the nickname "Popeye".

2 Lord Weidenfeld was suing *Private Eye* on some pretext or other.

October 1, 1980

TO JUDGE *Private Eye*'s Newsagent of the Year Competition I must sift through entries from about 400 newsagents, all hoping to be recognised as the one who has most reduced his order for "Sir" Feathery Goldfinger's failed news-magazine called **TOADY!**[1] The prizes will be announced and presented at a lavish banquet attended by many stars of stage and screen, on 28 November.

Many newsagents can report 100% reduction from 25 copies or so to none, but the average reduction in order appears to be around 80%. If this figure is typical, one trembles for its editor, the nice, red-faced, clean living Toady Shrimsley.

Poor Toady. I feel I may have been beastly to him in the past, and to his dear brother Bernard ("Slimy"), the former editor of the *News of the World* whose pathetic climb-down over his libel action should be seen as a cause for commiseration rather than glee.

Alas, I fear there is no truth in the rumour that the two brothers are thinking of joining the Roman Catholic Church. At any rate it seems most unlikely that there is any truth in the rumour as I have just this moment invented it. But history is often moulded by poetic visions of this sort, and I think I will send Lord Longford round to see them.

For myself, I propose to make a pilgrimage along the path of the old Crusades, lighting candles in all the churches on the way to advance this pleasant idea.

October 2, 1980

FIRST TO St Mark's in Venice where two huge candles burn side by side in honour of these unfortunate brothers, one for Toady, one for Slimy. Then to Ravenna where I light another two in the church of S. Apollinare in Classe under the wonderful Byzantine mosaic of sheep on a green background.

Soon candles will be burning all over the Adriatic and eastern Mediterranean, that God may see fit to lighten their sad lives and fill their poor shrivelled hearts with His love, giving them the fortitude to face the misfortunes and personal tragedies still in store for them.

October 4, 1980

IN THE Cathedrals of Corcula and Dubrovnik Croatian peasants cross themselves and pray before miraculous statues in the hope that one day God will remove the curse of socialism from their unhappy land, but four candles burn in the gloom with another purpose, for the salvation of the brothers Shrimsley, no less – two for Slimy, two for Toady.

October 8, 1980

CANDLES are burning, or have burnt, in Crete, at the Crusaders' Hospital in Rhodes and at the shrine of the Apocalypse in Patmos where St John dictated his incomprehensible Book of Revelations.

My spiritual adviser on the Swan's Hellenic Cruise is the Very Reverend Antony Bridge, Dean of Guildford. He disputes my theory that St John was drunk at the time and says he was talking in code, comprehensible only to Jews. This seems to be a most dangerous theory, which might be extended to the whole of the modern movement in art by unscrupulous persons for their own ends.

October 10, 1980

AT EPHESUS in Turkey where St Paul preached, there are no longer any Christian churches so it is impossible to light candles for the Shrimsley brothers – either for Toady or for Slimy – as I would wish.

By great good luck, I fall into conversation with a grave-robber, who sells me a small 2nd-century Hellenistic marble head of

1 Sir James Goldsmith's failing magazine called *NOW!*.

Artemis, otherwise known as Diana of the Ephesians. It might even be genuine, as the earth around here abounds in such objects.

In the absence of a Christian church, I set the head up in the Venus Bar of our cruise liner and sacrifice two mice in front of it on behalf of the gifted and charming Shrimsley brothers – one for Slimy, the other one for Toady. It is always a good idea to take out two insurance policies, in case the first insurance company turns out to be run by villains or Liberals or whatever.

Dean Bridge is most interesting on the subject of human sacrifice. He says that nowadays people tend to frown on this practice, regarding it as cruel, but we fail to understand that killing is only incidental to the main purpose which was to return to God something which God had given.

He is a most intelligent, articulate and agreeable man. I cannot think why they have never made him a bishop, especially when one sees the miserable specimens who receive promotion in the Church of England.

October 14, 1980

AT LAST Sir Michael Edwardes's appointment as the first dwarf to be chairman of British Leyland is explained. It was so that he could pose for photographs beside the new Mini Metro without giving away the fact that it was especially designed for childless dwarves.

The newspapers say that the whole country is engulfed by a wave of Metro Madness, with housewives scratching out each other's eyes in their anxiety to buy one. I suspect that this is the sort of press distortion which Tony Benn quite rightly complains about.

The Metro looks practically the same as every other car to me, except that it is much too small. In any case, I have always bought foreign cars since meeting a man in a pub in Dorset a few years ago who seemed to know what he was talking about. He told me that foreigners make them better.

October 29, 1980

WITH THE sad news of Sir Charles Wintour's retirement as Editor of the *Evening Standard* after sixty years, I reluctantly decide it is time to move on from the newspaper where I have been writing regular columns for nine years and reviewing novels every week for the last seven.

Wintour was one of the few civilised and effective journalists in Fleet Street. Something of his benign presence may live on, but

I am told that the new Editor, Mr "Lou" Kirby (late of the appalling *News*) has his hair styled at Celine's. He is also having to drop at least one libel action against the *Standard* before becoming its editor.

I think I will move my books column to the *Daily Mail* in the New Year. People will laugh at me for this, remembering that I once swore never to write for the *Mail* again while its editor (who likes to be known as "Mr English") was suing the *Spectator* for alleged libel. Such people ignore the important influence of Christian forgiveness and ordinary compassion in human affairs.

I have never met Mr English and hope I never have to do so, but I saw a photograph of him once and received the strong impression that he was wearing a wig. It is impossible to be angry for very long with a man who wears a wig.

October 30, 1980

TO THE Black Lubayanka, in Fleet Street, where Lord Thingers Maffews[1] has organised a small lunch party to mark my departure from Express Newspapers at the end of the year after nine years of faithful service. He has asked the Archbishop of Canterbury, Dr Runcie, Sir Iain Moncreiffe of That Ilk, Sir John Junor (of some other Ilk), Sir Melvyn Barg, the delicious, 23-year-old Lady Olga Maitland, mouth-watering Prue Leith and a bevy of beautiful women including Edna Healey, no less.

I must say, Lord Maffews is a jolly good host. He doesn't like the look of our *escalope de veau à la crème* so has a special dish brought to him, no doubt containing jellied eels, stewed whelks, parsnips, tripe 'n' elephant trunk pie and other homely delicacies. He says how very much he enjoys nearly everything I and other members of my family have ever written, and how sad he is that his own humble class origins make it impossible for me to go on working for him.

The other great sadness is that the lovely Lady Maffews is Not Ible to be Wiv Us. I hope all is well. If I thought there was any estrangement between them I might have to sell the story to my old friend Peter Tory, whose excellent William Hickey column in the *Daily Express* is the only thing worth reading in that doomed newspaper.

November 5, 1980

TODAY we learn that poor old Annabel Birley has fallen again and delivered another (legitimate) Goldsmith into the world in addition to the two Goldsmith bastards she has already saddled us with. It is a black day for England. These grocers breed like yeast, if they are given the chance, but Annabel

1 Waugh is referring to "Lord" Fingers Maffews, Cockney proprietor of Express Newspapers.

really ought to know better at her age. Perhaps the brute has been looking lustfully at her with his terrible mad blue eyes.

In the evening I go to a reception by the Apostolic Delegate at Archbishop's House to celebrate the second anniversary of Pope John Paul's election. Norman Stevas is not here, which should have put me on my guard. The Delegate himself is a charming man called Archbishop and Mrs Bruno Heim but the place is crawling with Soviet agents. I am not in the least surprised to see Cardinal Basil (or Vassall, or Vassily, as one prefers) Hume deep in conversation with born-again Tony Benn, the former Post Office Minister.

Cardinal Vass has been around long enough now for us all to decide that he is a profoundly silly, profoundly irritating man. I think I shall suggest he be sent back to Ampleforth or, failing that, poisoned – as Cardinal Hinsley was, by an infected oyster on 17 March 1943.

November 11, 1980

TO NEW YORK for the launching of the American edition of my book about the Thorpe trial (*The Last Word* – Michael Joseph – *hurry, hurry*). I am greeted by the news that Princess Anne is expecting a baby. I take the opportunity of a television chat show to issue a formal denial that I am the father of this child. Despite my strong objection to suing, I may be forced to take action against anyone who suggests that this may be the case.

When asked why I think it good news that another Phillips is on the way, I have to explain that from the medical point of view it is always a good idea for young women to exercise their child-bearing muscles from time to time. Otherwise the muscles may atrophy with consequent deterioration of related motor functions. An exception to this rule would seem to be my old friend Nora Beloff who, although childless, retains full motor capacity in every myofibril.

November 14, 1980

NEW YORK is in a very silly mood, with everyone pretending to have voted for Carter when everybody knows they really voted for Reagan. Now the Jews claim to be terrified of religious harassment and pogroms conducted by the muscular Christians.

I keep assuring them that Ronald is the most easy-going, genial and kind-hearted of men without the cruelty in him to drown a kitten, but then I hear that Michael Foot has been chosen as leader of the Labour Party and I begin to understand their point of view.

Foot is a perfectly decent fellow if you can get him alone. It is only when he's showing off to the lower classes that he becomes insupportable. But what terrifies me is the sort of adulation he receives from soppy

people of every age group, as if he came from the Osmond singing family instead of from the family of a jumped up Cornish solicitor and Lord Mayor of Plymouth.

Foot is not a Welsh negro like Jimmy Jones, but I still see the makings of a Footsville Massacre, with groupies clambering over each other to drink cyanide as the world comes crashing down over his silly, quivering Cornish ears.

November 20, 1980

THROUGH Detroit to the University of Michigan at Ann Arbor, where I have been hired to give a lecture on Lady Diana Spencer in the magnificent Gothic Law Library which is the greatest architectural glory of this Northern state.

With the aid of diagrams, slides and biological charts I demonstrate that she is as normal as any girl of nineteen can reasonably expect to be. But there are two good reasons why she should never be Queen of England.

In the first place, she is a close cousin of Charlie Vass, alias Charles Douglas-Home, fun-loving 43-year-old Deputy Assistant Chief Editorial Executive at *The Times*. Charlie has just failed on his twenty-fifth attempt at the coveted Miss World title, disguised this year as Miss Costa Rica.

The second objection is that through her father's second marriage to Raine Legge (*née* McCorquodale alias Lewisham alias Dartmouth) Lady Diana is the step-granddaughter of Barbara Cartland, the romantic novelist and Royal Jelly freak, who lost her virginity on the night of 23 April 1927. If Wales tries to get away with foisting Barbara Cartland on the country as our Queen Gran, he will have a revolution on his hands.

November 28, 1980

I NEVER thought I would find myself jumping to the defence of Bob Edwards, curly-headed editor of the *Sunday Mirror*, but things are getting serious. Bob's resignation from the Kennel Club may be at stake if senior stewards have their way after his clash with Buckingham Palace over whether or not Prince Charles was romancing late at night with his beloved on the Royal Train.

I was not there and so have an open mind on the crucial point of whether or not any romancing took place. But nobody can sit back idly and see a respected public figure like Bob Edwards – whose position does not allow him to hit back – have his name dragged through the mud by such proven liars as inhabit Buckingham Palace.

As Sir Bernard Levin writes in today's *Times*: "It cannot be emphasised too strongly, nor indeed put too extravagantly, that *the press has no duty to be responsible at all.*" If the Queen is "tired of press lies", as she informed the *Daily Telegraph*, then it is plain she is tired of life and ought to abdicate.

Rather an amusing lie has just occurred to me involving Princess Margaret, four black dustmen and a chihuahua, but perhaps this is not the moment to tell it.

November 29, 1980

AFTER three weeks' scrutiny we must all decide that 19-year-old Lady Diana Spencer is innocent, truthful, sweet and entirely delicious. What has Wales done to deserve her? More particularly, what has she done to deserve such a hellish fate?

At one level she might be held up as a shining example to all teenagers of what can be achieved by simply saying "no": no premarital malarkey; no Saturday night fever; no assignations with Martin Amis or Frank Johnson – and one day Prince Charming will whisk you away to a life of champagne, After Eights and opening the Stevenage New Town Senior Citizens' Afternoon Disco and Rest Room with a perfectly natural smile.

But it will be a black day for Britain when she finally puts the crown on her head. Millions of fathers of teenage daughters will have no further excuse for locking them up. What will happen when Caitlin Davies, to name but one, is let loose? I fear life will not be worth living for the nation's few remaining heterosexual males.

December 7, 1980

A PHOTOGRAPH in one of the Sunday colour supplements shows the Minister for Agriculture, Mr Peter Walker, sitting alone in what must be the ugliest drawing room in Europe.

It is Walker who, from this hideous room, has ordered the extermination of all British badgers. He claims they are a threat to the health of cows, but the biggest public health hazard in Britain is undoubtedly Walker's young son Jonathan, the demon shitter.

Soon after his birth ten years ago, Walker warned a Conservative party conference that by the time of Jonathan's 15th birthday the nation would need to build another 20 giant sewage works to accommodate the lad's single-handed production. In a time of government cuts, the case for gassing the Walker family now seems unanswerable. See Anthony Powell: *Faces in My Time* page 94 et seq.

December 9, 1980

SO. Farewell Oswald Mosley, as my colleague E.J. Thribb would almost certainly be inspired to write. Is there anything to add?

There were always rumours about poor old Tom Mosley – or "Kit" as he later became – that he was in fact Jewish. I never believed them, but it is true that he had one characteristic which I have noticed in some of my Jewish colleagues – no doubt it is the result of two million years' persecution – that he always had to be right. Kit could never get over how right he had been about unemployment in the 'thirties, about the Gold Standard, the Common Market etc. etc. etc.

As if anyone cared. I am afraid this insistence on how right he had always been made him something of a bore in later years. But I was never able to make up my mind on his main point, that it was a terrible mistake to get involved in the Second World War.

At the time we were told it was to protect the Poles, but then at the end of the war Churchill handed them over to Stalin and promised he could bash them up as much as he liked without any interference from anyone else.

Whether Mosley was right or wrong, we seem to have learnt our lesson. Nobody is going to help the Poles a second time.[1]

December 11, 1980

RAINE SPENCER tells me the royal engagement will be announced over Christmas, so it looks as if Prince Charles and his adorable bride will be competing with the Poles for news space. Christmas is tradition-

1 Strikes in the Gdansk shipyard threatened to provoke a Russian invasion.

ally the time for Russia to invade its neighbours.

Nobody in Britain can really claim the credit for persuading the Russians to this philanthropic act, but our wonderful Olympic sportsmen certainly did their best.

"In the event I feel I was right because it has kept the international lines between sportsmen open," said the handsome, tremendously intelligent Sebastian Coe, receiving his *Daily Express* Sportsman of the Year trophy from tremendously intelligent *Daily Express* chairman "Lord" Maffews of Shoreditch.

Now Sebastian has been voted third in the BBC's Sports Personality of the Year contest. Since he is obviously the most popular person in Britain, I think he should be appointed Prime Minister to give this country of ours the leadership it really deserves.

December 12, 1980

AS MY time to leave the *Standard* draws near after seven years as its fiction reviewer I wish some kind person would buy the paper from its present owner, Elephant Man lookalike "Lord" Maffews (as my friend William Hickey wittily describes him). Such a philanthropist could send this whelk-guzzling oaf back to Bermondsey, reinstate Sir Charles Wintour as editor and let me resume my novel reviewing.

December 14, 1980

I DON'T suppose the world will ever recover from Spiggy Topes's[1] death. In Somerset all the pigs set up a squeal through the night and even the cows weep. Television programmes are entirely given over to Turds' music and old Turds' films.

Even after all these years nobody in my house is able to tell the Turds apart. "That's Spiggy", shouts one. "No it isn't, it's George – or Paul, or Ringo," shouts everyone else. "That's Paul". "No it's not, it's Yoko." Nobody has spotted the obvious reason why he was shot – that Mark Chapman mistook him for Yoko Ono.

At last I see someone on the box whom I definitely recognise as Spiggy but it turns out to be Hunter Davies, the man of letters, describing how he once swam with Spiggy in a swimming pool for three days without exchanging a word. I do not see that Topes's untimely death adds much force to the argument for restricting gun sales in the US.

December 15, 1980

EXCITING NEWS about "Sir" Smelly Goldtooth,[2] the controversial grocer who keeps trying to draw attention to himself. Now he is hoping to get into Parliament as Conservative Member for Richmond.

1 John Lennon had been shot dead by a disturbed youth in New York.
2 James Goldsmith.

Last time he tried to get there it was as a Labour peer on Lady Forkbender's witty Resignation Honours list, which included such brilliant names as "Sir" Eric Miller, Mister Jarvis Astaire, Bernie Silver, Meyer Lanskey, Big Joe Kagan, Al Capone, Sam Guciano, Jeremy Thorpe, the late Ethel and Julius Rosenberg, etc.

Normally "Sir" Toothbrush would not stand much chance in a staid Conservative area of this sort. His opponent, Mr George Tremlett, is an honest, intelligent man who has devoted his life to the Conservative cause, reaching an important post in charge of Greater London Housing before his 40th birthday.

But Tremlett is not rich, and Richmond people fear that their Constituency Association will be dazzled by "Sir" Crocodile Skin's fish-like and grocerish gold, as so many better men have been dazzled before, usually with fatal results.

December 16, 1980

POOR MAD Wedgie Benn's story of attempts being made to recruit him for MI5 is an obvious lie. Apart from anything else, Wedgie is not and never has been a homosexualist.

He explains the strange request: "It came from a certain colonel in plain clothes" who offered him £1,000 a year; "which was more than twice as much as the income I later received as a BBC producer."

The Intelligence and Security Services, as well as being obliged by the terms of their charter to recruit only practising homosexualists, pay very badly indeed. I suspect that Wedgie was making a mistake. The "plain clothes colonel" was in fact none other than "Colonel" Harland Sanders, inventor of the finger-lickin' Kentucky chicken. Nobody would have been taken in by Wedgie as a spy, but with his mad blue eyes and general air of enthusiasm he might have made a brilliant salesman of finger-lickin' Kentucky fried chickens.

We shall probably never know the answer to this riddle as the bogus Colonel died yesterday of pneumonia at the suspiciously early age of 90. To think that if only Wedgie had been listening more closely he might have done something useful with his miserable, doomed existence.

December 26, 1980

VENICE at Christmas is the Mecca of the international pigeon-kicking fancy. Here the pigeons are fatter and slower than anywhere else on earth, and some have even been trained to give a little yelp of surprise on contact.

In hot youth I used to hunt the scrawny pigeons of Lucca and Siena, once landing a lucky kick on a bird in flight from the top of Giotto's campanile in Florence. While little more than a boy I was arrested for kicking a seagull by mistake in Bari. But I have never known anything like this.

The birds in Trafalgar Square are out of bounds, nowadays, having learned to take the corn offered them by sentimental, half-witted members of the public and then to cover their well-wishers with shit – just like the English "workers", as they are so amusingly called.

I hope nothing ever happens to Venice. The water levels seem dangerously low in the lagoon just now, and locals are saying that all the water has been drunk by armies of hacks from the *Sunday Times*, who descend on the city every other week to write about Venice in Peril.

1981

The Prince of Wales marries his beautiful virgin bride, Lady Diana Spencer, but Waugh notices a cooling of relations between himself and Buckingham Palace. Princess Anne produces another baby, which should be called Susan, but her husband is rumoured to be involved with a female television newsreader. Anna Ford retires from Independent Television News, rumoured to be involved with a fashionable West End hairdresser called Marc.

France elects a Socialist President, and over the whole of English politics there hangs the shadow of a threatened return by Mrs Shirley Williams. Her former lover, Sir Peter Parker, wreaks havoc throughout British Rail.

Harold Evans re-emerges as Editor of *The Times* in place of Sir William Rees-Mogg, and causes great sorrow, but Margaret Drabble tries to spread peace, love and friendship by hugging people in Conway Hall. The good news of 1981 is that a secret society is formed in Somerset, comprised for the most part of retired majors, ostensibly dedicated to the re-issue of Surtees novels but secretly planning to reintroduce National Service and bring everything back to normal.

January 10, 1981

A NEW GROUP is beginning to make itself felt in Somerset whose influence may soon spread to the whole country. Called the Surtees Society, after the great sporting novelist, it is at present largely composed of Somerset landowners, many of whom fought in the last war.

Our ostensible purpose is to re-issue the novels of Surtees in facsimile, and to this end we plan to bring out *Mr Sponge's Sporting Tour* later this year (details from Sir Charles Pickthorn, Bt, The Manor House, Nunney, Nr Frome, Somerset; or Maj. (Retd.) The Hon. Robert Pomeroy, Rockfield House, Nunney, Nr Frome, Somerset).

But it seems most unlikely that the Surtees Society will stop there. When we have teamed up with all the Gussetts and Frobishers in every public-house of England we will be in a position to make ourselves felt in the Corridors of Power.

Ultimately we may succeed in our deepest aims, to declare a state of martial law, reintroduce National Service etc. but our first target must be to nail the Great Drunkenness Lie being put about by Mr Patrick Jenkin, Health Secretary, and other members of the Government with the connivance of toadying journalists.

Patrick Jenkin (who has three nipples) alleges that Britain is suffering from an epidemic of alcoholism, and urges vast Budget increases on drink duty for "health" reasons. This is a lie. Britain is bottom of the league in alcoholism.

It will fall to senior members of the Surtees Society to see to it that if this monstrous lie prevails, and if the price of drink is increased for "health" reasons this sad, multi-papillated man is put out of his misery.

January 18, 1981

TO THINK that in two days' time I shall be basking on the sun-kissed shores of Uruguay. Viviane Ventura, the well-known expert in public relations, telephoned to ask if I can fly out with her to spend a week reporting on the Red Cross Ball which is being given in Montevideo, in the presence of Patric Leischfeld, the Royal photographer, Gina Lollobrigida, Sir Victor Lownes, Lord Nigel Dempster and all the beautiful people.

Uruguay, I am almost sure, is in South America. But I would go anywhere to support a really good cause like the Red Cross. I may even pick up some useful tips on how to organise a military coup, which is something I constantly urge on any member of the armed forces I meet.

January 19, 1981

VENTURA telephones to say the Uruguay trip is off. It was all an unfortunate mistake. She apologises for the clownish incompetence of her "public relations" enterprise by saying that she's absolutely furious, she has sent an angry wire to Uruguay's Head of State called "Doctor" Aparicio Mendez.

Never mind. I had never heard of the pox-ridden country anyway, or of its bloodthirsty military dictator, the arch-murderer Mendez. As for his calling himself "Doctor", I would as soon take my verrucas to the Yorkshire Ripper.

The Red Cross ought to be ashamed of itself for dancing to the cries of tortured political prisoners. Mendez has the appearance as well as the manners of a hog. We should all think seriously about supporting the Tupamaro guerrillas in their noble struggle for democracy and improved living standards among the oppressed coolies of Central Africa, or wherever it is.

January 24, 1981

IT COMES as something of a shock to learn that the youth who burned 26 people to death in Hull had changed his name from Peter Dinsdale to Bruce Lee, after the kung-fu actor.

Oddly enough, I have often thought of changing my name to Bruce. It seemed manly, classless, clean and wholesome without being prissy or pi.

In my own case I expect I was influenced by my admiration for Colonel "Bruce" Page, who was born Vernon Catterpox in a tree-house near Geelong, New South Wales. But I have always been discouraged by the example of Bruce Forsyth (born Sebastian Jonibagger in an outside lavatory near Barking).

Names like Auberon don't seem to carry as much clout as they used to do. Perhaps I shall end up calling myself Clive like everyone else.

January 26, 1981

AS A secret member of Opus Dei for many years I am puzzled that *The Times* should lend itself to a vulgar, blackguarding onslaught against us.

It is true that we are given light leather whips or *disciplinae* and encouraged to scourge ourselves at least three times a week, but nobody ever checks up to see we have done it. Monsignor Escrivas, our saintly founder, believed in operating on the Gordonstoun principle of trusting people to do these unpleasant things.

But even if some of our keener members or Numeraries do beat themselves occasionally, I do not see that it concerns Rees-Mogg. Flagellation may not be everyone's cup of tea but some people certainly enjoy it, and at least they are doing it in a good cause.

January 27, 1981

AT THE SAVOY for Granada's *What The Papers Say* awards I meet my old friend George Gale, who tells me the latest "Lord" Maffews joke.

Here it is:

"What is lower class, repulsively ugly and so keen to be a 'Lord' that it has bought a lot of rotten old British newspapers?"

"I give in."

"Rupert Murdoch!!?!"

January 30, 1981

A TERRIBLE night spent worrying about the poor and unemployed. Their position is now so desperate that the Salvation Army has set up a soup-kitchen in Mexborough, Yorkshire (where over 3,000 of the 17,000 population are out of work) to feed the starving.

In 90 minutes they served only one person. The others, I suspect, were already too weak to make their way to the soup-kitchen. Or they might have felt it was the Salvation Army's job to bring the soup round to them.

What is urgently needed is a Meals On Wheels to every household in the country. If people refuse to accept the soup, or if they are out, it should be poured through their letterboxes.

February 16, 1981

TO THE House of Lords with my dear old friend "Sir" Harold Wislon to protest against the Art Council's refusal of a grant to the D'Oyly Carte Company. I am disguised as Nanky-Poo, a wandering minstrel, Harold as a fat, raddled and probably dying former Prime Minister. But it is wonderful to see him up and around again.

My life's ambition has always been to stage a production of *The Mikado* with an all-Japanese cast in Tokyo. But the Arts Council can't even cough up a couple of hundred thousand pounds to keep the Gilbert and Sullivan tradition alive in England.

Plainly this is a calculated ploy by the flabby old Stalinist pooftahs, pseuds and charlatans who make up the Arts Council, to rub the public's nose in the moronic Communist propaganda they actually do subsidise. By refusing a grant to the D'Oyly Carte, they hope to demonstrate once more the extreme cowardice of Mrs Thatcher's government.

If Paul Channon[1] had half the officer qualities of the average fieldmouse he would stop all government subsidy to the Arts Council and take state patronage of the arts under the wing of his ministry. Then, by arrangement with the British Council, I might start interviewing Japanese schoolgirls for the parts of Yum-Yum, Pitti-Sing, Peep-Bo and the front line of the chorus.

February 20, 1981

WHY DID "Sir" Robin Day's daddy never tell him that you do not wear a spotted bow-tie with top hat and morning coat unless you want to look a bloody fool? The Queen must have thought he was some sort of lion tamer from the circus when he turned up at Buckingham Palace to collect his knighthood.

Mrs Thatcher has discredited the whole honours system with her awards to "Sir" Larry-Albert Lamb, the editor of the *Sun*, who put tits on our breakfast table and "Lord" Maffews of Shoreditch, the whelk-guzzling 1950s spiv who bought Express newspapers.

If I had been the Queen, I would have told Day to go home and get himself properly dressed before presenting himself again. But hers must be a very depressing job. The truth is that there is practically nobody worth honouring left in Britain, except for Peregrine Worsthorne, Michael Wharton and possibly Keith Waterhouse. All the rest are cowards, toadies, coxcombs, placemen. . .

February 27, 1981

THE SAINTLY William Rees-Mogg's retirement is as great a tragedy, in its way, as the retirement of Anna Ford from ITN. At least, in Anna's case, we can look forward to her new book about Men.

I hope it will be about real men – people like Sir John Junor and Captain Jeremy Phipps of the SAS – rather than about the effeminate hairdressers and namby-pamby publishers' touts who hang around in London.

Anna is rumoured to be romancing with a married, 52-year-old gentleman in the publishing business. I don't believe it myself, but as Dame Harold Evans says, there's nowt so queer as folks. The late Duke of Norfolk, God rest his soul, used to served mashed potatoes with steak and kidney pudding.

March 2, 1981

RATHER A charming letter from the Prince of Wales thanking me for my advice over the years on the matter of women. It was my article on the Royal Marriage Question in the *Spectator* before Christmas which finally decided him to take the plunge, he says.

All of which is quite gratifying. But passing Clarence House in a cab this afternoon I suddenly feel a twinge of pity for the innocent 19-year-old girl who is now a prisoner inside it. Never again will she be able to pop out to buy a newspaper or a packet of peanuts. For the rest of her life she will be accompanied wherever she goes by officious flunkeys and sycophants.

It is a terrible fate for a young girl and I am ashamed of my part in it. The least I can do is to arrange a daring, last-minute swap so that instead of marrying Lady Diana Spencer on July 29th, Charles will find himself marrying Lady Diana Cooper, indescribably lovely 86-year-old widow of the Tory politician who persecuted Wodehouse during the war.

1 Arts Minister.

Old Bat Ears will probably not notice the difference. In any case, he would marry anyone I told him to marry. The great question on everybody's mind is quite different: is Lady Diana Cooper a virgin?

Probably not. But when one contemplates her beloved son, 51-year-old Viscount Norwich of Aldwick, one can't really be sure, and I feel this is one of those occasions when one should give a beautiful lady the benefit of the doubt.

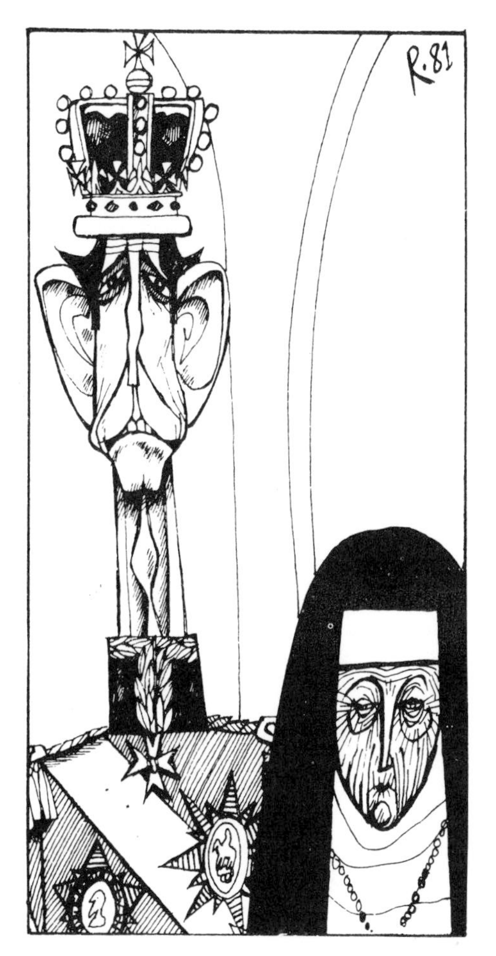

March 8, 1981

MAGDALEN COLLEGE, Oxford is to get rid of 50 College servants because they are over retirement age. The Senior Bursar, Mr Richard Johnson, explains that they are keeping younger people out of jobs.

The idea that any young person today would be capable of the duties of a College servant, or prepared to accept them, is, of course, absurd. One of the great truths of our time is that although there are 2,460,000 unemployed it is impossible to find so much as a gardener's boy in the labour market, let alone a trustworthy footman or under-butler.

Magdalen's action is part of a deliberate policy by middle-aged left-wing dons to make life as unpleasant as they can. Oxford and Cambridge are the only universities with an official policy of discriminating against public school candidates in favour of the semi-literate products of Mrs Shirley Williams's comprehensive battery system.

The result is that on average Oxford and Cambridge undergraduates are not only much lower class and uglier than their equivalents in the better provincial universities – frequently they are horribly pale with blotchy complexions, lifeless, discoloured neckfeathers and bald bottoms – they are also much stupider.

March 9, 1981

TODAY is the 100th anniversary of the birth of Ernest Bevin, a Somerset man who should not be confused with Aneurin Bevan, the fun-loving Welsh miner, or Lord Beveridge, a sort of drink. Bevin was Minister of Health, Bevan Foreign Secretary, as if anybody could care.

Richard Crossbum's latest volume of diaries throws strange light on the famous libel action of Bevan and others (Bevin, Beveridge etc) versus *Spectator*. Bevan, Crossbum and someone called Morgan Phillips sued the *Spectator* for saying they had been drunk at a socialist conference in Venice. They won £2,500 apiece after swearing on oath they had not been drunk. Solicitors: Goodman, Badman, Beggarman etc.

Crossbum now reveals that Phillips, at least, had been dead drunk for most of the conference. He congratulates himself for not having "let a cat out of the bag" in his evidence, concluding:

"So altogether you can say it was a very satisfactory result. I'm sure of one thing – that Mr Goodman, whom I regard as a pleasant villain, will sleep easier in his bed tonight now that he's got his verdict. . ."

For younger readers I should explain that Goodman, later beatified as The Blessed Arnold by Pope Paul VI, is now Master of University College, Oxford. Morgan Phillips, who was then General-Secretary of the Labour Party, is the father of Captain Mark Phillips, the Olympic swimmer, and also has a revolting daughter called Mrs Gwynneth Dunwoody.

March 16, 1981

A TELEPHONE call brings me the sad news of Maurice Oldfield's death – a strange thing to have happened on Harold Wilson's 65th birthday. I wonder if he was murdered. Maurice was one of only four men and women in this country, apart from myself, who knew the full story of Harold Wilson's resignation as Prime Minister in 1976, and he is the second to have died rather suddenly. Even Sir Harold was looking far from well when I last saw him.

Maurice was a fine man to have served under, and I doubt whether we shall see his like again. A few years ago I involuntarily did him a disservice which may have caused him some trouble. Commenting on the fact that nearly all MI6 agents were homosexuals (nothing wrong with that, of course) and seemed to spend most of their time murdering each other at the taxpayer's expense, I stated categorically that at least my old friend Maurice, although a bachelor, was perfectly normal in that way.

A few months later I learnt that this paragraph had been interpreted by the devious minds of MI5 as meaning that Maurice *was* a homosexualist. They put tabs on his flat at Marsham Court (an address once used by Jeremy Thorpe) who reported that he did, indeed, receive visits from strange young men with painted faces, stretched lurex trousers and high-heeled boots. For a time it looked as if he would fail his positive vetting.

But the explanation was quite simple. These fancy young men were in fact SIS agents who needed Maurice's signature on a bit of paper before they could get on with murdering each other, or whatever jobs they had in mind.

April 4, 1981

HAS ANYBODY ever actually heard Prince Andrew speak? It was I who put the nation's anxieties at rest about Lieutenant Mark Phillips, who was feared to be a deaf-mute, when I demonstrated that if you whistle at him he wets his pants.

Prince Andrew's problem may be different. Preparations for his 21st birthday party at Windsor in June include three bands with a gigantic battery of noise-making equipment, laser beams, dry ice and psychedelic projections. The idea behind it all is that on his first public appearance – although goodness knows how long they will be able to keep the secret – nobody will guess the Terrible Truth.

This is that Andrew, although a healthy enough boy in other ways, has never actually learned to speak. When he opens his mouth, a noise emerges which has been compared to the honking of angry geese or the trumpeting of elephants on the rampage, according to the time of day.

There is nothing amusing about a speech impediment of this magnitude and the Royal Family has every right to expect us to treat it with sympathy and restraint. So far as I am concerned, they need have no worries. Their secret will remain locked in my breast.

April 9, 1981

ANNA'S LAST appearance on News At Ten. Apart from Mary Whitehouse and Mrs Thatcher, Anna Ford must now be the most reviled woman in Britain. Scarcely a day goes by without further insults being heaped on her beautiful head by the back-biting sado-poofs of Grub Street, pretending to be jealous of her healthy affection for Monsieur Marc Boxer, 53, the talented West End hairdresser. But I must admit my own pillow is damp.

At difficult moments, I always turn to *The*

Times for guidance. Today there is a leading article on the railways, no doubt written by its exciting new Editor, Mr Harold Evans (*sic*):

CONTINUING THE AGE OF THE TRAIN

The railways are a national asset, but a wasting one. Not even the chirpy efforts of Mr Jimmy Savile travelling first class can entirely remove the burdens of obsolescence, peak loads and the schizophrenia of having to provide a public service at a time of public austerity.

Obviously there are several interesting ideas floating around here, if one can sort them out. Not *even* the chirpy efforts. . . can *entirely* remove these burdens, we are told. Chirpy efforts probably go a long way in the right direction, but what is the significance of Mr Savile's travelling first class? Is this more or less likely to induce the dread schizophrenia already mentioned?

I thought I understood the English language well enough, but just what the fucking, sodding, shitting hell is this idiotic sentence trying to tell us? Come along, Damie. Have another bash.

April 10, 1981

TWENTY YEARS ago when I lived in London, the place was full of women like Mrs Shirley Williams with bossy, fatuous opinions about education, redistribution of wealth and all that dreary rubbish.

In those days everybody drank filthy wine and served messed-up chickens with tomatoes in a sort of casserole. After a time, they succeeded in driving me out of London. But at least nobody thought their smug, half-witted opinions (which would require a gigantic police state apparatus to maintain) had anything to do with real politics.

Now this insufferably stupid woman is hailed everywhere as a great political moderate, the person who will save us from the deeper lunacies of Wedgwood Benn. But what on earth is one to do with these women?

The time is long past when one could thrash them soundly and lock them in their bedrooms. Perhaps some philanthropist will organise a Moderate Females' Mass Fun-Run down to the sea and over the cliffs at Beachy Head.

May 11, 1981

TODAY I leave the Westminster Hospital after three weeks of severe illness brought on by laughing at the sight of Vanessa Redgrave as Isadora Duncan on television.

A sad little *cri-de-cœur* from Jean Rook, loveliest of all the *Daily Express* columnists, under the heading GIVE US A BREAK PLEASE:

"Can't newspapers please tear the 'Yorkshire' label off 'The Ripper'. . . Won't somebody give us a break and remember that Yorkshire also produced pudding and Boycott. And me."

I was not aware that La Rook was a Yorkshire lass, but it comes as no surprise. She is part of the great invasion of Northerners who took over many key points during the 1960s.

Most of us are beginning to feel we have suffered from these people long enough. Perhaps Ms Rook has lost touch with the folks back home, the dismal left-overs after 70 years' emigration from the region, but I personally feel it would be more appropriate to refer to Mr Sutcliffe[1] quite simply as "the Yorkshire".

May 12, 1981

GOOD NEWS that Henry Fairlie has left the *Spectator* at last and gone back to *The Times* after 27 years. His recent dispatches from Washington have shown alarming signs of senility, most particularly a determination to confuse Ronald Reagan with Adolf Hitler, the discredited Yorkshire-born German politician who died in Berlin 36 years ago.

Henry never really recovered from Ronald's landslide victory. In the week of the American elections he wrote authoritatively in the *Spectator*:

> "Jimmy Carter will be the next President of the United States. The momentum is now with him and Ronald Reagan will not regain it. . . My prediction is really based on my reading of the mood of the country, of the nature of the electors. . . of the characters of the two candidates. . . and of the issues. . . In other words, I am not just making a guess. I'm reinforcing my political judgements of the past months."

Since Ronald has been President, Henry has taken to accusing him of planning the physical annihilation of Negroes and the urban poor. Foolishly, *The Times* prints a photograph of Henry with his first column, which runs painfully true to recent form.

After waffling for paragraphs about how old he is, and complaining about how fast news travels nowadays – "things which happen here are often known to even ordinary viewers in Britain before I know of them, simply because here it is not the time to watch television news" – he returns to Ronald and "the problems in trying to understand if President Reagan and his present popularity is [*sic*] genuine. His aimiability [*sic*] seems to conquer, but how deep are his triumphs?"

Oh God. Can nothing be done to save *The Times*?

May 21, 1981

A TELEGRAM of congratulation sent to François Mitterand, the new President of France. Giscard d'Estaing was an odious tyrant who, underneath his urbane exterior, frequently used to eat three French schoolchildren for breakfast.

A slightly embarrassing aspect of his presidency was the way he used to send me presents, sometimes as many as two a week – mostly ties by Pierre Chardin in execrable taste. Needless to say, I've sent them all to Oxfam, plus interesting soup stains, as of tomorrow morning.

Why did he do it? People might think he was hoping for a favourable mention in *Private Eye* or *Tatler*, but I believe he was angling for an invitation to one of my famous Combe Florey badger shoots when badgers are let out of a box, one by one, after dark and then shot at by sportsmen with torches who usually take the precaution of climbing a tree first. Badgers are very poor tree-climbers.

May 26, 1981

POOR BARBARA Cartland.[2] Perhaps I will give her my invitation to this wretched royal wedding. I am sure Prince Charles invited me to the Cathedral only for my fine singing voice, not because he really likes me. He still

1 Peter Sutcliffe, a Yorkshire lorry-driver, had been identified as the Ripper.

2 Barbara Cartland, step-grandmother of the bride, was not asked to the Royal Wedding.

obstinately refuses to introduce me to his lovely young fiancée, despite some pretty elephantine hints on my part.

Perhaps he does not feel quite so secure in her affections as we have been led to believe. He was never very subtle in his approach to women, always embarrassingly clumsy with his hands. If the adorable Lady Diana's affections are really on the wane, Mrs Cartland should be there to record it all exclusively for *Private Eye*.

With a trim military moustache and false beard, Mrs Cartland should have no difficulty in passing herself off as me. I would even lend her the morning coat my late Father wore at my own wedding on 1 July 1961, the very day, by coincidence, of Lady Diana's birth. If only I had known!

My own efforts to make friends with this exquisitely attractive young woman will obviously have to wait until she is Princess of Wales.

June 1, 1981

THERE IS always a long, nail-biting delay between Princess Anne's giving birth to a baby – or "experiencing an occupational hazard" as she wittily calls it – and a decision about what the "baby" is to be called.

Long discussions at Combe Florey have come up with Emma, Charlotte and Mary. Emma and Charlotte were fashionable in the Campari-sodden 1960s, and Emma has certainly travelled from West London hairdressers to Doncaster council estate *chic*, but I doubt whether either name has reached the Phillipses yet.

Mary has the great advantage that it would enable Captain Phillips to make jokes about Bloody Marys, but I personally feel the choice will fall upon Susan. Most people seem to be agreed that it is almost certainly the name of Captain Phillips's mother.

June 8, 1981

SO IT IS to be Zara. The reason for this strange name I learn is that the happy couple intended to call their darling little occupational hazard "Sarah", but the rest of the world misunderstood their strange pronunciation.

So now the poor little thing is stuck with a Jewish boy's name from the Book of Chronicles for the rest of her life. If ever I meet the unfortunate child, I shall call her Susan.

June 9, 1981

FRIENDS OF Peter Sutcliffe, the 34-year-old Yorkshire, are wondering what grounds he has in mind for his Appeal after confessing to so many yorkshires in the past and with the obvious intention of yorkshiring again as soon as he gets out.

I think he might claim, as a lapsed Catholic, to have been misled by the Second Vatican Council, like Bobby Sands, Raymond McCreesh[1] and the rest of them. For several weeks I've been trying to compose a letter to *The Times* exposing the fiendish Roman Catholic Bishop of Hexham and Newcastle, called Hugh Lindsay, who agreed with Cardinal O'Fiaock that to describe the hunger-strikers as suicides – or IRA killers as murderers, for that matter – "greatly over-simplifies a complex moral situation".

My problem is the opening. Since Dame Haroldo Ghastlysides first turned up to work at *The Times* in a track suit one obviously can't address the Editor as "Sir", let alone "Dear Sir." "Dear Dame" is facetious while the simpler form "Dame, my attention has been drawn. . . " – sounds a trifle peremptory.

June 10, 1981

POOR WEDGIE. I suspect there is nothing really the matter with him physically and they have invented this Guillain-Barre Syndrome to keep him in hospital.[2] When he complains of a strange feeling in his legs he is simply expressing a sub-conscious jealousy of Michael Foot's crutches, which have given the old fraud so much political sex-appeal in the Year of the Disabled. Now, of course, they will stuff him with drugs until he sincerely believes he is a poached egg.

Oddly enough I feel a strange tingling in my feet whenever I see Princess Michael of Kent, who seems to follow me around everywhere nowadays.

What is she up to? I never knew her when she was married to poor old Tom Troubridge and I don't see why I should know her now she is married to this German fellow. She keeps asking whether I think the Queen is tired, or suffering from nervous exhaustion, or needs a rest, and I suspect she wants me to say she ought to take over the job.

I just managed to stop myself kicking her at the Derby when I saw what had happened to Gordon Richards. He has to walk around in a slipper after trying to kick a rabbit. Nor can I ever forget my friend Jamie Mar who fell to his death from a Knightsbridge balcony six years ago when trying to kick an impudent and exorbitant pigeon.

June 14, 1981

SIR PETER PARKER should visit India where the tragic rail accident in Bihar State reveals that 3,000 Indians were travelling on one train. Never mind that they all drowned. That is not the point. So keen were they to let the train take the strain, that many of them were travelling on the roof.

Where has Parker gone wrong? Most of our trains are nearly empty. I never travel by train if I can help it, partly for fear of meeting Jimmy Savile, partly because I can't bear the sight of so many OAPs and "students" travelling much cheaper than I am. There must be a message in all this for British Rail.

June 16, 1981

IT HAS been a rotten Spring but all is not lost. Gilbert's *Pirates of Penzance* is the smash-hit on Broadway and Nottingham University has just voted to introduce a fagging system whereby first-year students will make the beds and wait at table for those in their final year.

Clive James's hideously unfunny "poem" about Prince Charles has been exposed for the grovelling rubbish it is in the *Sunday Times*, of all newspapers. The world is coming to its senses at last. Perhaps we should all think about making babies again.

June 21, 1981

THERE ARE some bad pitfalls in Debrett's new book on *Etiquette and Modern Manners*. Practically none of the really important

1 Two IRA terrorists who starved themselves to death in the Maze Prison, Long Kesh.

2 Wedgwood Benn was confined to hospital with a mysterious illness affecting his sight and balance. It was thought to be caused by excessive tea drinking.

changes in polite behaviour have been noticed.

For instance, it used to be normal when arriving at a country house for the weekend to bring a little gift for the hostess. Nowadays guests are expected to bring a present for the host – usually a case or two of sound Burgundy or claret. More than five cases is sometimes thought ostentatious, but the more modern-minded host will overlook such transgressions.

Guests arriving by train should take a bath immediately. It is very bad manners to tell stories at dinner about disgusting encounters on the train. Remember that some of the guests may have progressive or "left-wing" views. The secret of all good manners lies in consideration for other people's feelings.

Unmarried couples who propose to fornicate should never make their intentions clear, although married couples may sometimes boast about their sexual prowess, if they wish. It is very rude for husbands or wives to contradict each other on these occasions.

June 23, 1981

WHEN I SEE Tony Holden, the 22-year-old Royal biographer who has just been given an important post on *The Times*, I say how sad I was to read in the *Telegraph* this morning that his newspaper's circulation has sunk from 325,000 to 275,000, despite its abrasive and brilliant Editor, Dame Twankypoo Fancyshanks, 53.[1]

He denies this hotly, saying that under "Harry's" editorship so many more people want to take *The Times* that they are trying to discourage them, in case they find themselves with the wrong sort of reader.

June 25, 1981

IN TODAY'S *Telegraph* the newspaper's editor, Sir William Deedes, reviews Vol. V Part 2 of the *Winston S. Churchill Companion, 1929-35* (Heinemann, £65).

Young Deedes (who was Minister Without Portfolio in the last days of the Campbell-Bannerman Cabinet of 1905–8) draws attention to the fees which Churchill received as a journalist at this time:

"He wrote for British and American publications at rates which (*without* allowing for a £ worth 17 times more than today's) seem generous. The *News of the World*, for example, paid £4,200 for a series of twelve articles."

This works out at £350 an article or £5,950 in modern money – by coincidence, exactly what Lord Gnome pays me for my occasional pieces. But if Deedes *really* thinks that £350 an article is generous payment nowadays, this may explain why he has to write his own books pages.

July 6, 1981

A WEEKEND of violence at Combe Florey, sparked off by the Church fete on Saturday in the ground of Combe Florey House, leaves a bruised and bewildered populace wondering where we have all gone wrong.

Theft and looting – mainly by crazed nonagenarian whites – left two milk bottles broken beyond hope of repair, cakes from the cake stall seriously nibbled, and one book from my own stall of review copies badly foxed.

Needless to say, the police were quite unable to contain the violence, which is thought to be non-racial in origin. When I suggested to PC Barnes, our village policeman, that he use CS gas or even plastic bullets against a particularly quarrelsome group of old dears around the china stall, he revealed that he had not brought them with him.

Various conclusions can be drawn from all this. In the first place, geriatric terrorism must be recognised for what it is – the unacceptable face of the welfare state. This may mean arming the police and reversing the Government's entire economic policy.

Next, the Government must provide play schools for elderly folk where they can work off their aggressive instincts on each other. Massive government spending may be necessary. The overriding question must be whether we, as a nation, can afford a repetition of events at Combe Florey on Bloody Saturday.

1 Harold Evans.

July 22, 1981

PEOPLE WHO took CSE English in the South Western Region on 18 May this year were given a huge chunk from one of my early novels, called *Path of Dalliance*, on which they had to answer twenty comprehension questions and write an essay.

At first glance, the choice seems to suggest an element of sadism on the part of the examiners, but on second thoughts I feel their motive might have been revenge. The passage is all about a power-mad housewife called Mrs Sligger with ideas on education, who hopes to be elected a Liberal Member of Parliament to put them into practice. This character, needless to say, was based on Mrs Shirley Williams.

Now that Croydon Liberals have had the sense to send her packing the danger seems to be temporarily averted, but the important thing about Mrs Williams which nobody else seems to have spotted is that she is not only loathsomely conceited but actually insane. Her latest scheme is to foster out public school children into northern working class families under a Social Democrat government:

"Pupils from Eton might easily find themselves at a comprehensive school in Liverpool, which might seem rather a wild idea, but we have to break down the barriers," she threatened to the Secondary Head Teachers Conference in Sheffield. "It will be similar to wartime evacuation, only in reverse."

No novelist would dare invent a character so repulsive or so grotesque, which is one of the reasons why we should all stick to journalism.

September 1, 1981

ON OUR last night in the Languedoc we hold the first of what will become an annual series of Bernard Levin Commemorative Banquets. This, in plain English, is what we eat:

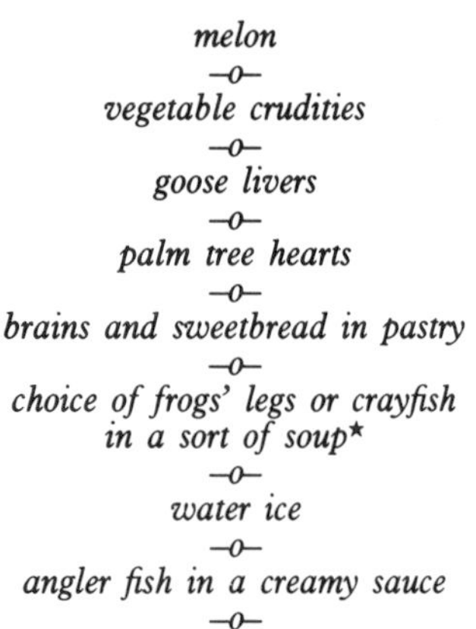

melon
–o–
vegetable crudities
–o–
goose livers
–o–
palm tree hearts
–o–
brains and sweetbread in pastry
–o–
*choice of frogs' legs or crayfish in a sort of soup**
–o–
water ice
–o–
angler fish in a creamy sauce
–o–

preserved duck with wild mushrooms
–o–
green salad
–o–
something rather like meatballs
–o–
cheeses
–o–
pastries
–o–
fruit

*Both in my case. Many diners had already retired, complaining of inner tensions.

I shall not reveal what we drink throughout this meal as it might set a bad example to the lower classes, who are said to read *Private Eye* in ever-increasing numbers.

Before the end of the meal I find I am left alone at the head of the table, thoughtfully finishing a pineapple.

This is appropriate enough. We enter the world alone and we die alone. Other people can never provide more than a temporary distraction from the ultimate loneliness of the human condition. Their company is generally much over-rated. There are certain great truths which a man should face in solitude. Tomorrow I must return to England and persecute Harold Evans.[1]

September 4, 1981

SAFELY IN London, I am greeted by a throng of ashen-faced toadies with the news that Tina Brown, the elegant and gifted editor of *Tatler*, has married. For the life of me, I can see nothing wrong with that.

Who is the lucky man, I ask. Many of us have felt that it was time the Duke of Atholl settled down. At 50, he is no longer as young or as beautiful as he once was. I suppose dear old Lord Barnby is a little old at 96, as well as being happily married, but my friend Kenneth Rose is still free, and then I suppose there is always Martin Amis.

"D-d-d-dame Haro. . ."

My head reels. Oh dear. I hope he does not try to intrude any of his horrible common friends on *Tatler*. Now I suppose I shall have to stop persecuting the brute. It is a sad day for journalism.

At 52, Tina presumably isn't much interested in That Sort of Thing any more. But her loathsome young husband, at an aggressive 26, may well expect her to do the most disgusting things. Can she know what she is letting herself in for?[2]

September 5, 1981

BIT BY BIT I learn more about the Wedding of the Year. The Prince of Wales like myself was unable to attend, but he sent Tony Holden[3] to report. He says Tony is really quite amusing about it all.

The ceremony took place at Bernard Braden's family home in Vancouver. Music was provided by a tape recorder hidden in a bush. Tea and fishpaste sandwiches were handed round by Tony Holden. My picture by Patric Leischfeld shows the radiant Dame enjoying a joke with Mr Gidley J. Kitchen,

1 Evans had published an extraordinarily violent attack on Waugh while the author was in France.
2 Brown was 26, Evans 53.
3 The Brown-Evans wedding. "Tony" Holden was a well-known toady to both Evans and Wales. It is unlikely that he was quite amusing about the wedding.

Editor-in-Chief of the Winnipeg and South Manitoba Stock Breeders' Gazette, one of the many notables present.

The special wedding breakfast menu was as follows:

Tea
—o—
Yorkshire Pudding
—o—
The Trimmings (ie gravy, boiled cabbages)
—o—
Café au Maxwell House
pasteurisé "Long Life"
—o—
*After Eights**

*This item was made possible by the generous sponsorship of Lillywhites' Sportswear Jockey Y-Front Promotions Inc.

The Prince of Wales laughed, but it makes me weep to think that Tina could have kept herself so long, just for this.

September 6, 1981

NOTHING MUCH seems to have happened during my long absence in France, so I think I shall go back there. London is scarcely inhabitable with its mad, diseased women and unpleasant taxi-drivers.

Only one man has so far stood out against them. Mr Peter McKay, the fearless *Daily Mirror* columnist, tells me he spent the night of the Royal Wedding in a police cell after hitting one of these impertinent brutes over the head with a shoulder-bag, forgetting for the moment that it contained a bottle of champagne.

He wins my nomination for Journalist of the Year, as well as the usual SAS Certificate for Proficiency in Class Warfare and a special mention in this Diary for Conspicuous Bravery in the Anti-Proletarian *Weltkampf*.

September 7, 1981

JOE ASHTON, "the Voice of the People", describes in the *Daily Star* how he was shocked and disgusted by all the bare breasts exposed on beaches in the South of France.

"The brazen hussies have no shame at all," he complains, while revealing that "like any other bloke who reads this paper" he normally turns to the hideous naked ladies on page seven "to have a look at the Diddies". In another passage he reveals: "As for the nudist beaches at St Tropez, I kept well away."

At last one understands why the French have been exposing themselves in this way. Our only hope of keeping the Joe Ashtons of this world at bay is to show them our private parts. This week I am off to St Tropez with a party of like-minded hacks from the *Sunday Telegraph* to learn how it is done.

September 12, 1981

FOR WEEKS now I have known about Mark and the spotless Angela Ripoff but my lips were sealed. We were all terrified the Queen would come to hear about it. But when I receive a peremptory telephone call ordering me into the Royal Presence at the hideously unsocial hour of 2 o'clock in the afternoon I know that the cat is out of the bag.

It is quite obvious to the meanest intelligence nowadays that the Queen does not like me anymore. We used to enjoy pleasant afternoons together, *thé-dansants*, when I would give her singing lessons or teach her a few elementary card tricks. Now she seems to see me as one of the Enemy. I think she may be going mad. It is quite untrue that I am "John Wood", the Australian journalist who broke the story in Australia's *Sunday Telegraph*.[1]

When she asks me if I will put it around in Fleet Street that there is no truth in these rumours about her daughter's marriage, I bow coldly. Then she has the bright idea of sending Mark Phillips abroad to "think things over". I point out what everybody in England knows perfectly well, that if he tried any such activity he would swallow his tongue, his eyes would fall out and his ears would disappear into his head. Next she suggests that Mark and Angela are simply

1 Rumours had appeared in the Australian press that Princess Anne's marriage was in trouble as a result of Captain Phillips's attachment to Ms Angela Rippon, the TV newsreader, with whom he had been writing a book about equitation.

writing a book together. I have to tell her that under those circumstances "writing a book together" would become another of those embarrassing euphemisms, like "discussing Uganda".

But when she starts talking to me about slow-acting poisons and disused mine-shafts in Cornwall I make my excuses and leave the room, backwards on all fours, occasionally rubbing my forehead against the carpet.

Oh dear. One is so very fond of them both. It is hard to know whose side to be on.

September 13, 1981

SUPERMAN John Aspinall seems to be in trouble getting his zoo licence renewed after one of his Siberian Tigers, called Zeya, ate two of her keepers and had to be shot by Aspinall in person.

Of course he has only himself to blame. I warned him against letting these big cats get a taste for human flesh at the time of Lord Lucan's mysterious disappearance. But Aspinall always thinks he knows best, and it was poor Zeya who had to pay the price.

Actually I think Aspinall is rather a disgusting man who shouldn't be allowed charge of a dead kitten. I hope he loses his case.

September 21, 1981

LAST NIGHT, unable to sleep for worrying about badgers, I watched Glenda Jackson in Ken Russell's *The Music Lovers*. Hideous woman, dreadful film. One can't really blame Tchaikovsky for preferring boys. Anybody might become a homosexualist who had once seen Glenda Jackson naked.

Since she has been kind enough to show it to us, I must remark that she has a most unusual configuration to her pubic hair. It seems to grow in a narrow tuft, like the hairstyle of the Last of the Mohicans. I wonder if Ms Jackson has any Red Indian blood. If so, it might explain why there are no more Mohicans.

September 25, 1981

AS PARLIAMENT is still in recess I am denied my usual afternoon's entertainment of sitting in the House of Lords to watch Lord Hailsham writhing and squirming on the Woolsack.

One likes to imagine that he is already suffering the agony of the damned. Younger readers may find it hard to imagine that this slippery old buffoon was once a very dangerous man, whose evil hysteria threatened one of the gentlest and best Englishmen ever born.

It was on 15 December 1944, as Iain Sproat reminds us in his newly published book *Wodehouse at War* (Milner, £8.95) that the pipsqueak Quintin Hogg, as he then was, stood up in the House of Commons, and demanded that P.G. Wodehouse should be brought to England and tried for treason.

The importance of Sproat's book is not so

much to prove that Wodehouse was entirely innocent of this foul charge, concocted by Duff Cooper and Bill Connor ("Cassandra" in the *Daily Mirror*) out of jealousy and spite – we already knew that – but to prove that by December 1944 everybody knew Wodehouse was innocent.

I have always said that when the frightful Hogg Hailsham dies I will go and dance on his grave. Perhaps with this new evidence we might allow ourselves the treat of taking him out and hanging him first. Sproat has recently been appointed to an important post in the Government and should be in a position to do something about this.

October 1, 1981

TO GOLDEN Square, where Granada have invited me to bring my family for a preview of their £11,000 million Gay Extravaganza *Brideshead Revisited*. If they are alarmed when we turn up 25 strong, with the family chaplain to advise on doctrinal points, Mr Derek Granger's exquisite politeness puts everyone at ease. A sumptuous feast is served to all my poor relations, who have not seen such magnificence for years.

It is a stupendous production. The British public will never have seen anything like it. I would not be surprised if television sets in the meanest and dingiest homes start sprouting baroque cupolas and barley-sugar columns. It will have a profoundly beneficial effect on the moral climate of the nation.

October 6, 1981

PEOPLE KEEP asking me to parties at Oxford but on my last visit I found it in a sorry state as a result of the university's determination to favour children from deprived backgrounds at the expense of brighter children from ordinary homes. The latest invitation is to celebrate Hugh Trevor-Roper's departure from Oxford and the Regius Professorship.

Duckworth is bringing out a volume of essays to celebrate the event called *History and Imagination* – a snip at £25. In his foreword, Trevor-Roper recalls how, many years ago, Evelyn Waugh wrote to the *New Statesman* (then a literate and widely regarded magazine) to correct some error in Roper's history.

"One honourable course is open to Mr Trevor-Roper. He should change his name and seek a livelihood in Cambridge."

Twenty-seven years later, Roper has done both these things, changing his name to Dacre (which sounds *much* nicer) and taking up a post at Peterhouse. Now everybody is saying what a good fellow he is.

October 9, 1981

UP TO LONDON for a short season to celebrate P.G. Wodehouse's centenary. Quite suddenly I am told that the train ticket need only cost £7 return, against the ordinary first class return of £31.40.

This is the brainchild of Sir Peter Parker, chairman of British Rail and former lover of Shirley Williams, who has been described as the silliest man in Britain. In order to benefit from his proposal you have to be prepared (1) to arrive in London in the mid-morning, by which time most people are drunk, or asleep, or gone out to luncheon (2) to travel second class among the "workers", students and old age pensioners, many of whom may be carrying plastic bags filled with anthrax-contaminated soil from their housing estates.

The trouble with Parker is that he sees the British Rail fare structure as an instrument of social justice rather than as a means of paying for the railways. If he dropped all his bargain fares – for OAPs, students, lower class black men whose surnames begin with A-K on alternate months after 5.30 but before 3.45 – and simply halved the ordinary fares for everyone, people might use his trains again.

As it is, I shall start taking to the buses when the present cheap rate ends in November. They are much cleaner and you don't have to look at photographs of Jimmy Savile.

October 10, 1981

TO BRIGHTON with a huge party of Lord Gnome's minions where we celebrate P.G. Wodehouse's centenary with a feast in the Royal Pavilion.

We start drinking at 11.08 am as the train pulls out of Victoria Station and I am still drinking at 1.30 in the morning at a club called something like Scroffles in the Kings Road.

It has been an eventful day. In Brighton the talk was all of a new magazine launched by Richard Branson, a millionaire who makes gramophone records, which seems entirely devoted to exposing *Private Eye*. Everybody was very excited about this, wondering how much money he pays for exclusive information.

I did not tell them that the next issue of this magazine will have a centrefold spread of myself in the nude, full frontal, on a *chaise longue*. I was asked to pose by a pretty woman called Jennifer Sharpe whom I met at a party, and gladly consented. It should sell like hot cakes.

October 13, 1981

I HOPE the picture, when it appears, does something to cheer up the Princess of Wales. On learning that I wanted to meet her

this beautiful person was thrown into a state of great excitement, but her lily-livered husband forbids it.

Now she refuses all food and is visibly pining away, prompting speculation among gutter journalists that she may have *anorexia nervosa*. Poor lovely creature. Will her cruel husband remain obdurate, must she die to prove the point that wives are no longer their husbands' chattels? Or will she be allowed her heart's desire? Time alone will tell.

October 27, 1981

LITTLE DID the Prince and Princess of Wales realise it when they arrived at Swansea Station this evening, but they were being closely watched by my younger son, Nathaniel Thomas Biafra Waugh, who happened to be waiting for a connection to Haverfordwest.

It just goes to show that they can't be too careful. Mercifully Charles was not in a sportive mood or making dirty jokes about husbands being present when their wives are giving birth. This would have shocked the lad terribly, and probably turned him into a Republican.

The reason that husbands have always been kept away on these occasions lies deep in our surviving links with the animal creation. The humblest female mammal always seeks privacy to give birth, and male rats are so outraged if they find themselves present that they eat their young.

No doubt the Prince of Wales would be able to restrain himself from eating the next Heir to the Throne. So abject have English males become, he will probably just blush to the roots of his hair. But I believe that Captain Phillips, who was bossed into watching his wife produce one of her tiresome setbacks – later identified as Baby Susan – ate a polyester teddybear and two plastic ducks, no doubt in some confusion about what he was expected to do.

It is only because women are mad and have forgotten which sex they belong to that they make these unnatural suggestions. Husbands whose wives are behaving oddly should give them a glass of sherry and an aspirin.

October 28, 1981

ONE RESULT of all this is that fewer and fewer babies are being born. If the lovely Princess of Wales does not produce an heir it will almost certainly be because of the threat of this red-faced, swallowing, bat-eared gentleman being present.

Mr Harold Brooks-Baker, managing director of Debrett, claims that so few babies are now being born as a result of these uncouth practices that the Western European nations will soon disappear. The Swedes will vanish in three or four generations, he says, the English and others shortly afterwards.

He should know. A world without Swedes may be one of the happier ideas of our time, but I don't like the thought of all those shattered, elderly Englishmen sitting around and comparing notes with each other about births they have attended.

November 1, 1981

WHATEVER HAPPENS, I must be back in Somerset by December 1 when Mrs Shirley Williams comes to address a rally of the Social Democratic Party in Bridgwater. Suitably enough, this hellish woman has chosen the local Comprehensive School as her venue.

Rotten eggs and cowpats can probably be acquired locally, but stink bombs and more sophisticated devices should be brought with you. Hoax bomb calls and maniacal threatening letters should be addressed to Bridgwater Police Headquarters. Tea and biscuits will be served at halftime.

November 22, 1981

AFTER A three-week fact-finding tour of the Far East I find myself in Manila with time on my hands to buy a few servants for my dear Wife and eat a dog or two.

They do not taste at all bad – the Filipinos are brilliant cooks. I think I will propose it for the menu of the next annual dinner of the Dog Lovers Party of Great Britain. We meet at the Imperial Hotel, Barnstaple on 4 August every year – the anniversary of Jeremy Thorpe's arrest – to drink long and solemn toasts to the memory of Rinka.

November 24, 1981

I'M FLYING over the Hindu Kush in a Jumbo Jet at 40,000 feet when the news is flashed to me that Jocelyn Stevens has been sacked from Express Newspapers. Champagne corks start popping immediately and even the economy class passengers in their huddled masses at the back of the plane break into a feeble cheer.

It is only when we are flying over Turkey, with the Anatolian Mountains retreating beneath us, that I begin to have second thoughts. Jocelyn Stevens looks disgusting, of course, and is indeed a thoroughly disgusting person, but he was practically the only person left on Express Newspapers with any claim to be upper class.

Not much claim it is true – I don't suppose he could get past the butler at Combe Florey, for all his blond curls and self-confident, bottomy walk. But at least he tried. Now that the *Daily Express* does not have a single person on its staff who can begin to hold a knife and fork properly, I fear it will just sink into the London sewers with a horrible gurgle.

Which is exactly what is happening to *The Times* under its ghastly new editor. When Murdoch appointed Dame Harold Evans rather than bushy-tailed Charles Douglas-Home (alias Charlie Vass) he wasn't to know that Vass would turn out to be the first cousin of the Princess of Wales. Murdoch must be kicking himself now, stuck with this boring, undersized piss-pot and his court of lower class sycophants, while even the Queen Mother has changed to the *Daily Telegraph*.[1]

November 26, 1981

BACK IN ENGLAND I find Fleet Street is in a state of turmoil. Peter McKay has been missing from the *Mirror* for a week – presumably the police have caught up with him over the incident when he assaulted a London taxi driver with a bottle of champagne in a carrier-bag after the Royal Wedding. He spent the night in the cells but they had to release him when there was nobody to lodge a complaint after the wretched fellow died. He claims to be holidaying in Scotland.

Next I learn that there is a new William Hickey in my old friend Michael Leapman – another refugee from the sinking *Times*. Today he reveals that the Duchess of Rutland has just had a baby, which is jolly interesting as the Duchess doesn't seem to be aware of it. But he publishes a photograph of the lad, so I suppose it must be true. Perhaps after a certain age one doesn't notice these things.

It is an ill wind. I think I will try and sell him the story told me by McKay about how the Cockney philanthropist Lord Maffews goes to bed with his wife Queenie. It is incredibly funny, involving a sack of goose feathers, a bowl of jellied eels, the inner tube of a tractor tyre and 3lbs of peppermint bullseyes but I'd better not tell it here or he won't pay me.

1 Murdoch lost no time in replacing Evans with Douglas-Home. See *infra*.

November 27, 1981

NOW HICKEY has taken the baby away from the Rutlands and given it to an old Oxford acquaintance called B. Sweeny. I hope it ends up with someone who'll look after it properly.

Lord Scarman's Report[1] has driven my Books Page off the *Daily Mail.* This is a serious error of judgement on the part of the Editor, who is called "Mr English". The Report – fatuously suggesting that black men be given priority treatment to help them forget their natural disadvantages and stop them misbehaving – is worth about five lines on an inside page.

I think Scarman may be a rival to Sir Peter Parker for the title of Silliest Person in Britain. Every judgement of his I have read – against *Private Eye* in Goldenballs, against the little Asian ladies at Grunwick – has been mind-bogglingly silly.

December 3, 1981

ALARMED to receive a telephone call from someone called Miller at the Palace saying the Queen wants to see me immediately. Can she have guessed my secret? Surely not. Still, to be on the safe side, I stuff my trousers with cardboard and other protective materials.

But it is all right. A huge crowd of journalists is gathered to be given a morallers on hounding the Princess of Wales. In particular, we are told, we must all turn our backs whenever the Princess is buying wine gums. There are certain things which a young girl must be allowed to do in private.

Many of the editors present are weeping. It would be a horribly sad thing if we drove this delightful young woman mad, but she simply must realise that we have our jobs to do. Somebody must teach her to hand the wine gums around. Even the dirtiest hacks honour the journalists' Code in this matter.

December 10, 1981

THE HEADLESS bodies of two fully grown brown bears have been found floating in the river at Hackney. Immediately one begins to feel alarmed for several of one's friends. Peter McKay is all right. He has reappeared in the *Daily Express*, trying to drive the Princess of Wales mad. But I have not seen Geoffrey Wheatcroft for some time.

If anything had happened to Lord Gowrie I am sure someone would have claimed credit for it – if not the IRA perhaps the National Front, or even me.

Of course it is possible they are just two brown bears who happen to have lost their heads. If so, I expect they were given as a bribe to Mr Heath by the Russians. Wandering around Grocer's bachelor pad, they

1 On previous race riots.

probably got caught in the super-efficient mousetraps with which he protects the wine gums in his sweets cupboard. Horrible really, but one can't help laughing.

December 11, 1981

ON A TRAIN journey to Durham, I sit opposite someone pretending to read the *New Statesman* and take it away from him. The man is obviously very ill. He puts up no resistance.

It is the first time I have seen this magazine for years, although I was a subscriber for 18 years before that and wrote a regular column in it for nearly three years. Today's issue has a huge photograph of Peter Tatchell[1]: "The Purge is on. If Tatchell goes, what will be left of Labour?"

Inside, it asks more searching questions of its readers: "Whose party is it anyway? What sort of party is it that cannot tolerate Peter Tatchell?"

If you have any answers to these questions, you will have to keep them to yourselves as I see the Editor no longer prints readers' letters. Probably his readers are too illiterate to write, in any case.

Or perhaps there aren't any readers left. Looking closely at the young man sitting opposite me in the train, I see he is dead. Poor fellow, he doesn't look as if he had a very enjoyable life. I put the magazine back between his lifeless fingers and wander down to the Buffet for a thoughtful pork pie.

December 18, 1981

THE *SPECTATOR*'s annual Christmas lunch is held in Claridge's this year as a protest against our treatment by the Ritz Restaurant last time.

So we have Claridge's drawing room to ourselves. As the new proprietor, Mr Algy Cluff, is rather richer than last year's one, Mr Henry "Scotch Eggs" Keswick (he is a former lover of the beautiful widow of Mao Tse-Tung) there are more people and much bigger helpings of food.

The chief oration is given by Sir Peregrine Worsthorne (*né* Cock de Doodle – his late father, the Colonel, used sometimes to be seen in bed with Eartha Kitt although it is thought that no impropriety occurred) who urges everyone to support the Conservative Party.

This causes much merriment. There are no women present, so we have great fun debagging George Gale and trying to stuff him into the teapot. I cannot remember such a jolly office party for ages.

December 23, 1981

NEWS REACHES me in Somerset that a group of Lesbians in Publishing (LIP) which publishes a Newsletter called *Lipwash* has awarded me a Prize for my journalism this year. It takes the form of a marzipan pig covered in pink icing sugar.

This does not strike me as very generous but as it seems to be the only Prize I have won this year, and as I am rather partial to marzipan, I decide to journey up to London to receive my Pig.

Imagine my annoyance when I search the whole of London without finding it anywhere. Possibly it never existed, and was simply a lie told by these silly women in order to draw attention to themselves.

It is this sort of behaviour which gives lesbianism a bad name. Personally, I am coming round to the view recently expressed by Pope John-Paul II that they have no business whatever to do whatever it is they do together.

December 31, 1981

LORD SNOWBUM ends his year as Handicapped King of the World with a heart-rending plea to Anthea Hall, of the *Telegraph*, that blind people should be allowed into the cinemas unaccompanied.

Anthea is a susceptible lady – I kissed her once at a children's party in north Oxford 25 years ago – and has plainly fallen for the tiny Old Etonian Welsh bore. She calls him "Compassion's Champion" and forgets to ask him why on earth blind people want to go to the cinema anyway. But Snowbum had his answer ready: "There are a lot of bad films which are better just heard," he says.

1 Homosexual Labour Candidate in the Bermondsey by-election. He was not elected.

1982

Jon Pilger, the left-wing journalist, claims to have bought a female Thai infant on *Daily Mirror* expenses for £85. This makes Waugh suspicious; he claims the normal rate is £12 a baby. The Falklands War seems to offer an opportunity for sinking Pilger in an aircraft carrier, just as W.T. Stead, a previous crusading journalist, was sunk in the *Titanic*, seventy years earlier.

Despite Waugh's advice that he should stay away, Pope John-Paul II visits Britain. A new form of venereal disease, called *herpes*, reaches epidemic proportions in England. It can be cured only by massive doses of a most disagreeable cheese, called Lymeswold. Peter Walker, a Tory politician, continues his genocidal campaign against badgers and Mrs Thatcher, soon to become demented by conceit after her Falklands victory, persists in her cruel persecution of Sir Peregrine Worsthorne.

The good news is that Princess Anne announces she is not expecting another child, and that many British "workers" remain on strike throughout the year. The Princess of Wales gives birth to a son, and a Great Debate rages about whether or not it should be circumcised. It is suggested that the matter should be put to a National Referendum. Further good news is that Harold Evans is sacked as Editor of *The Times*, Mr Bernard Shrimsley as Editor of the *Mail on Sunday*.

January 1, 1982

NEW YEAR's Honours and the Prime Minister has once again refused to award Peregrine Worsthorne the knighthood he so richly deserves. Instead she "honours" Steve Ovett and "Seb" Coe, the two athletes who taunted the enslaved masses of Eastern Europe and disgraced their country by prancing around at the Moscow Olympics.

I was never among those who felt that the two should be hanged on their return from the Soviet Union, but I did feel very strongly that they should have their passports cancelled and be forced to spend the rest of their lives there. At the time Mrs Thatcher agreed with me, but she was overruled by Soviet agents in the Foreign and Commonwealth Office.

January 2, 1982

IN THE late morning the Prince of Wales drops in, hoping for a glass of cherry brandy. He tells me his wife is pregnant, which I already knew. What should he call it, and will I agree to be Godfather?

As the child will be nearly half English, this seems a reasonable enough request. The Royal Family hasn't been doing too well recently, what with Master "Peter" Phillips and poor little Baby Susan, whose godparents are Bruce Forsyth, Duncan Goodhew and Diana Dors. I tell him that of course the child should be called Auberon, if it is a boy. If it is a girl he can call it anything he likes except Shirley.

January 4, 1982

JOCELYN STEVENS is holidaying in Gstaad with his girlfriend, the moustachioed hell-cat Vivien Clore, 66. From there he announces that he is trying to catch up with his reading: "I want to rejoin the human race," he says.

This seems to me a great mistake. The human race has taken some bad knocks recently, and I think it is time it was given a rest. In Jocelyn's case it would involve endless, painful surgery to no very useful purpose: his tail would have to be cut off, his scales trimmed, his terrible poisonous fangs would have to be filed down. He says he has ambitions to be involved in television, but if he is not careful he will spoil his chances of an appearance in David Attenborough's brilliant *Life on Earth* series.

January 9, 1982

AMID ALL the conceited buffoons who sit on the British Bench it is good to acclaim one who combines wisdom and mercy with a knowledge of the real world in which we live. Many readers may have thought that Judge Bertrand Richards's fine of £2,000 on a motorist who raped a hitchhiker was rather stiff for what appears to have been a momentary lapse.[1]

But then rape is plainly rather an unpleasant experience – perhaps comparable to being beaten on the bare bottom by a drooling schoolmaster. And young people today take it very hard if they are made to do anything they do not want to do.

The father seems as much to blame as anyone. But the main issue is as the Judge pointed out: hitchhikers are tremendous bores, with very little conversation and often quite a disagreeable smell. If they are not prepared to offer any form of sexual comfort in exchange for the boredom of their company, they should carry a little notice saying what they *are* prepared to do: sing songs, do card tricks, tell funny stories or play a musical instrument.

January 11, 1982

NOW THAT the Irish are giving up corporal punishment in schools, Britain will be the only country in Europe to retain it. On the whole, I have always favoured abolition, but a pampered childhood simply does not prepare young people for the day when they have to go out into the world and be raped, or mugged, or accidentally shut in the lavatory, or insulted by a taxi-driver. Many react to these minor setbacks by going mad.

I would feel more favourably towards organisations like Women Against Rape if,

1 There had been an outcry at the leniency of this sentence.

in addition to telling us what they are *against*, they would tell us what they are *for*. What do they propose to put in its place?

Last week my pink marzipan pig finally arrived from the organisation called LIP (Lesbians in Publishing) and it was perfectly delicious. Whoever cooked it would probably make a lovely little wife for some lucky man.

January 14, 1982

PETER WALKER, the horrible former protégé of Grocer Heath who still hangs around in the Conservative Government as Minister of Agriculture, takes a half page in the *Observer* to explain his determination to go on gassing badgers.

Where cows are suffering from bovine tuberculosis, he says, badgers are often found to be similarly affected. But even Lord Zuckerman acknowledged in his notorious report that nobody knew whether cows catch it from badgers or the other way round. Walker does not mention this point.

Zuckerman's possible motive for urging on the destruction of the British badger population is often discussed. There are no badgers in South Africa, where he was born, unless one counts the African Honey badger or Ratel, which is really a sort of weasel. To get its honey it farts into the bees' nest until all the bees are senseless. Perhaps his parents wiped out all the true badgers in South Africa before little Solly arrived.

Or perhaps there is a more sinister explanation. There can be no doubt that Zuckerman is frequently mistaken for a badger as he wanders around London Zoo and this may account for his hatred of them. Peter Walker's motives, I imagine, are more complicated. He feels that the more badger's sets left empty, the better his chance of using one as a bunker or bolt-hole for small, lower-class conservative parties when the nation eventually comes to its senses and sweeps me to power.

It won't work. I shall appoint Lord Zuckerman my Minister of Agriculture and instruct him to go around farting into all badger sets which seem unoccupied. Walker shall not escape.

January 15, 1982

IF JOHN ALDERSON, the retiring Chief Constable of Devon and Cornwall, is adopted as a Liberal candidate at the next election, this will cast a curious light on the behaviour of his Force in the investigations which followed the murder of a certain dog called

Rinka on Porlock Hill over six years ago.

John Alderson may be a man of many qualities. His enthusiasm for "community" policing rather than actually combating crime has been widely praised. But many of us remain unconvinced that he was sufficiently concerned about our Dumb Friends.

Once again, public duty calls. Any Liberal constituency party which adopts this garrulous oaf will find me standing against him as Independent Social Democrat, Dog Lovers and Law Enforcement candidate for a Cleaner Britain and Better Deal for *all* our dogs. God save the Queen.[2]

January 20, 1982

WHEN MAURICE Oldfield died last year it was officially announced that he had died for health reasons – the same, in fact, as caused him to resign from being head of security in Ulster a few months earlier. At the time, I expressed my doubts about this and said that I thought the old boy had probably been murdered by members of the Secret Intelligence Service, which he headed for several years before his retirement in 1977.

Normally when SIS officers murder each other it is the result of some poofish quarrel or lovers' tiff inside the Service. On this occasion it may have been a misguided desire to protect the good name of the Old Firm. I gather that members of the rival – and slightly more respectable – Home Security Service had been breathing down the necks of their glamorous colleagues in the SIS about various wild allegations being made in Belfast.

If these had received a thorough airing and Maurice's name had been dragged through the mud, it would have been a poetic revenge for what the SIS pooftahs had done to the reputation of my old chief Roger Hollis.[3]

Today Jim Prior makes an official announcement that nobody in the Northern Ireland office, no policemen and no politicians are involved in inquiries about a homosexual ring of Belfast youth taken into care.[4] Just the same, he has decided that the inquiry will be conducted in private. So perhaps we shall never know the guilty men.

January 21, 1982

ONE MILLION five hundred and eight thousand and forty-six morons now buy the *Daily Star*. Perhaps nearly half of that number even "read" some of it. It has a higher percentage of young "readers" than any other national newspaper except, I suppose, *Beano*.

The good news is that it is losing buckets of money. Lord Maffews has to scatter millions and millions of pounds in bingo money among its ignorant yobbo "readership" before they will consent to take it to their sheds at the end of the garden.

The bad news is that all the newspapers now face ruin as a result of this half-witted competition for "readers". If the leadership of the National Union of Journalists were more than a collection of creepy lower-class power maniacs and left-wing fanatics – it would organise nationwide pressure to stop any newspaper offering any prizes whatever to its loathsome "readers". They have done nothing whatever to deserve it. Then journalists might be able to undertake urgently needed refurbishment of their stately homes, repair their works of art etc.

January 22, 1982

THE PRINCE of Wales tells me he will not be going to Princess Marie-Astrid's wedding in Luxembourg today as he would be too embarrassed, so I decide not to go, either.[5]

1 Belonged to Norman Scott, the former friend of Jeremy Thorpe.
2 Alderson contested Teignmouth, Devon, in the Liberal interest in the 1983 election, but Waugh does not seem to have noticed.
3 Former head of MI5, accused by SIS (MI6) of having been a Soviet spy.
4 This refers to the Kincora Boys' Home allegations, that an orphanage was run as a call-boy service. The scandal never broke.
5 This refers to a much earlier scoop by Dempster, the *Daily Mail's* gossip columnist, in which he revealed that the Prince of Wales was secretly engaged to Princess Marie-Astrid of Luxembourg, a Catholic. Nothing further was heard of this scoop.

Apparently they have found some Hun to marry her who looks all right on paper, even though he is half her age.

Nobody who was there has quite forgotten the earlier, rather muted civil ceremony at which Nigel Dempster and I were the only witnesses. Everybody, on the other hand, seems to have forgotten the unknown baby – did we decide to call it Jean-Charles or Charles-Jean? – now farmed out to a Belgian peasant woman in the Forêt de Jambes, poor little chap.

Perhaps one day he will come to claim the throne of England but my lips are sealed and so, I am sure, are Nigel's. Neither of us minds that we were not asked to the wedding at St Paul's. Neither of us minds that we've not even been presented to the lovely young bride. We can keep our mouths shut.

But it will be a charming gesture if the Prince of Wales decides to call his first-born son Auberon, as he has promised to do. The lad will be in remainder, among other things, to the Dukedom of Marlborough. If he has a second son – and I don't see why he shouldn't – it might be a kind thought to call him Prince Nigel.

January 25, 1982

WONDERFUL NEWS that in the teeth of fierce competition I have been appointed Wine Correspondent of *Tatler* magazine. I must not let success go to my head. There will be many embittered losers and jealous hacks who will now be my enemies. They will have to be dealt with.

All my life, as I now realise, I have wanted nothing more than to be *Tatler*'s Wine Correspondent. Wine merchants will doff their caps to me and bring out their choicest wares. Cases of wine will arrive at every delivery. Unbelievably beautiful model girls will drape themselves over me every time I sip a little-known *apéritif* from the Loire.

As I pen my first column for April – about a terrible *faux-pas* by Alan Watkins, the Islington gormandizer – I realise I've discovered a new art form. I can't make up my mind whether to write it under my own name or pseudonymously as Crispin de St Crispian, which should be a pretty impenetrable disguise.[1] I wouldn't like to upset my old friend Alan.

January 30, 1982

KEN LIVINGSTONE is everywhere these days, spreading his words of wisdom like rhinoceros droppings all around. Today, at the North London Polytechnic, I hear him describe the Law Lords as "vandals in ermine" who have acted to please the Government because "they all come from the same class background".

Ken is obviously smarting from the bitter attacks on him in the capitalist press. He says he has been accused of "everything from invading Poland to eating babies". He could not possibly have invaded Poland, whatever the papers say, as he simply has not had time with all his London engagements. I never knew they had accused him of eating babies.

He does not tell us whether he is innocent or guilty of this charge. Personally, I would not be surprised. Many people from his class background are as greedy and as lazy in their eating habits as they are in everything else they do.

February 1, 1982

LAST YEAR I wrote of my shock at discovering that Mr Patrick Serjeant, 56-year-old City Editor of the *Daily Mail*, was paid a mere £143,542 a year. It seemed almost obscene that an old man like that should be paid so much less than I am at half his age on the same newspaper.

Now I learn that they have paid attention to my criticism and have jacked up his fee by £112,104 to £255,646. I suppose a middle-class fellow of simple tastes can rub along on that.

February 4, 1982

I SHALL be abroad at the time of the Pope's visit in May in order to avoid embarrassment, but already I hear plans being cooked up by the unspeakable English hierarchy to humiliate this saintly man.

The idea of sending him to Toxteth,

1 Waugh wrote it under the pseudonym of Crispin de St Crispian.

among the most vicious and criminal populations of England, was cooked up within Archbishop's House on Mossley Hill, Liverpool, the lair of oily Archbishop Derek Worlock. No doubt he hopes to suck up to all the most brutal and evilly disposed elements in his northern Province.

But the ultimate humiliation has not yet been announced – that either on Merseyside or in Archbishop's House, Westminster, the Pope will be forced to meet (and be photographed with) Mrs Shirley Vivien Teresa Brittain Williams, the Social Democrat politician. Political simpletons in Archbishop's House feel that this will give a boost to "moderate" policies in government, as represented by this egocentric female.

Not since one of the early popes was decapitated as he sat on the papal throne has any pontiff been exposed to such indignity. By taking Communion twice in one day in a desperate attempt to impresss the half-witted voters of Crosby with her Catholicism, "two-wafer" Williams showed her contempt not only for them but also for the Catholic Church.

She succeeded in making a fool of Archbishop Worlock; now she hopes to make a fool of Pope Ringo, but Ringo is a man of many surprises. With a bit of luck he will pronounce a Papal anathema on this wretched woman and have her burned as a witch outside the Senior Citizens' Portakabin Complex behind Toxteth Town Hall.

February 8, 1982

TO GRANADA's *What The Papers Say* lunch in the Savoy to see my beloved proprietor, Lord Gnome, acclaimed as the Greatest Newspaper Proprietor of All Time. Marmaduke looks very distinguished in a champagne corduroy jacket, slightly foxed, over green trousers in drip-dry tomalin, trimmed by a jiffy zipp. What a wonderful man!

The occasion is completely spoiled by the behaviour of Dame Harold Evans who has piteously enough been appointed "Best" Editor of the Year. He insists on making a speech and blubs into the microphone about his ratty little newspaper.[1]

I hope that Brian Inglis, Tony Howard[2] and the others responsible for this tasteless joke feel thoroughly ashamed of themselves.

February 10, 1982

WANDERING DOWN Park Lane at lunchtime I find that I seem to have joined an

1 Evans was about to be sacked after his brief editorship of *The Times*.
2 Two journalists.

Usdaw picket outside the Dorchester Ballroom entrance. We are protesting about a Foyles literary luncheon being held inside in honour of Esther Rantzen. One of our placards says "Foyles Lunch the Stinking Rich".

Quite apart from the use of the verb "lunch", which I would have thought an upper-class colloquialism, I find this slogan interesting because although we all knew that Esther Rantzen was extremely rich I have never heard it suggested that she has a body odour problem.

If so, I wonder if it has anything to do with breast feeding. She has brought her new baby Joshua along to breast feed it during the lunch. Recently, the *British Medical Journal* published a terrifying account of the dangers of breast feeding from the point of view of the baby, but there was no hint of this additional hazard.

I expect the explanation is simply that Joshua was imitating his namesake the High Priest who stood before the Angel of the Lord in filthy raiment (Zechariah iii 3). Even so, it was quite right of responsible trade unionists to draw attention to the possible health hazard.

February 28, 1982

JEREMY, JEREMY, bang, bang, woof, woof. How nice it was to have Mr Thorpe back in public life. I had been missing this blameless and distinguished man more than I can say.

People who complained that he was not the best person to head the British section of Amnesty International are missing the point. Amnesty's purpose is to rescue people from prison, and nobody in the country has better experience of staying out of prison than our Jeremy.

His new job[1] would have involved standing up and announcing that the Russians were torturing Georgian nationalists in Tiflis, pulling out people's fingernails in Riga. The question must arise whether anyone would have believed him.

I think I would. I believe almost anything about the Russians.

March 6, 1982

ONCE AGAIN I write off applying for the job of Editor of the *New Statesman*. This must be my fifth application in 16 years. One day these foolish people will see the light. The trouble with poor old Colonel Bruce Page, now demoted to being the office electrician, is that he never understood about boredom.

The same is true about *The Times*. For many years it hovered tantalizingly on the edge of being a really dull newspaper. But under the great and good Sir William Rees-Mogg there was always a sort of loony inspiration behind it which might pop up at any moment, like a naked streaker at somebody's memorial service. Since he left, it has quite simply become a very dull newspaper, with occasional embarrassing displays of loutishness and ignorance.

Perhaps I should apply for the editorship of *The Times*, too. On the other hand, I don't think so. There is rather a poor class of person to be found in Printing House Square these days. But I am glad I turned down the chairmanship of the Arts Council when it was offered to me. There are wonderful things to be done with the *New Statesman*. I am off to Cuba.

March 12, 1982

Havana, Cuba

IT TAKES a whole week in Cuba to see Fidel Castro. The problem is that one can't just turn up at his front door because nobody knows where he lives. One has to send a message to his office at the Communist Party Headquarters in Revolucion Square and then hope for the best.

I hinted that I was an intimate friend of Edward Heath, which is not strictly speaking true, but it worked. Fidel came round to my hotel and said he got on famously with Heath when the kippery old Grocer visited Cuba recently. It seems that Grocer was looking for hints about how he can return to Power in Britain.

After a few opening pleasantries, the Cuban dictator and mass-murderer asks me why I want to see him. This is a bit

1 Thorpe's appointment as Director of Amnesty had been cancelled after an outcry.

embarrassing. One always likes to call on the people in charge of any country one is visiting, even if they are murderous flea-bags like him. It is a question of good manners.

To put him at his ease I ask him if he has ever met the Emperor of Japan. He says no, he hasn't. After a pause I reveal that I am not only Wine Correspondent of *Tatler* magazine but also Assistant Chief Executive Managing Political Editor of *Private Eye* and wish to ask him about his sex life. Nobody in Cuba knows if he is married, or has a woman, or what he does.

He gives a horrible blood-curdling laugh and says he is particularly interested in scuba-diving. This is a new one on me, although I had noticed a rather strange Cuban fish called a *manjauri* which might, I suppose, give one a *frisson* if one was that way inclined. But fancy doing it with a fish! It certainly takes all sorts.

March 20, 1982

ON THE return journey I keep receiving garbled messages about the power struggle at *The Times*, but I have lost all interest. I decided it was time for Harry Lauder to go last summer,[1] but I have no curiosity about his successor.

Little Charlie Vass was my fag many years ago in college at Eton, but he never impressed me much by his coffee making. Perhaps it has improved.

The best man for the job would undoubtedly have been Alexander Chancellor, 22-year-old Hispanic-looking editor of the *Spectator*. He hates women, and might be persuaded to sack the social editoress who refused to mention my 40th birthday the other day.

At least Vass, being a public school man, will not disgrace us all by blubbing on television when he is sacked.[2]

March 22, 1982

SAD TO see Sir John Betjeman, our beloved Poet Laureate, lend his lustrous name to a round robin in *The Times* with the usual collection of frauds, voluptuaries and monsters to support a National Arts Day on June 24.

The first signatory to this disgusting letter is Sir Hugh Casson, so I suppose he is responsible for the prose style, a mixture between social workers' protest and margarine advertisement:

> "Arts Day can become a source of renewed national consciousness and community spirit. We applaud this initiative which will set aside a special day each year for showing how the arts can enrich our lives – every day."

1 Harold Evans had printed a violent attack on Waugh, written by a disgruntled actor, the previous summer.

2 Evans had just been sacked from the Editorship of *The Times*. Charles Douglas-Home replaced him.

Perhaps Sir John has to sign these letters to earn the hog's head of mead and haunch of venison he receives every year as his screw for being Laureate. But he must also know that people like Hugh Casson, Martyn "Book Bangs" Goff and Henry Moore (to name only three of his fellow signatories) have given us nothing to celebrate.

Will anybody volunteer to form a national committee to sabotage the Arts Day?

April 2, 1982

JON PILGER, the *Daily Mirror*'s repulsive and sinister "heartthrob" reporter writes about how he bought an 8-year-old girl in Thailand for £85 on *Mirror* expenses. He blames the government of Thailand, and now the newspaper is full of hate-letters against one of the very few decent governments left in South East Asia.

He might have mentioned that the trade is illegal and punishable by 10 years in a Thai gaol. Never mind. When I was last in Bangkok they said the price was £12 for a Thai baby – perhaps some error of transmission occurred in the *Mirror's* expense account department – and I seriously thought of buying a couple to be raffled at last summer's Church Fete in Combe Florey.

April 10, 1982

ON THE first leg of a world tour to find out more about Jon Pilger, the sinister and repulsive *Daily Mirror* heart throb, I stop over in Hong Kong where my cousin, Capt. Andrew Waugh, RN, commands the Naval Station. He expresses quiet confidence in the Colony's ability to withstand any threat of a Pilger invasion from the sea.

At the Foreign Correspondents Club I deliver an address on the 70th anniversary of W.T. Stead's being drowned in the *Titanic*. One of the reasons we should always oppose the raising of the *Titanic* is in case the remains of this odious prig are brought to the surface.

He it was who, by publishing a lot of prurient filth about child prostitutes in the *Pall Mall Gazette* at the end of the last century, founded the shrill, self-righteous school of British sexual journalism which has done so much to make our Sundays miserable ever since. In those sensible days they first of all sent him to prison, then they put him on the *Titanic* and sank it.

As we drink good riddance to this dreadful man, it occurs to me that the Falklands crisis[1] offers a wonderful opportunity for the editor of the *Daily Mirror* to do something about Jon Pilger. Nobody will be sadder than I when *HMS Hermes* is sunk, but if Jon Pilger is on board the sacrifice will at least make a sort of sense.

April 14, 1982

ON ARRIVAL in Bangkok I find there is already a 40-strong Jon Pilger Society meeting weekly at the Foreign Correspondents Association in Oriental Arcade. They provide me with trunkfuls of material on this curious man, going back to his earliest years. Soon I shall be in a position to present my findings for the James Goldsmith Prize.[2]

April 25, 1982

HOW ARE the mighty fallen! Ferdinand Mount who has been Political Correspondent of the *Spectator* since I gave up the job 12 years ago has now been appointed Chief Adviser to Mrs Thatcher, head of her think-tank and probably the most powerful man in Britain after Jimmy Savile.[3]

To have deserted to the enemy after so many years of honourable service! Now he puts the seal on his treachery, pours salt into every ignominious wound by being hailed as a good fellow, one who has seen the light, in the *Sunday Times*.

What on earth should one do: write a

1 Mrs Thatcher had sent a task-force to reoccupy the Falklands after an Argentinian invasion. It was still in mid-Atlantic.

2 Goldsmith had announced a £50,000 annual prize for journalists who exposed subversion in the media. It was never awarded.

3 A television comic.

letter of condolence to his poor, lovely wife? Offer to take his blameless children into care? Or just rend the garments and howl?

April 29, 1982

ON MY return to Combe Florey I am surprised to find a signed copy of Captain Mark Phillips's new book *My Romps With Angela Ripoff* (published by David and Charles and Tim and Julian at £8.95).

It is not entirely devoid of interest. At the time of his wedding he reveals he was so nervous that he fouled himself and had to change trousers with his best man, Captain Eric Grounds-for-Divorce. This explains much which puzzled us at the time.

Now he is happiest when giving Baby Susan her bath or playing football with his four-legged son Peter Phillips. Or so he says. But then he also claims to like cuddling his wife, the Princess-Dame, in front of their television set. Oh, yeah. If people believe that, they'll believe anything. Go on, Captain, try pulling the other one.

May 6, 1982

CONVERSATIONS in the pub become unpleasantly heated. Someone is bragging about how the Argentinian army has no experience of fighting anyone except its own civilian population, when I have to point out that the British Navy does not even have this experience.

For years I urged that the Royal Navy should be used against the dockers of Liverpool and elsewhere. They might even now take a few biffs at the nation's 8m health workers, just going on strike for the sixteenth time this year.

I can't really make up my mind about the Falklands dispute. Galtieri has always struck me as a decent, reasonably sound sort of person, but I don't care for some of his friends – Tony Benn and Ken Livingstone in particular.

Mrs Thatcher should use this as a golden opportunity to blow up the huge grain silos in Northern Argentina, containing all the wheat intended for Russia. In fact I was urging her to do this long before the Argentinians invaded. But nowadays she listens only to Ferdinand Mount and Jimmy Savile. I might as well babble of green fields.

May 7, 1982

SUNSHINE IN St James's Park. A pretty English girl is dallying with an Arab on the grass. Everyone looks clean, well-dressed and happy. Alexander Solzhenitsyn says we have nothing to smile about, no right to smile, because soon we are going to be socialists and slaves:

> "The ferocious desire to appear happy at all times humiliates and undermines humanity. As to us in the East, the inertia of accumulated suffering had freed us of that joyful air. In the face of the camera, our faces remain the way they are in real life – downcast."

It is true that the Russians have always been gloomy buggers, and they have plenty to be miserable about. Throughout their history they have done nothing but tyrannise each other, treating themselves as little better than animals. Socialism might almost have been invented to let them go on doing it, keeping themselves poor, hungry and oppressed.

As for Solzhenitsyn, I suspect that when he has had his fill of the West's slackness, indiscipline, lack of moral purpose and distasteful – not to say insane – air of happiness, he will be welcomed back to Russia as a national hero, just as Dostoievsky was before him.

May 12, 1982

TO THE *Spectator* for lunch. They seem less drunk than they used to be, which is a worrying sign. I hope Chancellor is not getting a sense of moral purpose over this Falklands rubbish. Or perhaps Algy Cluff, the proprietor, finds his oil business less profitable than formerly.

When I call for port Chancellor says there isn't any, and in any case he doesn't know where it is. Mr "Lavish" Mactavish, the magazine's Argentine-born manager and general factotum, leaves the room looking mysterious.

Fifteen minutes later the door bursts open and a madwoman comes in making a terrible noise with her mouth. Nothing can stop her.

Before this rising tide of garbage, the guests slink away one by one.

Brooding about it afterwards, I decide she must have been summoned by telephone from some agency along the lines of Singing Telegrams Speed The Parting Guests? Rent-a-party-wrecker Inc? If anybody can give me the address and telephone number of these enterprising people I should be most grateful.

May 14, 1982

BAD NEWS from the Law Courts. Apparently *Private Eye* was justified in calling Desmond Wilcox a plagiarist but not justified in suggesting he had abused his position at the BBC to commit plagiarism.

So this nasty little man gets away with £14,500 in damages (on top of the £20,000 or so he had received for his plagiarism) and £80,000 in expenses, which he was never in danger of losing because the BBC was paying his expenses out of public money.

If the *Eye* loses its next big battle – against Gordon Kirby, consul in Jeddah at the time of Helen Smith's murder[1] – it will be the end of the *Eye*. Once again the plaintiff is being staked by taxpayers' money, this time from the Foreign Office.

The decision to use Foreign Office money to pursue Mr Kirby's personal grievance was taken by Lord Carrington. Nobody was sadder than I when the Curse of Gnome struck him down so swiftly.[2] His successor, Mr Pym's Number One, seems a shifty sort of individual. The more often he appears on television, the faster we count our spoons.

I wonder what will happen to him. Perhaps he will fall into the beautiful mahogany lavatory in the Foreign Secretary's suite one day after he has done his famous Number Ones and be flushed away to a new life in London's sewage system and out of the history of our time.[3]

May 15, 1982

STREET VIOLENCE of a kind familiar to London and Liverpool has at last broken out in Combe Florey, where an old age pensioner in the village reports that her cat has been shot by an air-rifle.

A nice Taunton CID man who calls at the house for permission to interrogate some of my tenants admits the police are baffled. A check is being made on all registered aliens but I'm afraid we may need to look into our own hearts and into the nature of our own community for the answer to this one.

Whether do-good schoolteachers are to blame for it, as most sensible people seem to think, or unemployment, as left-wing extremists maintain, or the decline and

1 Helen Smith, a nurse, was pushed off the roof at a drinks party in Jeddah. *Private Eye* suspected a Foreign Office cover-up.
2 Lord Carrington, a politician, resigned from the Foreign Office when Argentina invaded the Falklands.
3 Francis Pym, another politician, was sacked as Foreign Secretary immediately after the 1983 General Election.

collapse of organised religion, as Prince Philip avers, this epidemic of mindless violence has now reached a point where the traditional forces of law and order can no longer cope.

With Charles Bronson's example in mind, I am organising a task force of vigilantes who will patrol the village street from sundown to sunrise, disguised as cats, but with shotguns, crossbows and special Worlock cat-to-person missiles slung under their bellies.

First we will need about 500 cat skins, but they should be easy to organise. There is a New Spirit abroad in the land, the spirit of Deathwish. Let the world's Galtieris ignore it at their peril.

May 19, 1982

BEEN LAUGHING all morning at the news from Liverpool, where NUPE workers insist on inspecting all patients to decide if they are ill enough to be operated on. The thought of Liverpudlians showing their varicose veins, piles and diseased livers to the ward cleaners and dustbin executive disposal operatives for approval somehow tickles me.

This is what a People's Health Service should be all about. As part of their plan to win the next general election, Labour hope to introduce the same system into the newspaper industry, so that lift boys, electricians and tea persons will have to pass anything before it is printed.

May 20, 1982

I HAVE refused all invitations to meet the Pope, giving as my official reason that one goes to Marseilles to eat *bouillabaisse* and to Rome to meet the Pope. One has to be rather strict about filling up the house with odd people one has met on one's travels.

My real reason is slightly different. I told the Pope not to come and I think he tried to explain this to Cardinal Hume but that wily old fraud pretended not to understand his English. The Pope's visit is a disaster because it lends a mantle of respectability to the Portakabin Merseyside welfare office adjunct which the Catholic Church in Britain has become.

Within the space of 15 years, as shown in last week's TV programme: "A Church in Crisis", the English Catholic Church has changed from being a bastion of dignity and truth in a disintegrating world to one of the most repulsive aspects of its disintegration.

It has now fallen into the hands of a tiny minority of community freaks who preach their poisonous rubbish, week after week, to an ever shrinking band of the *lumpen* faithful.

By giving this ugly strain his blessing, the brave and good John Paul has done more harm to Catholicism in Britain than the Communist Party has yet achieved in Poland. He should never have come.

May 21, 1982

FOR NEARLY a month I have been drinking nothing but Californian wine as part of a fact-finding enquiry for *Tatler* magazine: does it promote incoherence, psycho-babble, moral collapse and even homosexualism among its devotees? I rather fear it might.

Another problem is whether one can seriously urge the impressionable rich to spend their money on wine called things like Stags Leap, Inglenook and Napa Valley Zinfandel, however nice it seems to taste. This is not just a question of snobbery, but represents a serious moral dilemma, like "modernising" the Prayer Book.

At lunchtime two Oxford undergraduates arrive, saying they want to write a book about me. I do not catch the girl's surname, but she seems quite exceptionally graceful, intelligent and pleasing. This is most unlike the usual Oxford undergraduate nowadays, but even so I shoo them away after lunch, having to write some rubbish for the *Daily Mail* about snooker.

Some time later, I learn she comes from a famous ducal family, is the daughter of a proper earl and a first cousin once removed of the Queen. Damn, *damn*, **damn**! It proves my point, that one should never approach a bottle of wine without carefully studying what is written on the label.

May 28, 1982

IGNORING THE Papal junketing I go to the 95th Birthday Party and Grand Retirement Celebration of my old friend Sir Charles Wintour, who has edited the *Evening Standard* for the last 60 years. He gave my grandfather, Arthur Waugh, his first job in Fleet Street in 1911. Sir Charles is one of the few decent and honourable men to have survived the Street of Shame.

Dinner at the Hyde Park Hotel might have been rather a gloomy occasion since it is being paid for by "Lord" Maffews, the cockney eel-pie manufacturer who bought Express newspapers in a job-lot a few years ago. This objectionable man stands on his tiny legs to Pie a Tribute to the colleague we have all known since before "Lord" Maffews learned how to use a lavatory.

Then halfway through this terrible speech I remember the great "Lord" Maffews joke, first told to me by Peter McKay at Lady Melchett's ball. After I have told my neighbours, the joke travels all around the table and soon people are falling backwards off their chairs and rolling under the table.

Maffews, who is boring on about Sir Charles's "glittering and distinguished career in journalism", thinks he has made a tremendous hit. I'm afraid it will only encourage him to give more of these gruesome dinner parties.

June 1, 1982

NO SOONER has the Pope left than they start cutting up the carpet he stood on to say Mass in Cardiff. S.A. Jones of Newport is selling it in little crosses at £5 a piece, with a certificate of authenticity signed by four Roman Catholic bishops. Profits will be shared out between Jones the Carpet and the Catholic Church.

This practice – the trade in sacred relics – is called simony. It was first condemned by ecclesiastical law at the Council of Chalcedon in 451, and has frequently been anathemised since.

But I suppose it is too much to expect any of the damp-eyed nursery school attendants who pass for priests in Archbishop Worlock's "new sort of church" to know anything about their religion. They pretend to drool over sickies and to get their kicks from soppy communal love feasts, but really they are just in it for the money.

June 3, 1982

I WAS rather pleased to be asked to the Hopalong Beano at Windsor Castle, reckoning that few of my rivals would be there – not even the great and good Sir Peregrine Worsthorne seems to be asked this time – but it all turns to ashes when I see Anthony Andrews.[1]

Princess Margaret is not in the least bit amused when I ask him to show us his bum.[1] I find it hard to know what will amuse her nowadays, but she is looking much less ugly than she did a few years ago.

We discuss why the Queen is glum. Perhaps she is worried about Prince Andrew. One theory is that Argentine lies are quite true – the *Invincible* was sunk several weeks ago, and only the Queen knows it. The Queen Mother, God bless her, thinks the Queen is worried about Prince Edward's "A" levels.

My own theory is that she is upset at Mrs Reagan's refusal to curtsey to her. I know that this sort of boorishness would sicken me if I were Queen. If I didn't love Hopalong[2] so much, I would have refused to come.

June 6, 1982

TO THE Drury Lane Theatre for Michael White's production of *The Pirates of Penzance* with Tim Curry and Pamela Stephenson. I do not think I have ever enjoyed an evening's theatre more in my whole life.

After Shakespeare, under whose massive shade all writers in the English language must somehow struggle to survive, it seems to me that Gilbert and Sullivan are the finest examples of the British genius. Now the Americans have taken them up, there is hope for the New World.

Someone in the Arts Council recently decided to close down the D'Oyly Carte

1 Andrews, as Lord Sebastian Flyte in the televised version of *Brideshead Revisited*, frequently displayed it. Not to be confused with Prince Andrew, the Queen's second son.
2 Ronald Reagan.

Opera Company. When this Soviet agent has been identified, we will know how to deal with him. But if this miserable decade has no other justification, at least it has produced a fine *Pirates of Penzance*.

June 10, 1982

A PROUD father, taken to court for refusing to let a midwife near his girlfriend while she was having a baby explains that he wanted the baby to be born by natural methods, with the mother standing up.

They had learned this new method of having babies from an Esther Rantzen TV programme, they said, and wanted to give it a try. Now, of course, they are in serious trouble, thanks to Esther.

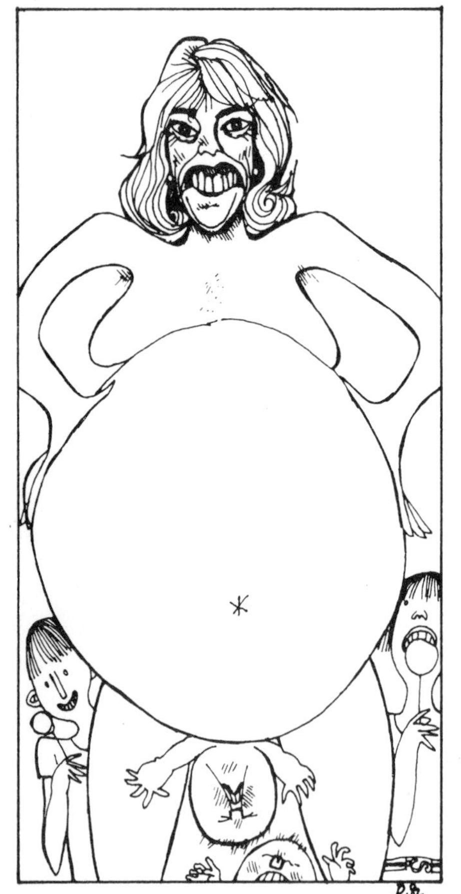

June 16, 1982

PARTIES, parties, parties. Jawn Wells[1] has got married to lovely, frail mother of eight Tizzi Gatacre and wants me to celebrate the event at Mrs Heinz's house at Ascot with 57 varieties of tomato ketchup and other bottled sauces. I don't think I will go. Jawn has been celibate for a very long time and his sexual passions must have been accumulating for something close to 47 years. I do not want to be present when they explode. My advice to bridegrooms in these circumstances is to take things slowly.

Peter McKay is giving a joint birthday party with Mr David "Dave" Cash, the brains behind *Private Eye*'s financial empire. Both claim to be 40, but I have my doubts.

In the end I choose a younger scene. Miss Caitlin Davies, daughter of the dreaded Argentine "Hoonta" Davies, is sharing her 18th birthday party with Jane Brien, daughter of the drunken Hampstead spermatologist,[2] at Ronnie Scott's.

It is terribly noisy. Caitlin and Jane do a sort of striptease in nappies. I suppose people enjoy this sort of thing. I think I will go to Wimbledon and see if I can find a young girl to rub myself against.

June 21, 1982

EVERYBODY looks to me to know what the Royal baby will be called, but the Royal Family have such boring names, and none of their relations is particularly distinguished. The Princess of Wales, on the other hand, is quite well connected, being a cousin not only of little Charlie Vass, funloving teenage editor of *The Times*, but also of Lord Gnome and even of myself.

Hickey makes the witty suggestion that the child should be called Stanley, after our famous victory in the Falklands. But as the child is born on Midsummer's Night, I should have thought that a better name would be Auberon.

Auberon Princeps. Auberon Cornwall. Auberon Wales. Auberon Rex. I find myself so exhausted by all this celebration that I think I'd better go to Wimbledon again and rub myself against a young girl.

1 A comic.
2 Alan Brien.

June 27, 1982

STAYING at Gnome Towers for the weekend my wife and I are rudely awakened at 11.00 in the morning by an ashen-faced footman who draws attention to a scurrilous attack on Lord Gnome in the pathetic *Mail on Sunday*.

This article, by the notorious pimp Willie Donaldson, reeks of envy and class hatred. It is a monument to declining journalistic standards in our "see-through" society – exactly the sort of thing his Lordship had in mind when he first launched this crusading organ.

The worst insult which Donaldson can think of is to say that his Lordship is rich. No doubt Marmaduke is reasonably well to do, but I could tell the wretched hack that his Lordship frequently makes anonymous gifts to little-known charities in such third world places as the Cayman Islands. In any case, the rich are by no means always greedy, cruel or mean. In my experience, it is the poor who are generally over-rated.

But Marmaduke seems extraordinarily cheerful at Morning Service in his private chapel, singing "Praise my soul the King of heaven" lustily. When we retire to our room at the end of the day, we hear an extraordinary noise which my Wife puts down to rats in the baronial wainscoting.

But I know better, having heard the sound before. It is his Lordship laughing. What can this mean?

June 28, 1982

THIS morning everything is explained. Mr Bernard Shrimsley, the slimy, snivelling Editor of *Mail on Sunday*, has been sacked once again – this time after ten issues. Is it a record?

Lord Gnome is convulsed with merriment all morning and increases my wages on the spot. We discuss who might get the job next. Dame Harold Evans, I understand, is frightfully keen but when I mention this his Lordship has another fit of laughing. The Dame, you see, is also under the Curse of Gnome.

July 2, 1982

NEARLY 2,000 readers have written to ask my advice on whether or not Prince William of Wales should be circumcised. It is not an easy question to answer, and I have the impression that much more may hang on this little point than anyone realises.

It all depends on what sort of a monarchy people want. Uncircumcised males generally tend to the sciences rather than to the Arts. Their terror at being exposed makes them cowardly and unreliable in a tight corner, but they are sometimes good at games like ping-pong and Monopoly.

For all I know there may be sound reasons for leaving the little chap alone. I feel it should be made the subject of a national plebiscite, like the Common Market referendum. We have to think of something to keep us amused now the Falklands are over.[1]

July 18, 1982

AFTER A rainstorm, a huge slug appears underneath one of my fig trees. If I say it is two feet long nobody will believe me, so I had better say it is a foot and a half. The children, for some inexplicable reason, decide to christen it "Jon".[2]

One of the most revolting and sadistic things anyone can do is to put salt on a slug's tail. First it gives off a sort of yellow foam, accompanied by a nasty smell. Then it starts thrashing around like Lawrence Olivier trying to act Richard III's death scene on the field of Bosworth. Before long the wretched creature expires.

So long as salt is freely available in the shops, a small minority of people will continue to torture slugs in this heartless way. Responsible newspapers like the *Daily Mirror* should campaign to have salt withdrawn, being administered only by qualified health visitors who are also members of COHSE.

Salt is far too dangerous a substance to be left lying around. Using figures supplied by the Thatcher Government, it has been calculated that 20,000 Old Age Pensioners sniff it in the Solihull area. That is a conservative estimate.

1 Argentina surrendered on May 20, 1982.
2 Jon Pilger, the left-wing journalist, had initiated libel proceedings against Waugh, paid for by the *Daily Mirror*. They were later dropped.

July 21, 1982

TO HATFIELD, for the 81st birthday party of Barbara Cartland, the romantic novelist who has recently been appointed Queen Mother Apparent. It is a fine gathering of the old gang: Rebecca West, 92; Malcolm Muggeridge, 81; Gloria Swanson, age unknown; Sir John Junor, 83; Sir Nigel Dempster, 71; Lord Goodman and Lady Diana Cooper both 85; John Wells, 47; Sir Arthur Rubinstein, 106. . .

I had hoped for something of a feast, as Ms Cartland is extremely rich, but on this occasion she offers nothing but Royal Jelly and natural bran flavoured with vitamins, A, B_2, E and F.

The oldies fall on it greedily, but I can't face the thought of all those vitamins. Instead I find an aged pekingese asleep on a pink satin cushion, and eat it morosely. There is nothing funny or commendable about old age. It is a miserable affliction which brings a sort of imbecility to those who suffer from it and distresses everyone else.

July 30, 1982

Aude, France

FOR A WEEK I have done no work at all, and marvel at the stamina of the English, who somehow manage to do none all their lives. After a few days, I found myself in a state of nervous exhaustion and moral collapse.

August 6, 1982

OLIVER CROMWELL'S face was entirely covered by warts. To have shown him without them would have been like painting Telly Savalas in a wig, or Lord Hailsham as a sylph in a ballet-dancer's leotard. When Cromwell asked for "warts and all" in his portrait, he was merely insisting it should be recognisable.

Now the idea has caught on that no portrait is complete without some warts. That is my only criticism of a fairly grovelling portrait of me in the *Observer* by my old friend Alan Watneys: he has added warts where none exist on the beautiful, bland countenance which confronted him.

He opines that I may be tormented by sexual jealousy – not only of the horrible Lord Gowrie, who is Mrs Thatcher's token blackamoor in the Northern Ireland Office, but also of Dame Harold Evans, the controversial Welsh dwarf whose brief editorship of *The Times* caused so much pain.

That seems to box the compass pretty well, from massive vassals to frigid midgets. Is there nobody who escapes my sexual jealousy? Jon Pilger is frightfully good-looking, I agree, but I don't think he excites my sexual jealousy. No, honestly. Believe me.

August 8, 1982

TONIGHT is celebrated as Jeremy Thorpe Night throughout the Langue d'Oc, where once the troubadours sang. It marks the anniversary of Jeremy Thorpe's arrest on various foul charges of which a London jury later acquitted him.

Farmers, farmworkers and drunken peasants march up and down the lane all night with lanterns, singing at the top of their voices and beating the hedgerows with long staves or alpenstocks.

It is a very jolly occasion indeed, and makes me think of the Buddhist New Year in Chiang Mai, Northern Thailand, when everybody pours water over everybody else, laughing uproariously. There are still little corners of joy in this blighted, Pilger-infested world.

August 14, 1982

ON THE twentieth anniversary of Marilyn Monroe's death I have to deliver a lecture to the Thomas Aquinas Society of Dominican seminarists attached to Toulouse University and take her murder – some would call it a martyrdom – as my theme.

At this late stage, we will probably never know which of the Kennedy brothers it was who delivered the lethal injection under her armpit: Robert Kennedy, the Attorney General and father of eight, with whom she had just ended a love affair; or Jack Kennedy, who in addition to being the father of three children, was also the President of the United States, with whom she had had a couple of one-night stands.

So far as I know, she never went to bed with Teddy Kennedy, the father of eleven who still hopes to be President. If she had, of course, the poor girl would not have stood a chance. But the appalling readiness – one might call it eagerness – of these Kennedy brothers to murder their former girlfriends demonstrates a failure in traditional Catholic morality, or so I tell the Thomists of Toulouse.

Because murder and adultery were regarded as equally grave sins – and equally easily pardoned – Catholic adulterers had very few inhibitions about murdering their girlfriends. If the last Vatican Council had been able to achieve a single useful thing, it might have been to adjust this emphasis which explains the behaviour of the IRA as well as that of the Yorkshire Ripper and Kennedy brothers.

But modern Catholics are not in the least interested in questions of personal morality, only in socialist economic theory. The more advanced among them probably accept Lenin's conclusion, that occasional murders may be justified for the good of the community as a whole.

August 30, 1982

AFTER many years as a political correspondent and commentator, I have decided the best way to judge a government, ignoring all the communist propaganda pouring out from *The Times*, *Sunday Times* and BBC, is by the pound's rate of exchange against those few civilised currencies that matter: the French franc, the Italian lira and the Thai baht.

By this measurement, Mrs Thatcher's government, which gives us more than 12 francs to the pound, is very good indeed. I shall vote for her at the next election. The annual Bernard Levin Memorial Luncheon, held this year in the Hotel de France, Auch, has four extra courses to celebrate the new rate of exchange. They are:

Fresh ducks' liver with grapes
Oyster stuffed with goose livers,
sauce Bernardaise
Preserved goose with small peas
Panache of goose and duck livers
au nature

Afterwards we drink endless toasts to Mrs Thatcher and sing variations on the theme of "For she's a jolly good fellow" until the last person has fallen asleep. There is something to be said for socialism in other countries.

September 10, 1982

THE *SPECTATOR* has sent me a copy of *Brief Lives* by my old friend Alan Watneys. Soon to be published by Hamish Hamilton at the exorbitant price of £8.95, it is a collection of obituaries of all his friends – some of them, like myself and Lord Gnome, still alive. The trouble with writing obituaries is that one does not get paid for them until after the subject is dead, and I suppose Watneys grew tired of waiting.

Among them is an obituary of Tom Driberg, the former MP and Chairman of the Labour Party who died six years ago. Tom not only worked for the KGB and MI5, like most homosexualists in public life, but also for *Private Eye*, and frequently came to *Eye* lunches.

We assumed that he came for the food, most particularly Monsieur Balon's exquisite Israeli-style *goy chumpkfa* in Brown Sauce. Not so, according to Watneys:

"The real reason Driberg was such an assiduous attender at these lunches was that he conceived a passion for Patrick Marnham, likewise a regular attender. Marnham, who was heterosexual, did not respond to his advances."

Marnham, I should explain, is an impoverished writer. To think that none of us dreamed of the dramas going on under the table during all those years! One thing puzzles me. If this is true, why did both of them go on attending these lunches? I do not pretend to know the answer, but I think we should be told.

September 11, 1982

BROODING ABOUT Marnham and Driberg, I remember another embarrassing episode during a lunch for *Spectator* writers at the *Daily Mirror*. The story is told by Alicks Chancellor, the *Spectator*'s highly motivated, croquet-playing Editor.

He took Peter Ackroyd[1] along with him. Ackroyd is a very sensitive, artistic sort of person. He found himself sitting next to a bronzed, blond bombshell from Bondi Beach. As the claret gave way to the port and the port to brandy, Ackroyd's flirtatious manner gave way to more explicit amorous advances.

Imagine Chancellor's horror when he recognised Ackroyd's victim as none other than the *Mirror*'s fearless award-winning ace heart-throb reporter . . .

Jon Pilger ! ! !

September 15, 1982

Zimbabwe

ON MY first day in Harare I am ushered into the presence of the lovely Ghana-born wife of Zimbabwe's exciting new Prime Minister, Comrade Sally Mugabe. She is also Minister for Women's Affairs. After I have introduced myself as an Arts Council-sponsored poet from England, we talk seriously for a while about Zimbabwe women – how good they are, how much they cost etc.

When my attentions become more pressing she sighs and says: "All you poets are the same" – before leading me by the hand into an inner chamber, crooning the ancient Dagbani love song "*mba mba cho p'keti maa'la*". . .

Actually this is not completely true. I had various introductions to Mrs Mugabe, and three people I meet in Harare assure me they can arrange an interview with no difficulty, but they all come to nothing. Perhaps Comrade Sally is just another of those women I seem destined never to meet, like the Princess of Wales. If I seriously imagined I was never going to meet the Princess of Wales, I think I would die.

September 18, 1982

TODAY I see my first pair of hippopotamuses mating in the shallow waters of the Zambesi River, much reduced by the drought.

Nowadays we are programmed to associate sexual activity with skinny, cream-coloured teenagers who are gracious enough to take off their clothes for the glossy magazines. I bet none of them could provide half the satisfaction of a mature female hippopotamus of some fifty-five or sixty summers, wallowing in the soupy waters.

It must be the perfect life, really, to be a male hippopotamus.

September 21, 1982

AT THE Serima Mission, in Victoria Province, I am shown around by an enchantingly pretty African nun called Sister

1 Literary and Arts editor of the *Spectator*. A bachelor.

Balbina. The mission was founded by Swiss Bethlehem Fathers and is famous for its African carvings of Bible-related subjects.

Sister Balbina is one of the loveliest women I've seen in the whole of Africa. She cannot be more than 25, and has the most delightful figure. How poignant that she should have dedicated her life in this way.

When we come to the bell tower, I ask her to climb up the ladder in front of me. It was rather a caddish request, I suppose, but I had often wondered. Black petticoats and pink knickers. To think I had to come all this way to find out.

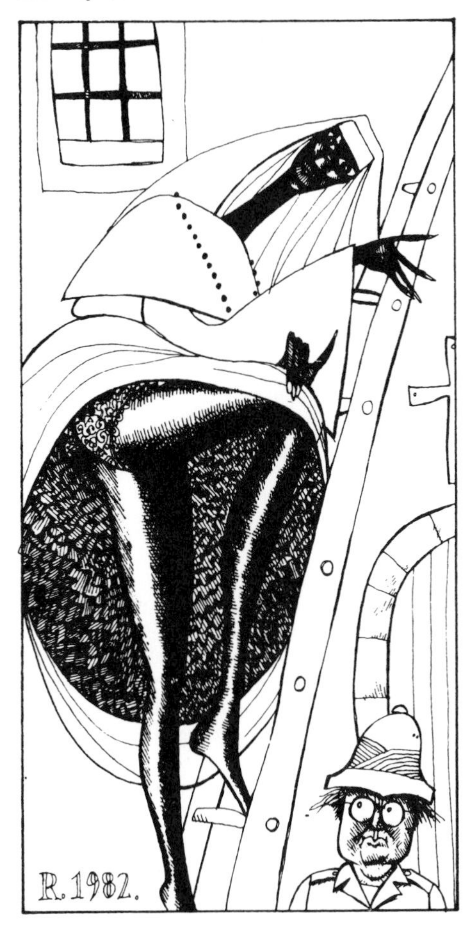

October 4, 1982

IT IS seldom this Diary shoulders the unpleasant task of naming a Shit of the Year, but the moment has arrived. Step forward "Lord" Beaumont of Whitley, publisher of dirty books, formerly known as "The Reverend" Tim Beaumont. Lord Disgusting would be a better title.

He it was who published all the dirty drawings by Aubrey Beardsley which Beardsley, on his deathbed, implored his publisher to destroy. He it is who now calls for a 20% tax on public school fees in order to "smash the ruling class".

Let us take a glance at Lord Disgusting's background. Born immensely rich, he was not content to go to one public school like the rest of us. He went to *two* public schools. People may ask why he went to two public schools. I do not know the answer.

Perhaps his father thought Gordonstoun was "smarter" than Eton after Prince Philip had gone there. Perhaps he thought there were too many Jews at Eton. Perhaps there was some other reason. I do not know. Lord Disgusting may care to tell us.

After sending his own four children to such exclusive schools as Gordonstoun and St Margaret's, Bushey, he started associating himself with strange organisations like Exit, the Liberal Party and "Make Children Happy: The New Kind Of Charity For All Our Kids" – an organisation which I exposed some months ago.

Now his last child has safely left school, he calls for a huge tax on school fees as "the best blow for equality since the Reform Bill". I would propose Lord Disgusting as the White's Club's Shit of the Year except that even White's has to draw the line somewhere, and this degenerate voluptuary has never got in.

October 7, 1982

A SUMMONS from my beloved proprietor to attend on him at Gnome Towers without fail at 10.45am. This is a bad sign, as it is exactly the hour at which His Lordship generally goes to the lavatory.

What can he want to talk about? I suppose it is Jon Pilger, and groan inwardly. I do not particularly wish to see Lord Gnome laughing on the lavatory. He might do himself some terrible injury at his age.

In fact Marmaduke wishes to talk about *herpes*, the exciting new venereal disease being promoted by the *Sunday Times*. He has

personal knowledge of the condition, which is incurable, having contracted it many years ago in Algeciras, apparently from his stepmother.

He tells me that far from its having any deleterious effects, it is entirely beneficial, promoting an active sex life, vigorous hair growth and a lively interest in the affairs of young people. Indeed, it is to *herpes* that His Lordship attributes much of his success in life. Unsightly symptoms may be kept at bay by eating Lymeswold, the new full-fat soft blue English cheese being promoted by Peter Walker and the British Cheese Council.

Young women, especially, benefit from the new *herpes* look, which imparts a glowing radiance to the skin such as might cost many hundreds of pounds at a beautician's parlour. Any young woman wishing to learn more about this unique opportunity should write, enclosing photographs, to the Social Secretary at Gnome Towers, L18 2EP.

October 14, 1982

ONE OF my many jobs in life is to keep an eye on Soviet and other Iron Curtain infiltration into Fleet Street. This brings me into fairly frequent contact with the Special Branch, the only wing of the Security Service which is heterosexual and uninfiltrated by Communist agents. Perhaps it is as some sort of reward for my good work in the past that a friend in the Special Branch now gives me photocopies of all Prince Andrew's love letters to Koo Stark,[1] written from *HMS Invincible* in the South Atlantic. They were found in Koo's flat during a routine security check.

I must admit, I can't help laughing. Andrew really must make efforts with his spelling. Besoms are a type of broom, and "pussee" is an Anglo-Indian word for afternoon. But I don't think I will publish them. They might make the Princess of Wales blush.

October 23, 1982

MOST Saturdays I worship at the Reform in Seymour Place but today I choose the Finchley Progressive Synagogue in Hutton Grove, where the singing is sometimes thought to be even better.

Who should I meet there but my old friend Patrick Marnham, the famous bachelor?[2] He asks me across the road for a quick "drinky poo". Patrick is terribly worried about the Animal Libbers who have been protesting about the Princess of Wales wearing furs. It is not that he approves of cruelty, he says, but a lot of poor families make their living from the fur trade.

Patrick is nearly 40 years old now, and we are all getting tired of telling him it is time he found himself a nice young Jewish girl. Soon the mothers are going to start asking questions about why he has not married before, with all his mink underwear and other fur accessories.

In fact I think I may have just the job for him. Owing to a lucky breakthrough, I *may* be able to introduce him to a really lovely young girl – 18, good family, very dainty and all the trimmings. Better not reveal her name, but I tell him the father is half-Jewish,

1 An actress with whom the Prince was infatuated.
2 Marnham, a poor writer, had described Waugh's Jewish ancestry in *The Private Eye Story* (Deutsch, 1982).

old-Etonian, Welsh, very, very small, titled and with royal connections.[1]

Patrick asks me if there might be a bob or two in the background, and I tell him not to worry. Very wealthy indeed.

October 25, 1982

GORE VIDAL, the brilliant American author whose name is sometimes mentioned in the same breath as Shakespeare, Proust, Gide, Liberace and Larry Grayson, accuses me of having lost him a Senatorial election in California by suggesting, in a New York book review, that he had homosexual preferences.

This is very puzzling. I always assumed that Vidal was a practising homosexualist. Now it appears that he regards homosexuality as such a vile and unnatural perversion that he's even prepared to sue me for alleged libel.

Perhaps I have got it wrong. If so I must certainly apologise and give him back his seat in the Senate. Can anybody throw any light on the puzzle? Any first-hand reminiscences, letters, holiday snaps, home movies etc will be gratefully received, as will any examples of his published work which point conclusively in one direction or the other.

October 28, 1982

A NEW STUDY of the rare genetic disorder called porphyria – to which our own beloved Royal Family is tragically prone – links the disease with the legend of Count Dracula.

Sufferers of porphyria, according to Dr Lionel Millgrom of Imperial College, London, become sensitive to light and can only emerge after dark; their gums shrink, making their teeth appear exceptionally large; they grow hair on their hands and faces and develop an animal nature; they show an aversion to garlic, which contains an enzyme which is especially harmful to their condition.

Worst of all, they feel a craving for iron, says Dr Millgrom, and "one of the most effective ways of taking it is by drinking blood".

None of the Royal Family likes garlic, but only Prince Andrew shows the characteristic tooth formation which ignorant people used to identify as the mark of a vampire.

Unlike his great uncle, Harry "Bonkers" Gloucester, he has not yet started growing hair on his hands and face; nor, so far as I know, has he yet started murdering prostitutes like his great great uncle Albert Victor, Duke of Clarence – otherwise known as Jack the Ripper.

1 Presumably a reference to Lady Sarah Armstrong-Jones, only daughter of Lord Snowdon and Princess Margaret.

But many of the symptoms are there. Among all his girlfriends – Finola, Gemma, Julia, Xenia, Sandy, Carolyn, Karen, Kim, Kirsty and Koo – the only thing they have in common is that they did not seem to last very long.

I hope future girlfriends remember to sleep with a wreath of garlic around their necks.

November 1, 1982

A FULL page advertisement in the *Daily Express* paid for by an organisation called IFAW – the International Fund for Animal Welfare – urges us all to take action against the menace of Canadian seal pups now poised to invade the Commonwealth. IFAW suggests we should write letters of complaint to the Prime Minister.

I am not sure that is enough. These animals are highly dangerous, being carriers of *herpes* in their poisonous spittle. Fortunately, they are easy to identify, resembling large white caterpillars at the half-way stage between grub and chrysalis; they also give a high, menacing squeak when kicked.

We should be on the lookout for these vicious little animals. Some may have slipped into the country undetected, like German parachutists disguised as nuns. Any person suspected of being a seal pup in disguise should be kicked and then, if it squeaks, clubbed and skinned.

Crypto-seal pups are not always easy to identify, but in recent months I have found myself growing more and more suspicious of Melvyn Bragg.

November 10, 1982

ON BOARD *HMS Herpes* for a celebration of our victory over Argentina, I dance the night away in hornpipes and Irish jigs with specially selected soldiers, sailors and SAS heroes.

Our host for the evening is "Lord" Maffews of Kilimanjaro, the genial philanthropist of Express Newspapers. Barons of beef, boars' heads, saddles of lamb, winkles, whelks, lobsters, jellied eels, elephants' trunks and great stews of hippopotamus belly are washed down by 1,000 bottles of champagne, all supplied by the noble patriot. And lashings and lashings of Lymeswold cheese, which the cunning old rogue had bought at 38p a pound cheaper under its original brand name of Danish Saga Blue.

Never mind. As we line up to be sick over the deck rail into the mysterious waters of Portsmouth harbour 200 feet beneath us, we all agree it has been a jolly good show.

November 14, 1982

ANDREW BARLOW, heart-swap Romeo, is dead three years after being given the heart of a 17-year-old youth at enormous public expense in Papworth Hospital, Cambridge.

According to his wife, he came out of hospital a different man, obsessed by sex. He announced he wanted to go to bed with as many women as possible, settling eventually for a divorced lady some 11 years older than himself.

"I made up my mind that if I was going to die, I was going to have a superb time first," said this 32-year-old print worker before he died.

So he did, and now he is dead. Has it been worth it? A hundred elderly men could have drunk themselves to death on Lafite '45 for the price of keeping this one goon for three years in his "superb time". I think I may be going to vote Labour at the next election.

November 17, 1982

BACK TO *herpes*. An American girl, Ms Susan Lintrop, of Miami, Florida, is suing the man she claims she caught it off after a "one night stand" – for £60,000! Sexually transmitted *herpes* is now at epidemic proportions in the United States.

Lord Cowdray claims that traditional rubber appliances, as used by the working classes, are an effective prophylactic. But then he would say that, wouldn't he? London Rubber Company has a virtual monopoly in these goods.

No, the only cure is to eat as much Lymeswold as possible, before and after. It is a particularly nasty cheese, tasting of banana-flavoured toothpaste, but people should think of these things before they decide to be irresponsible.

December 4, 1982

TORY MP, Mr John Carlisle, claims to have evidence of young Asian girls being offered for sale in England at £1,000 a piece. Mostly they are sold to Indians who want to come to this country, but if Mr Carlisle really does have this evidence he should produce it immediately, as I would certainly be interested in buying a couple.

Asian women make the most delightful companions: affectionate, loyal, clean, hard-working, intelligent, attractive – as different from the typical modern Englishwoman as it would be possible to imagine. The most puzzling thing is why these Indian johnnies still want to come to England.

December 10, 1982

MORE HORROR stories about the treatment of old people. A gang of thieves in St Albans has been giving them drugged tea and

then robbing them while they slept. Or so it is claimed.

The reason why old people are at risk nowadays is that they are so rich. When their pension was only a few shillings a week, everybody left them alone. Now they are to be seen hobbling away from the Post Office every Monday morning carrying great fistfuls of £5 and £10 notes, even my fingers begin to twitch.

Something must obviously be done about this epidemic of granny bashing, and the first thing is for the Government to stop giving them so much money.

1983

A fairly uneventful year in comparison to those which preceded it. A new plague, called AIDS, threatens to wipe out all the world's homosexuals. Reactions to this development vary. More serious for others, puritan elements in Westminster's Conservative City Council start a campaign against massage parlours.

Despite this, Waugh decides to vote Conservative in the June General Election, thereby helping to secure Mrs Thatcher's victory. He also supports his old school colleague Roy Hattersley in Hattersley's successful attempt to secure the Deputy Leadership of the Labour Party.

Mrs Thatcher amazes the country by appointing the country's first black Minister, G. Gowrie, chosen as Minister for the Arts, in her new administration. Waugh joins in applauding this enlightened move.

January 1, 1983

EVERY JANUARY I go to Farnborough Abbey, Hampshire for the solemn Requiem Mass in memory of the Abbey's foundress, the Empress Eugenie of holy memory.

She built the Monastery so that the monks could pray for the souls of her husband, Napoleon III, who died at Chislehurst in 1873, and her son the Prince Imperial, who was hacked to death by Zulus in 1879.

Unfortunately for her intentions the monks were ordered to stop praying for the Bonaparte family by the then Bishop of Portsmouth, Monsignor Derek Worlock, about 10 years ago. Worlock found that the idea did not fit in with his own pig-like socialist priorities, especially as the ceremonies had become centres for pilgrimage by all the unthroned families of Europe, praying for the restoration of their dynasties.

Since Worlock has been sent to Merseyside, the good monks continue to pray for the holy Empress on the grounds that she was born de Montijo, in Spain and was a Bonaparte only by marriage.

The Empress lies in a marble sarcophagus above the Tabernacle; the Emperor is to the right of the Crypt altar, arrayed as a Knight of the Garter. Prince Lulu lies to the left, in small pieces. Elsewhere in the Abbey they preserve the patch of veldt where Lulu fell, displayed in a glass case.

January 5, 1983

TWO LETTERS in the post cause intense irritation. The first is from the Central London branch of the National Union of Journalists, announcing it has increased my subscription to £88 a year. These greedy, self-important shits know they can demand any sum they choose in black-mail, since membership of the Union is now compulsory.

The second is a begging letter from Christ Church, Oxford, asking if I will contribute to a hideous new quad they are planning to build in St Aldate's so that their new Comprehensive intake and lower class research students can be accommodated in the comfort they expect.

I expect all old Christ Church men will treat this appeal with the contempt it deserves. If I could pay them not to build the new quad – and to pull down the terrible Comprehensive Wing they built in Blue Boar Lane 10 years ago – I would happily do so.

One problem with the lower classes, as they emerge from centuries of richly deserved obscurity, is that they are greedy. Another problem, of course, is that they are ugly, boring, humourless and desperately conceited.

Perhaps when they have built the new St Aldate's quad I'll go and set fire to it and see if I can roast a few.

January 10, 1983

New York

A BUSY week in New York. Between meetings of the Avenge Marilyn Committee I have been demonstrating my Lymeswold cure for *herpes* to a listless audience of venereologists at the Frippelbaum Institute. They are interested only in the new disease called AIDS.

This is how the hysteria is described by Dr Lawrence Mass, writing in *New York Native*, the mass-circulation Gay newspaper:

"I don't think it's sensationalistic to report the serious reality that escalating numbers of sexually active gay men are currently experiencing a health crisis."

What all this means is that homosexualists are toppling over in the street like ninepins. They suddenly lose all immunity to illness. AIDS stands for Acquired Immunity Deficiency Syndrome but when they tell me this and ask what they should do about it, I give up. Try ordinary Cheddar cheese with an aspirin, I say weakly.

January 14, 1983

IN THE smoke-filled hall of the Algonquin Hotel there is a sudden commotion. A woman screams, chairs are overturned.

It is one of the glories of New York that these dramas are always happening. Every day the *Post* – easily Rupert Murdoch's best newspaper – tells of demented Negroes running amok and skinning each other alive, decomposed corpses being found in the cold store of Kosher restaurants etc.

On this occasion, however, it is just that news has come through from England that Tina Brown, the lovely 22-year-old editress of *Tatler*, is resigning her post. Like the retirement of William Rees-Mogg, this marks the end of an era. Miss Brown, by hiring some of the best talents in the country including the best wine correspondent in the world, caught the spirit of the entire age.

One of her last acts as editress was to give me an air ticket to Manila for the film festival. We will not see her like again.

January 16, 1983

BACK IN England for a few days to pick up my post, I glance at the newspapers. *The Times* tells me only that a huge number of people seem to have died, some of them old friends.

Tristram Hillier, the painter, has died at 77; Alex McKay, a nice man whose murdered wife was cruelly fed to pigs by some Pakistani tailors in Kent, at 73; John Cutts Lockwood, the former Tory MP, at 92; Dr Lovell Cocks, one-time Free Church Moderator and father of Michael, at 88; Colin Watson, the writer, at the extraordinarily young age of 62. And the Duke of Norfolk has broken his hip.

Oh dear, oh dear. Various reasons might be adduced for all this bad news.

My own theory is that they are all dying and falling around from boredom at the new *Times*. These are the people who have not had the resource to change to the *Daily Telegraph*.

January 22, 1983

OF ALL the things which have happened in my lifetime, the one which causes me almost the greatest pain is the sad decline of Bernard Levin.[1]

I write of a man I have loved for many years. Today he explains how, on going to see the film *E.T.*, which most of the Glendas were writing about months ago, he could not find a cloakroom at the Empire, Leicester Square because it had been turned into a kiosk selling souvenirs of the film.

"I have no serious expectation of ever coming across a more comprehensively perfect symbol of the combination of simplicity, indifference to the customers and hog-like greed that has brought the cinema in this country to the edge of destruction," he splutters.

All of us have been caught short at one time or another in our lives. It can be jolly embarrassing. The most sensible thing is to make some homely accommodation with a litter bin or empty milk bottle and hope nobody notices. The thing not to do is to make a great fuss, demand to see the manager and wave your Press Card around.

O Bernard, thou wast slain in thine high places. How are the mighty fallen!

February 20, 1983

OFFICIALS of the Church of Scientology deny that their founder, Ron Hubbard, is dead or incurably insane, although he has not been seen anywhere for two years. Is this true or untrue? In either case, does it matter?

None of us can really be sure that we exist. My whole life, as this Diary shows, is a lie. All the characters in it are invented, none bears any resemblance to anyone living or dead. People who claim to find themselves here, like the ludicrous Jon Pilger, the angry wee Harold Evans or the incredible Bernard "Slimy" Shrimsley, must know that the only real existence we can any of us claim is in the imagination of God.

As soon as He stops exercising His imagination about these tiresome people they will simply vanish, leaving not so much as a tooth or a dental plate behind.[2] That is one of the great comforts of religion. In fact, all three of them seem to have vanished already. Has anybody seen a tooth?

March 8, 1983

A MOMENTOUS decision taken in the small hours of the morning. Faced by the

1 A journalist.

2 Teeth and dental plates were turning up in a house at 195 Melrose Avenue, Cricklewood, scene of a mass murder.

appalling boredom of Somerset in winter I have decided to sell a few pictures and buy a flat in London. Everybody says that Brook Green, Hammersmith, is now the smartest place to live.

Alexander Chancellor has already bought a house there. So have Major Libby Purves,[1] Marc Boxer, Terri Wogan, Patric Leischfeld and all the Diana set.

Another advantage is that it is next door to St Paul's School, whose girls, under the ferocious, yoghurt-eating Widow Brigstocke, are said to be among the most interesting in London. If one does not move fast, one will soon be too old for this sort of thing.

March 26, 1983

I HAVE not been asked to David Frost's[2] "wedding" and would certainly not attend if I had been asked out of sympathy for the bride's poor father.

If the Duke of Norfolk were not such a good Christian, he would probably have taken the easy way out and shot himself. He is right not to do so, but I am afraid that I will be among those who avoid the Norfolks for the next few months. I hate it when brave men are reduced to crying on my shoulder.

April 19, 1983

MEMORIES RUSH back when I see a picture of Princess Anne with her grinning, speechless husband Commander Gibbs, in the Imperial Palace in Tokyo. The Emperor Hirohito is telling them a joke, and Princess Anne wears her "nasty nip in the air" face.

It is true that the Emperor's breath smells horrible, but this is because he eats nothing but raw fish.

When I last went to see him a few years ago, the Emperor seemed obsessed by the subject of pubic hair. I don't suppose Princess Anne had anything of interest to tell him about this – or, indeed, about anything else.

April 24, 1983

THE ENTERPRISING Manchester couple called Dennis and Lillian Rolph who are advertising their unborn baby for sale in the *Daily Mirror* reckoned to get £20,000 for the child when it is born.

I wonder if they have taken Capital Gains Tax into account, currently running at 30%. They should allow £5,000 for that, and then another £2,500 for VAT – babies are not exempt, as far as I can see, unless they count as farmstock or meat. If they sell the child at Christies they will also have to pay £2,000 commission plus £300 VAT on the commission, plus a couple of hundred if they want the brat illustrated in colour for the Christies catalogue, plus £200 insurance and carriage.

Then they will have to pay a fine and go to prison for three months for trading in babies. This is the way the Government treats anyone who honestly wants to be rich. Personally, I should value the baby at about £14.50. Delightful Asian babies – from the Philippines, Thailand and Vietnam – can be bought rather cheaper, sometimes with their mothers.

April 26, 1983

THE LATEST party game in London is derived from the ancient art of Siang Mien, introduced by a beautiful Chinese lady called Lailan Young in her book *Secrets of the Face*. It enables you to tell people's past history, present characters and future prospects by studying the various regions of their face.

I hope to run an occasional series of portraits with commentary derived from this ancient art. In time they will be collected in a book with foreword by the Duke of Edinburgh, published by Snipcock and Tweed at £48.50. The money will go to spastics or youth opportunities, or something of that sort.

Number One is the Right Honourable Roy Hattersley MP.

Called a "Shit face" this shape belongs to an essentially stupid, ambitious, greedy person, more or less unscrupulous in pursuit of

1 New editor of *Tatler* in succession to Tina Brown. She did not last long.
2 A former television celebrity who announced his engagement to a daughter of the Duke of Norfolk.

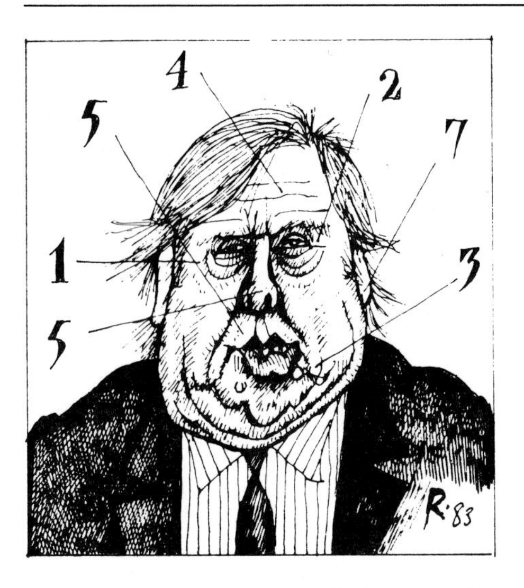

his own ends but with a certain base cunning (betrayed by the "*gunge*" marks under the nose) which sometimes carries it to a temporary position of authority.

Note the combination of hairiness with yellow flab in the Love Region.This indicates a lecherous nature, but also an awareness that prowess may fall short of desire. The ducks' feet or "wankers fingers" effect in the Health and Efficiency Region probably mean only that he has recently eaten a lot of toasted cheese.

Shit Faces usually do very well as ratcatchers and sometimes progress to rabbits. They should not be set against anything bigger than a hare.

Next week – Jon Pilger, Baby Susan Phillips, and Sir Hugh Casson.

April 29, 1983

HOW SAD to read that Sir Harold Evans, the former journalist, has died at the age of 71. I certainly never dreamed he was as old as that.[1] One's thoughts go out to his widow.

What else is there to say about this melancholy event? Perhaps one should pass on to the next thing. I am off to Lourdes with a party of 500 pilgrims from the North of England to pray for Professor Trevor-Roper's soul.[2]

May 2, 1983

FOR TWO days I have been receiving telephone calls from various toadies who say that Solzhenitsyn is coming to London and wants to meet me. But why should I wish to meet the nasty old flea-bag?

For a time he was my hero, when I thought that through heroic suffering he had become the first Russian to realise what unspeakable shits the Russians are and always have been. Socialism has nothing to do with it, except that it might have been invented to cater for their peculiar tastes.

In all their repulsive history they have done nothing but oppress each other and be oppressed. Since Solzhenitsyn came to the West he has revealed the same hatred of freedom in any form. His only real quarrel with Soviet oppression is that the Soviets do not use religion to justify it.

In any case I have just received a summons to Gnome Towers. That must take precedence over all social frivolities.

May 3, 1983

LORD GNOME receives me in the usual place. Marmaduke Gnome, I should explain, is one of the most remarkable men who have ever lived. Intensely shy, he can talk to his subordinates only when he is seated on the lavatory. He seldom looks at them and never refers to them by name – with the one exception of myself, who for some reason he always calls "Peregrine".[3]

"Kneel down, Peregrine," he says kindly, as I am ushered in. A long silence follows. Plop. He says that he has received a letter from lawyers representing Dame Harold Evans whose untimely death at the age of 71 I recorded last week.[4]

1 Sir Harold Evans, Bt, Macmillan's former press officer. Not to be confused with "Dame" Harold Evans (*vide passim*).
2 Professor Trevor-Roper had "authenticated" some bogus Hitler Diaries for the *Sunday Times*.
3 Peregrine Worsthorne had recently written an admiring portrait of the *Telegraph's* proprietor, to mark Lord Hartwell's 70th birthday.
4 See April 29, 1983, n.1.

"Dame Evans is dead," says Marmaduke. Plop. "You shall never again refer to him by name. Nor to his house, to his wife, his manservant, his maidservant, his ox, his ass, nor to anything that is his." Plop. Plop.

This is a bitter blow. Nobody in his senses would want to write about the smelly old corpse of Dame Evans. But am I never to be allowed to mention his beautiful 24-year-old widow, Tina, the hope of her generation, whose eyes are like almonds, her breasts like pomegranates? Murmuring "Not my will, O Lord, but Thine be done," I back away from the Presence. Perhaps I shall move to *Punch*.[1]

May 4, 1983

I REFUSE to be drawn into the Great Debate about whether or not Joan Collins is bald. It was started in the *Daily Mirror* by Anne Robinson, who announced that the 49-year-old actress was as bald as a coot.

Collins denies this, and calls her hairdresser, Mr Hugh Green, as witness. Unfortunately his evidence is slightly equivocal. "When you are an actress, there are occasions when you have to wear hairpieces. They all do," he says mysteriously. "She may have worn a swatch of hair, but that doesn't mean her hair doesn't look great without it."

The question I ask myself is, does it matter? Is a woman's hair really essential when one gets down to the nitty-gritty? Could one not become rather fond of a completely bald pate, so long as it was soft, matt, feminine and silky, rather than the sort of shiny, hard, greasy thing offered to the fairer sex by such as Gerald Kauffmann and "Sir" James Goldfish?

I do not pretend to know the answer to these questions.

May 5, 1983

A WONDERFUL new book about picnics, wittily called *The Picnic Paper* (Hutchinson £89.50) contains the solemn advice from Princess Margaret that one should always take one's butler with one on picnics. With the most grovelling respect, Ma'am, I would disagree.

Part of the story is told by Susanna Johnston, one of the book's editors. "I once had a romance that ended at a picnic," says Susanna. "No, I'm not going to tell you the details. I couldn't possibly. But before it poured with rain it was all on, and afterwards it was all off."

I suppose it was sporting of her not to reveal to the reptiles of the gutter press what everyone must have realised, that I was the other person involved. Like a fool, I had brought my butler along. At a particularly crucial moment when we were sheltering from the rain under a haystack – somewhere between the "all-on" and "all-off" situations – I heard someone clear his throat. It was my man, Wheatcroft.

"Has her ladyship considered the desirability or the possibility of some asparagus?" said this imbecile. It was the end of everything.

May 6, 1983

MY BOUQUET of the week goes to Mr Lionel Kellaway, a zoologist at University College, Swansea in charge of the University's snake-pit. He has taken 500 young adders and set them loose in a popular holiday area above the Gower Peninsula overlooking Swansea Bay.

This action was strongly criticised by Swansea's Chief Environmental Health Officer, Eddy Ramsden: "The area will be swarming with campers, caravanners and walkers in the next few months," said Eddy. "Conservation is one thing, but it isn't up to Mr Kellaway to restock the area with snakes which can kill."

Kellaway hits back: "I'm doing this because the snake population has been greatly reduced in recent years through people killing them and through the destruction of their natural habitat."

I think he is one of the great heroes of our time. We should do all we can to help him.

1 From that day since, *Private Eye* has never mentioned Evans nor referred to his existence in any way. After innumerable legal actions, he had succeeded in achieving the status of "non-person".

Mindful of how many years have passed since the black panther last walked the forests of West Somerset, I have been releasing two black panthers a week on Exmoor. So far they have not caught a single camper, caravanner or walker but it must be only a question of time.

May 7, 1983

AFTER LONG and hard thought I have decided to vote Conservative in this election[1] if I can pluck up the courage to face all the risks of infection involved in a visit to the polling booth.

My reason for this is Labour's policy on hunting. They propose to pass a law against all hunting dogs, while subsidising the lower classes in their lonely, cruel and beastly killing of fishes.

This must betray an insane hatred of dogs of the sort which brought about the downfall of the old Liberal Party. To confirm it, there is a picture of Worzel Gummidge[2] on the front page of the *Daily Telegraph* waving a huge stick over his dog Disraeli on Hampstead Heath, plainly about to beat it to death.

1 The forthcoming General Election of June 9, 1983.
2 Rt Hon. Michael Foot, Leader of the Labour Party.

May 8, 1983

NORMAN TEBBIT strikes me as the only person to have made a significant contribution to the great election debate. He describes the unspeakable Shirley Williams as:

"shifting, equivocal, weak, disunited, unreliable, indecisive and stinks of cheese."

He has convinced me that I am doing the right thing in voting Conservative this time round. Personally, I should have added that she is also fat, ugly, stupid, conceited, bossy and rude.

Of all the disagreeable qualities of this disgusting woman, who once insulted my friend Alan Watkins, the worst is that she is disunited. It is not widely known that she wears a wig, or that her teeth are false, her eyes are glass, her legs are wooden, her arms made of plastic, her bottom of rubber. . .

May 14, 1983

WITH TWENTY seaside resorts planning to open up nude and topless beaches this summer, I really do not see that we have any need to keep the Elgin Marbles in Bloomsbury any longer.

But then I do not see any good reason for

giving them to the people who now populate the Athenian conurbation, unless to teach those short-legged, furry, goatish creatures what Greeks used to look like 2300 years ago. Models in plaster of paris would be just as instructive.

But the British have become so ignorant and so brutish, so dedicated to proletarian values in the irreversible shift of wealth towards ordinary working people and their families, that there is no possible excuse for keeping the Elgin Marbles here. They should be auctioned, and the money spent on more ice creams for the moaning, underprivileged kiddies of Merseyside.

May 16, 1983

TO LONDON, for a luncheon of Egon Ronay's British Academy of Gastronomes at the Inigo Jones restaurant, Garrick Street. This is a rather expensive way I have devised of avoiding the fortnightly *Private Eye* lunches. These have degenerated into scenes of near-total hysteria.

The Gastronomes turn out to be a convivial crowd, mostly old friends, but I think I detect a certain nervousness about the political scene. Socialists are fanatically opposed to gastronomy as they are to all the good things of life. A peasant from the Sichiuan province of China has just been imprisoned for two years for killing and eating a giant panda.

It is a sad thought that I who have eaten squirrels in Somerset, crocodile meat in Cuba, dogs in the Philippines, raw horse in Japan, toads in Egypt and snakes in Northern Thailand may never eat a giant panda, unless this abominable curse of Socialism can be driven from the earth.

May 17, 1983

WESTMINSTER City Council, for all that it is supposed to be run by Conservatives, is inspired by the same hateful puritanism. For years it has been harassing the City's massage parlours which provide some of the few delightful and harmless services available in London. Now it has started persecuting restaurants and clubs, alleging breaches of its food hygiene regulations.

Even places which do not serve meals, like the Connolly Room in Dean Street, Soho, have suddenly been ordered to clean themselves up. This club, named after the late Cyril Connolly, a notoriously dirty book reviewer of the 1950s, has always been a centre for those who like drinking in filthy surroundings. Regulars include Francis Bacon, the celebrated piss-artist, and R.D. Laing, the loony doctor.

Hygiene is the worst enemy of good food, and every cook knows that the health risks of dirt are greatly exaggerated. Those who like eating cockroaches and mice droppings in their food will now be able to find them only in the great London hospitals – St Thomas's, Middlesex, Westminster – which do not

come under the iron heel of the local government inspectors.

It might be a good idea if these same hospitals could supply a massage service, using their beautiful, soft-hearted, highly-trained nurses. I keep urging this, but nobody pays the smallest bit of attention.

June 4, 1983

WORZEL[1] AND I stand on a rostrum in driving rain at a mass rally in Hyde Park to welcome the People's March for Jobs. In the event, only fourteen People turn up to demand jobs.

They stand around in the rain grumbling quietly about their money. It seems that local union branches promised them £400 each in bribes and "expenses" but thousands of press photographers and television crews make up the crowd.

I congratulate Worzel on an absolutely brilliant speech he has just made, quoted in the *Daily Mirror*:

"WE ARE HERE TO PROVIDE FOR ALL THOSE WHO ARE WEAKER AND HUNGRIER, MORE CRIPPLED THAN OURSELVES," piped Worzel, according to the *Daily Mirror*. "THAT IS OUR ONLY CERTAIN, GOOD AND REAL PURPOSE ON EARTH."

If Worzel is really interested in providing only for those who are more battered and crippled than he is, it should be an easy enough task. Perhaps half a dozen people in the country will qualify. They can be put up at Claridges, and the rest of us will get on with our own business.

I call this a really exciting programme for national recovery.

June 6, 1983

SOME WEEKS ago, Gummidge asked me to organise a "Stars for Worzel" parade to help him in the election. Even then I had my doubts whether he was quite the man, so I organised a strange collection of dead-beats to make him look ridiculous.

Larry Adler, the 72-year-old American who claims he can still play his hand-organ, gave a performance; so did something female called Maureen Lip-man; and Colin Welland, the lower-class bore. But dear old Melvyn Barg[2] really stole the show with his thundering slogan:

"The arts are a complete vindication for socialism because they are fundamentally funded by the State."

Heh, heh, heh. My crowning achievement was to have been Esther Rantzen, topless, singing a coy little song about Worzel's willie, but the hag refused. Still, I feel I have done my bit for the People's party.

June 10, 1983

THE SIGHT of Gerald "Curly" Kaufman blubbing on early morning television, and telling the great Sir Peregrine Worsthorne to wipe the smile off his face moves me to a most agreeable reverie.

Now this rubbish is out of the way we can concentrate on things that really matter, like whether or not the Princess of Wales is pregnant. But first let's bomb Russia.[3]

June 20, 1983

I LEARN to my delight of Mrs Thatcher's imaginative appointment of a black man to be Minister of the Arts. Some of my friends are a bit doubtful about this, pompously suggesting that the Arts are too important to be entrusted to a former picture dealer in the modern end of the market.

But I think nothing is more important than Race Relations. This is the sort of problem we are up against. The fact that Grey Gowrie has also been involved in the commercial side of selling "modern art" to discriminating punters is no disqualification. Making money – "wealth creation" – is what Conservatism is all about. In an ideal world, all black men should be employed as Ministers for the Arts.

1 Michael Foot led his party to a disastrous defeat in the June 1983 General Election.
2 Melvyn Bragg, a pseud.
3 The Conservative Party, under Margaret Thatcher, had won a resounding victory in the General Election held on June 9. Kaufman, noted for baldness, is a "moderate" Socialist politician.

July 3, 1983

I AM ON an inspection of the French nuclear deterrent, when news reaches me that Marc Boxer has replaced Major Libby Purves as Editor of *Tatler*.

I wonder if this time Boxer may not have bitten off more than he can chew. Major Purves put up a splendid fight against the wasp-waisted Negro pooftahs and deliciously slim anorexic nymphomaniacs pitted against her. But she is used to such things, having once accounted for two enemy machine gun posts single-handed in the Dardanelles.

Boxer has a good wit, it is true, and a certain anxiety about style which should help him. But he also has a deeply boring left-wing commitment – poor chap, he grew up at a time when it was considered smart to be left wing – and this will not help at all.

July 5, 1983

A LONG NIGHT sitting up with Nigel Lawson, the new Chancellor, who is tremendously upset by the thought that he may have to cut dole money and other handouts for the unemployed. This would create another 700,000 jobs when people on the dole found it worthwhile to accept lower-paid jobs at £80–£100 a week.

Unlike me, Lawson comes from a fairly humble background and he is distressed by the thought of all the suffering – even hunger – which will result from this necessary measure.

I tell the sobbing figure to take heart. The error in his reasoning is to suppose that jobs are necessary or good things. The English lower classes do not like "working" for the most part, and they are certainly no good at it.

If he wants to put the economy on its feet again, he has simply to say that there will be no tax on earned incomes after the first £25,000. The result will be a happy, prosperous, hardworking country where nobody is on the fiddle, politics loses most of its attractions and those who do not want to work can live in dignified retirement.

July 15, 1983

TO DURHAM, for the Centenary Miners' George Galer. I am trying to whip up support for my friend Roy Hattersley to win control of the Labour Party and be the next Labour Prime Minister.

Ever since we were at Eton together Roy has had this amazing ability, as he puts it, to "understand the working people of this country". He has even persuaded a few that he is "one of them".

Of course Roy is wonderfully intelligent and really runs rings around the thick shits of the Labour movement. Instead of saying, like Mrs Thatcher, that he wants a fair deal for the rich and that strikers should be put in prison, he says things like:

"We can only win if we inspire the idealism of the British people. That requires a further restatement of the socialist principles that will guide us when we are in office."

They all cheer like lunatics. Even his enemies have to agree that he looks very like a potential government. The Labour Party would be the most tremendous fools not to choose him.[1]

July 18, 1983

TERRIFYING figures for sexual harassment of female undergraduates at Oxford have been released by the University Student Women's Committee.

This vitally important committee circulated a questionnaire to all 3,000 women undergraduates demanding to know the details and extent of sexual harassment they had suffered. Only 41 complained of any sexual harassment at all, of which 22 claimed that they had been the objects of unwelcome sexual attention from dons. If one knocks off half a dozen of these complaints as being satirically inspired, we are left with a total of 16 cases of misbehaviour by dons.

No doubt some of these 3,000 women are hideous, or dirty, or mad, but they are all at the most nubile age when such sexual

1 Hattersley was thought to be standing against Messrs Kinnock and Benn for the Labour leadership. He did not go to Eton.

attraction as they will ever possess is at its strongest. What on earth is happening to the dons of Oxford?

July 27, 1983

OVER 1,400 people turn up for the *Spectator*'s summer party in Doughty Street. If half as many people as attend its parties actually bought the *Spectator*, the magazine would be safe.

My problem at parties is that I can never recognise anyone so I spend my time smirking inanely at total strangers. At last I think I recognise my old friend Howard Hughes, the American eccentric, and bound up to shake him by the hand.

Then I remember that Howard Hughes is dead. The person whose hand I am shaking is Charles Vass, Rupert Murdoch's brilliant 18½-year-old editor of *The Times*.

But what on earth has happened to Charlie Vass? The handsome, boyish figure whose mother once accused me of touching his privates in a public swimming pool now has a straggling beard down to his waist, and burning eyes which have sunk so far into his head as to be invisible. He walks with three crutches on a sort of mobile trestle with pulleys.

I think he probably needs to eat more spinach. But as we all get older and more feeble, these parties lose their point. It is time they were stopped. Later on I try eating a wine glass to amuse a young person and break one of my teeth.

August 24, 1983

Montmaur, Aude, France

MY CHIEF anxiety in taking such a long holiday is that I may not be pulling my weight in the great struggle to make Roy Hattersley Prime Minister, or at very least Deputy Prime Minister on the Dream Ticket.

It is not just that Roy is an old school friend. At Eton we used to call him "Fattersley" or occasionally "Al Fahta" – probably in reference to his Pakistani background. He cannot have found it easy being the only Pakistani at Eton, but he carried it off very well, with hampers of Tandoori chicken delivered daily from Fortnums.

Now he has to persuade all the oicks of the Labour Party that he is the best man to lead them into the future. Some of them are so thick as to be suicidal. Hattersley is a world statesman of the Douglas-Home class. With his experience as a Junior Minister in the Board of Trade, he can speak to the world's leaders in their own language – while still retaining the common touch if it is ever necessary for him to talk to the lower classes.

That is what an Eton education does for you. I think he is wonderful.

September 1, 1983

FOR SIX weeks my only contact with the outside world has been a copy of the *Daily Telegraph* rushed to Southern France by aeroplane, motorbike and every resource of modern technology to keep me up-to-date on world affairs.

Today's arrival brings a horrifying picture of Princess Michael of Kent taking thirty square inches at the top of the front page. She is holding two young Burmese cats to her bosom. The *Telegraph* solemnly announces they will replace Kitty, a Burmese cat whose dead body was found squashed (allegedly run over) three weeks ago.

"Of course, they will never replace Kitty," says the "Princess", "but I am absolutely delighted with them."

I feel it is time I returned to England. In my absence, this unattractive daughter of a former hairdresser seems set to take over the entire country. Soon she will start bullying the Queen into granting her whole menagerie the style and precedence of a marquess's younger son.

Then, when these two animals have been squashed or allegedly run over, she will turn up in an even bigger photograph on the front page of the *Daily Telegraph* with four of the brutes. My country needs me.

September 2, 1983

UNABLE to sleep at all in my *wagon-lit* for worrying about these cats. So long as she keeps the skinny creatures to her breast I don't suppose that much harm can result. But I am haunted by the fear that she may plan to put them in her knickers.

This may seem unlikely, and it is true that I have no particular reason to suppose that she has any such intention. But I would not be being honest if I denied that the thought had crossed my mind.

It is quite a normal practice in the Australian outback, where aborigine women believe that furry animals carried in this way afford some sort of protection, in the manner of a cushion, if they should happen to sit on a poisonous cactus.

But wild cactuses are few and far between in Gloucestershire. I feel that under English conditions the practice is unhygienic and also rather cruel. The appropriate authorities should be alerted.

September 4, 1983

AMAZING people creep out of the woodwork to address the British Association in the summer months. This time Dr Nuala Sworts-Isherwood, of the Technical Change Centre, London, comes forward to suggest that the age of the microchip poses a massive threat to women.

It is true that since the dear creatures gave up their traditional role as sex-objects and home-makers, their general situation has been somewhat parlous. Now their confused menfolk have started lusting after silicone chips.

One of the cruellest aspects of this nasty development is its commercialism. Adverts in the *Sunday Times* offer luscious little Taiwanese microchips (1.5mm x 0.6mm x 1.4mm) for as little as £18 – the price of short time with some disease-ridden bag in Soho.

Microchips are not only cheaper than women, they are less temperamental, cleaner and in many cases more intelligent. They last almost for ever and can easily be traded in for a new model.

Dr Nuala Sworts-Isherwood does not reveal that many women are desperately trying to meet this challenge by making their breasts bigger – either filling them with silicone or, in extreme cases, applying small foreign animals like Burmese kittens or Texan iguanas.

It may work, although I have always been a medium-tit man myself. But give me a little brown microchip from Japan, tittering politely into its hand, and I will give you Raquel Welch any day of the week.

September 12, 1983

MY OWN theory about the breakout of IRA detainees from the Maze Prison is that it was engineered by the Northern Ireland Office to distract attention from Sir George Terry's report on the Kincora Boys Home in east Belfast.

This boys' home was used as a male brothel and homosexual call-boy service by the Ulster political establishment – including, or so I have heard, some customers very high up in Intelligence. But Sir George Terry's massive dose of whitewash suggests there is no truth in any of these claims, and absolutely no need for any public enquiry.

"In the light of the report, the Secretary of State for Northern Ireland Mr James Prior believes that an expensive public enquiry into the scandal, at which names and wild allegations would be freely aired, is not warranted," we read.

But this will not satisfy those of us who happen to enjoy naming names and airing wild allegations. If Mr Prior thinks he can sit indefinitely on this very natural human urge of ours, he will find he ends up with a very sore bottom indeed.

September 13, 1983

IN THE studios of a Radio 1 programme called Front Line, where I have been hired to insult the North of England, I meet Sir George Young, the strange Government Minister who first emerged leading a Temperance Crusade in the DHSS.

He is now Undersecretary in the Department of the Environment and seems deeply concerned about unemployment on Merseyside, inner city deprivation and all the rest of it. Poor chap.

I think he should encourage unemployed school-leavers in the area to spend their days hunting hedgehogs. These could then be sold to a Welshpool crisp manufacturer of hedgehog-flavoured potato crisps, and used by Liverpool's archbishop Monsignor Derek Worlock, as Communion wafers.

The archbishop, I should explain, suffers from the rare Cœliac disease, or gluten enteropathy, which means that he cannot take bread in any form. For an archbishop to miss out on his spiritual sustenance in this way is a very serious thing.

If these crisps are adopted throughout the

whole of Merseyside it might also stop the frightful Mrs Shirley Williams in her tracks next time she goes on a Communion-guzzle in the area. Special wafers might be made for her with the hedgehog prickles intact, thereby solving about eight of the country's main problems at a stroke. The sheer intelligence of the scheme is enough to take one's breath away. Mrs Thatcher might take note. Until she starts employing outside "brains" like these she will never put Britain on its feet.

October 10, 1983

I NEVER thought my heart would lift up to arrive in Blackpool, but after a week at the Labour Party Conference in Brighton I feel like a jungle explorer who has returned to civilisation. Conservative women may be boring, but at least they are not interested in politics and most of them are reasonably clean. Some are agreeably plump. One usually manages to have quite a good time at Conservative Party conferences.

October 13, 1983

AT THE Young Conservatives Ball in the Winter Gardens I find myself unexpectedly closeted with Margaret Thatcher, whom I have not seen since she came to a *Private Eye* lunch over ten years ago.

She obviously expects me to ask her to dance, but it would be as much as my reputation in Fleet Street is worth to be seen dancing with her so I make my excuses, saying I have a particularly violent attack of AIDS. Also, I was rather hoping to find someone younger and juicier, although it might be rude to say so.

Instead I ask her why she has not yet adopted a sensible suggestion in George Gale's *Daily Express* column – Pungent, Penetrating, Pissed – and sent Grocer Heath to be overlord of Ulster in place of James Prior. With a bit of luck, he might get blown up, I explain helpfully.

She replies that she has to wait until the Kincora Boys Home Scandal has been laid to rest before sending another bachelor to Ulster.

October 17, 1983

ONE OF the alleged kerb-crawlers arrested in Nottingham for allegedly trying to chat up a policewoman disguised as a prostitute is allegedly called William Waugh, 34, of Pierrepoint Road, West Bridgford. Or so my *Daily Star* alleges.

I do not know whether William is any relation of mine, but whether he is or not he has my deepest sympathy. Any of us who

saw a woman police constable on the kerbside pretending to be a prostitute might be tempted to exchange a few ribald remarks, if not actually to prod her suggestively with our umbrellas.

I never thought so before, but I am honestly beginning to think that the police in this country are getting above themselves. As for the newspapers who co-operate by printing the names of police victims, their behaviour is beneath contempt.

Perhaps all the Glenda Slags who wax so indignant about kerb-crawlers secretly fear that professional prostitutes offer a cheaper, better service. They need not worry. I would sooner take a tumble with the *Mirror*'s Ann Robinson any day. Men have to be really desperate to go to English prostitutes, who are famous for being the laziest, ugliest and greediest in the world.

The best we can do for these unfortunate men is to strike back. From now on whenever I see a woman police constable in uniform I will make an indelicate proposition to her, and I hope everyone else does the same.

October 29, 1983

THE CASE for Dennis Nilssen[1] is put to me by my taxi-driver on the way to lunch. Strange how much simple wisdom there is to be found inside the deformed head and unprepossessing carcase of your typical London cabbie.

Most of Nilssen's victims were deeply unhappy men, he says. Worse than this they were drifters, many of them drawing £100 a week in Social Security payments. By knocking off 15 of them, Nilssen has saved our hard-pressed Social Security Services £1,500 a week.

If he had been allowed to continue his operations, instead of being put in prison at enormous expense to the taxpayer, he planned to knock off 500, thereby saving £50,000 a week or £2,100,000 a year. Nilssen should be hailed as a hero.

I am not sure I can follow this horrible man all the way. There is still the cost of clearing all those drains to be taken into account. But I must admit it would be lovely to have more money to spend on the things that really matter.

November 7, 1983

ANY DOUBTS I ever had that the *Daily Express* is doomed roll away and the sun shines again. Mr Bernard Shrimsley has joined the newspaper at last.[2]

But to keep up morale, "Lord" Maffews has offered to give *Daily Express* readers the chance to own their own racehorse. Here it is. I suppose somebody must want it.

1 A mass-murderer of homeless homosexual youths.
2 Shrimsley, sacked from the editorship of the *Mail on Sunday*, had once sued Waugh for alleged libel when editor of the *News of the World*. He was sacked from that post, too.

November 8, 1983

JOHNNY ROTTEN, the singer and musical entertainer, will always be remembered for one *bon mot*, when he described sex as "two and a half minutes of squelching".

In an interview with Christena Appleyard in the *Mirror*, he wishes to amend this aphorism. It is more like five minutes now, he says, because he has mastered a new technique.

Johnny's large blonde girlfriend, with whom he is rumoured to have been squelching for the last three years, refuses to confirm or deny this. I feel we should keep his famous saying as it originally came out. It is more poignant in its original form, and I suspect that after five minutes of squelching many young people nowadays would begin to find the whole thing a bit of a bore. Johnny is growing old.

December 8, 1983

THE FIRST Christmas cards begin to arrive. In 44 years I've never sent anyone a Christmas card, but nobody seems to take the hint.

On the other hand I send out about twenty letters a day in the normal course of events and the terrible jumbo-sized Christmas stamps we have to buy at this time of year create an additional hazard.

It would make sense if we could employ some of the millions of unemployed from Merseyside to come and lick them for us. They might not be much good at the job but it would be practice for them when they have to lick Gerald "Curly" Korfmann's bottom after the next election.

December 14, 1983

A MYSTERIOUS case of wine arrives in Somerset. It is a 1975er Zeltinger Himmelreich Spätlese Mosel and comes in a Corney and Barrow box. But when, in a pompous attempt to find out who is bribing me I ask Corney and Barrow about it, they say they have no record of any such order. It tastes quite nice.

I imagine that my benefactor must be the Prince of Wales, who would be bribing me to insult once again the wife of his unfortunate cousin, Prince Michael of Kent. It is typical of Bat Ears to suppose that everyone shares his taste for expensive German wines.

December 20, 1983

AS THE whole country cowers under a new Police Terror it is heartening to learn that a police woman, posing as a prostitute, has caught one of her own number. According to WPC Janet ("Street") Walker, she was mincing around Nottingham's vice area in jeans, sweater and bomber jacket when she was approached by Detective Chief Inspector Robert Warner, head of Lincolnshire's Fraud and Drug Squad, who asked: "How much is it?"

She replied: "What for?" He said: "Straight sex." She promptly booked him under a law of 34 Henry III (Justice of the Peace Act 1361) against kerb crawling.

Chief Inspector Warner claims WPC Street Walker is lying and their conversation was quite different. Certainly one or the other is lying, if not both. My sympathy goes to Warner, who is a married man, rather than to the officious pseudo-tart Walker. I hope something horrible and embarrassing happens to her before very long.

But aren't our police funny?

1984

Year of the great coal strike. Waugh suggests a solution might be for the Government to offer a bounty of £50 for the scalp of any Yorkshire miner. Mass starvation is reported in the north of England. A controversial new Bishop of Durham called Dr Jenkins adds to the confusion.

Greatest sorrow of all is the death of Sir John Betjeman, the beloved Poet Laureate. The death of Yuri Andropov is also noticed by the Junior Common Room of St Hugh's College, Oxford.

Mrs Thatcher appoints the first Negro to be a member of the Cabinet. The seal pup menace continues unabated. A mysterious Bulgarian called "Captain Robert Maxwell" buys the *Daily Mirror*. Pope John-Paul II denounces sex in marriage.

January 19, 1984

ROY PLOMLEY was a terrible fool to have asked Princess Michael of Kent on his desert island, but he is quite right to refuse to let her take a cat with her.

She says it must be Burmese, and preferably pregnant. It is a strange request from someone with her record. Last year a Burmese cat of hers was found hideously squashed but she claimed it had been run over by a car. Then she bought two new kittens. The fact that she wants to take only one with her on the desert island suggests that the other has been squashed too.

But why does she specify a pregnant cat? Perhaps Roy Plomley suspects as I do that she wants the poor creature with her so that she can sit on it. There is a long tradition for sitting on pregnant cats in Australia. Lord Carrington tried to discourage it when he was High Commissioner there, but obviously without much success. Carrington's whole life is a long record of failure, when you come to think about it.

January 20, 1984

ARRIVING early in the office I find it has been broken into and the whole place turned over by criminals.

Being totally uneducated, they missed all my Fabergé bibelots, my picture of Diana the Huntress by Boucher and a delightful *fête champêtre* attributed to Fragonard, stealing only a Sony Walkman which belongs to the boy who sticks my articles on pieces of cardboard.

I spend the whole morning trying to comfort the sobbing lad. It seems possible that these miscreants were looking for the Koo Stark tapes, letters and video which I bought recently from an antiquarian bookseller of my acquaintance.

They will find them rather disappointing. Prince Andrew, whatever his other qualities may be, is no Madame de Sévigné.

Koo looks quite fetching without any clothes, but we have all seen her like that often before. Prince Andrew has some interesting nodules under his left arm, but otherwise seems a depressingly ordinary young man.

January 22, 1984

WHEN A couple in the Cornish village of Tywardreath, near St Austell, decide to show a little initiative and turn their semi-detached home into a massage parlour, they are immediately "exposed" by a local reporter, raided by the police, prosecuted and forced to leave the neighbourhood.

The creep of a local reporter is called Simon Heppenstall. I have already reported him to Friends of Massage. If ever he seeks employment in Fleet Street, he will be a marked man.

January 23, 1984

ALL MY coalminer friends are up in arms against the Government's new idea to send women down the mines. They are terrified that their wives will discover what a cissy job they have, and also frightened their women will discover about the Gay Scene underground.

Many miners nowadays spend their entire shift in the palatial underground hairdressing *salons*, having their faces massaged and toenails polished.

Then, after they have been delicately sprinkled with coal dust from an outsize powder puff, they come to the surface bleary-eyed and ready for the first round of Black Velvet at t'Club.

January 26, 1984

"THERE'S NO substitute for a wife and at my age I have no desire for a mistress. The thought makes me slightly queasy. I'm fussy, not chaste, but at 76 the fires are slightly banked. When you're 76, your thoughts don't often stray to copulation."

Thus Lord Hailsham, Lord High Chancellor of England, talking to Ms Lynda Lee-Potter, the *Daily Mail*'s piquant young interviewer. Just what, one wonders, has this dirty old brute been up to? What is he trying to hide?

January 29, 1984

MY FRIEND Alexander Chancellor telephones that he has given up editing the *Spectator* after a difference of opinion with the magazine's exciting young proprietor, Archy Clough or "Cluff". When I asked my friends if I should resign, too, they all say: "Yes".

Shit. There goes another £8,000 a year. But at least I won't have to pay £4,800 of it to Mrs Thatcher so that she can go on poisoning the nation's old people with unnecessary pills.

February 1, 1984

JILL TWEEDIE has bought six acres of land and cannot think what to do with them. I suggest she use them to breed hedgehogs.

They are pleasant and affectionate animals which make very little noise and are quite palatable to eat. She could give them away free to the hungry unemployed.

There is always the possibility that if we

could spread enough hedgehogs around the country, Princess Michael of Kent might mistake one for a Siamese kitten and sit on it.

February 5, 1984

HALF WAY through church I discover to my dismay that this is Peace Sunday. We have to sit through half an hour of platitudes on this grisly subject.

I think it is time I went to see Dr Runcie for discussions about whether to join his lot. Unfortunately he has gone off to Uganda for discussions of a different nature. But I observe he has left his fun-loving wife Rosalind behind. Ugandan Customs Officers are liable to charge corkage on visiting wives. Perhaps I will go round and see her.

February 6, 1984

SO. Princess Anne now emerges as a cross between Mother Teresa and Grace Kelly.[1] I don't care. In this tiny corner she will be preserved for the nation as the Princess Anne we always knew and loved, whose poisonous spittle could stop a camel in its tracks at 20 paces and blind a Press photographer for life at twice the distance.

Here at least she will be remembered with her grinning, speechless husband who wets himself whenever you whistle at him, her enigmatic four-legged son "Peter" and the mysterious Baby Susan who is said to have grown a long yellow beak, black feathers and to croak like a raven.

February 8, 1984

NEW EVIDENCE about the younger generation comes from Oxford where, to everyone's dismay, they have allowed a bright twelve-year-old girl in among the ghastly, drooping, undersexed females at St Hugh's.

Recently there was a Motion proposed among the snivelling unemployables in the St Hugh's Junior Commonroom which noted "with sadness" the death of President Andropov. Just as the scurf-ridden, sobbing androgynes were about to concur, up stood the youngest undergraduate in Oxford's history, twelve-year-old Ruth Lawrence, and gave them a piece of her mind.

Andropov was a torturer, mass-murderer and stupendous shit, she cried. There was no possible reason to be sad about his death. They should be glad. As the pungent, lank-haired social catastrophes marched out of the room in ranks, she went on to say she did not approve of all this Peace business either.

February 26, 1984

I GRIEVE for Sir Sidney Yobbo,[2] who has lost his libel action against the BBC at a cost of £75,000. Of course he should never have brought it, but it is the only stain in an honourable record.

However silly or wicked it might be thought for a journalist to go whining and blubbing to lawyers, the BBC's posture in labelling his behaviour as an attack on free speech was even more hypocritical. Few people can have forgotten how the BBC staked a libel action brought by Desmond Wilcox[3] against *Private Eye*, in which the slimy plagiarist was awarded £14,000.

March 1, 1984

LATEST entertainment idea to hit the London scene is a group of hideous naked women and one man called the New Naturalists. I saw them first at a party given by Naim Attallah, the Palestinian philanthropist, but now they are everywhere.

They come on stage completely naked except for combat boots, their bodies painted in green and blue. Also painted blue is what could be described as the man's generative organ or virile member, but might more accurately be called his Willy.

1 Princess Anne had won general praise for her selflessness and pluck while touring Africa on behalf of the Save the Children Fund.
2 Mr Derek Jameson, a former Fleet Street editor.
3 A plagiarist.

Then they start peeing all over the stage and everybody shrieks with laughter. Those who stayed on at the Quartet party had the enjoyable experience of seeing it all cleared up afterwards by Miss Bridget Amory, one of the most enduringly beautiful of Naim's string of delicious debs.

March 5, 1984

NIGEL DEMPSTER reveals today that Diana Quick the piquant actress has broken up with Albert Finney and is "extremely anxious" to become a mother by someone else.

Diana seems to have had a rough time. Finney could not produce a baby and when she was in bed with Jeremy Irons during the filming of *Brideshead* he insisted on wearing underpants.

That was the time Diana showed us her bosom. It was jolly pretty and one would quite like to see the rest of her, but I am afraid she may have a taste for the rough trade. Perhaps she has grown out of that. Anyway, she knows where to find me.

March 9, 1984

DR GERMAINE GREER has a beautiful face, a pretty wit and a warm heart, but she will always remain a mystery to me. I doubt if I will ever get underneath the dough to the jam at the centre.

When in *Sex and Destiny* (Secker and Warburg, £9.95) she describes the male attitude to sex as "squirting jam into a doughnut", she is in fact quoting some foreigner who made the observation first.

What neither of them seems to realise is that the jam is not put into doughnuts this way. You lay your dough flat, put a teaspoon of jam in the middle then wrap it round the jam before deep frying.

Germaine may be the greatest expert in the world on the politics of human fertility, but she knows nothing about making doughnuts. I wonder if this explains why she is still unmarried – and whether, in fact, she really understands how babies are made.

March 12, 1984

MY EFFORTS to talk things over with the Archbishop of Canterbury are constantly frustrated. After his Ugandan discussions he has now gone on an 11-country tour of the Caribbean, explaining that by talking to black people in the Bahamas he will be helped when he comes to talk to the black people of Lambeth, where he happens to have a Palace.

I wonder how his cheerful, fun-loving wife feels about the old goat wandering off like this. I think I will really have to go and call on her in her bedroom in Lambeth Palace to discuss my problem, like Mr Fagan

with the Queen.[1] This behaviour will be impossible after the Criminal Trespass Act, but if Dr Runcie does not come home soon I will be in there like a rat up the gutter.

March 15, 1984

TO ST PAUL's Cathedral for the unveiling of the new 10-ton white marble sculpture called "Mother and Child" by Henry Moore. I suppose it could represent a mother and child. Someone else suggests it might be the cross-section of a nephritic kidney, enormously enlarged.

I prefer to see it as an eloquent protest against government cuts in the Health Service which mean that some mothers in Maternity Hospitals now have to supply disposable nappies for their own babies, just as they did in Hitler's Germany.

But however one looks at it, it is a bloody fatuous object. Perhaps the only way to make it popular would be to start a rumour that it has miraculous properties like so many Virgin and Child statues on the Continent. They should rename it Our Lady of Herpes, and encourage sufferers to come and rub their affected parts against it.

March 20, 1984

SIR MICHAEL HAVERS has some unusually interesting things to say at a Law Society seminar in Oxford on the vexing problem of when it is a citizen's duty to break the law. He cites the example of Nazi Germany.

I would have thought that a similar situation might arise where the government is too wet, or the police too cowardly, to enforce the Common Law of the land. Despite prodigious boasting Mrs Thatcher and the police have not been able to keep open more than 35 of the country's 175 coal pits despite the desire of miners to work. Under the circumstances I should have thought many responsible citizens would decide they have a duty to go out and bash a Yorkshire picket.

When I was a boy the police offered a bounty of 5p for every grey squirrel's tail you brought them. If they now offered a bounty of £50 for every Yorkshire miner's scalp they would save enormous government redundancy payments of up to £36,000 per miner, and give the unemployed of Merseyside the chance to earn a little extra beer money. I am sure that such an announcement would be greeted by dancing in the streets of Liverpool.

I keep solving all Mrs Thatcher's

1 Fagan, an unemployed person, wandered into the Queen's bedroom in Buckingham Palace while looking for something to drink. She engaged him in conversation before summoning the police.

problems for her but never receive any thanks. No doubt she'll produce this sensible scheme as her own idea in a few weeks' time.

May 1, 1984

BACK FROM a month of foreign travel, I feel slightly jealous of Pope Ringo who is still cavorting among the proud Wahgi tribesmen of Papua New Guinea, in their prized head-dresses of Cassowary and Bird of Paradise feathers, worn over wigs of human hair in the grotesque shape of Georgian naval hats.

Their faces are starkly blackened by ochre in contrast to their whitened eyelids, they wear nothing but beaten bark belts, and their bodies gleam with freshly-daubed pig fat.

Oddly enough, these magnificent creatures may be distantly related to me. According to Charles Mosley's nine-volume *History of the Waugh Family* (to be published by Debrett in October at £640 the set) there were two migrations of Waughs from Dunks, Lancashire, in the early eighteenth century. One settled on the slopes of Kilimanjaro, straddling the Kenya-Tanzania border, and became known as Wachagga; the second, in what is now Papua New Guinea, the Wahgi.

Both, miraculously, retained their Christian faith, and still celebrate the liturgy in a form of pidgin English scarcely to be distinguished from the Mickey Mouse language used by English Catholics today.

May 2, 1984

THE MYSTERY of how these sturdy kinsmen of mine – the Wachagga and the Wahgi – retained their Christian faith over hundreds of years must be explained by the fact that they have never been exposed to the English Catholic newspapers. I have no doubt that it was by trying to read these frightful publications that Michael Bettaney, the MI5 would-be traitor, changed from being a raving Roman Catholic into a Communist loonie.

Worst of them all is *The Tablet*, once a respectable weekly but now quite devastating in its silliness and ignorance. It is closely followed by the *Universe* and *Catholic Herald*, both now firmly in the grip of the Mickey Mouse brigade.

I am delighted to learn that the Superior of the Brompton Oratory, Father Charles Dilke, has now banned the sale of all three in his church, on the grounds that they constitute a scandal and an obstacle to Christian belief. I hope other parish priests follow his excellent example.

May 14, 1984

FOR SOME months now I have been corresponding with the editors of the Oxford English Dictionary about the derivation and etymology of the English verb "to pilger".

Observing that it is sometimes used in the sense of employing extravagant and emotive language to make a bogus political point, they ask if there is any connexion with the fact that Queen Victoria, in the privacy of Osborne, used to refer to her Foreign Secretary, Lord Palmerston, as "Pilgerstein" (*vide Palmerston* by P. Guedalla, Puttnams, 1927).

No, the word obviously originates in the German stem *pilger–*, meaning a pilgrim; hence *pilgerfahrt*, a pilgrimage, *pilgermann*, any Australian heart-throb reporter who earns more than £60,000 a year by championing the underdog.

One final unsettling point has been put to me by an American scholar living in Mexico: the briefest glance at the etymology of pilger/pilgrim (twelfth-century Provençal *pelegrin*, Latin *peregrinus*) leads one instantly to *peregrine*.

This is surely the last, locked door of Bluebeard's Castle. I dare not go further in terror of the possible discovery that my beloved Sir Peregrine Worsthorne, the suave, silver-haired Belgian thinker and Jon Pilger, the blond bombshell from Bondi Beach, are really one and the same person.

May 15, 1984

THE MOMENT John Betjeman died the sun went in and the heavens opened. Like so many other Englishmen at this time of desolation, nursing their private grief, I wander around my rain-swept acres killing adders.

When a great nobleman dies we are all diminished. But with the death of Betjeman even the fields and churches of Somerset seem to have shrunk.

May 17, 1984

IT IS TYPICAL of biased reporting in the so-called media to cry "Intimidation!" when the lads decide to paint a few cats in Nottinghamshire. In fact this is an old tradition among miners' communities in the north of England.

In the colliery village of Dunks, Lancashire, where I grew up (before winning my scholarship to Eton, meeting Terri Wogan etc), we used to paint all the cats of the village different colours every Easter morning. Then we would lead them through the streets in bonnets made out of chicken feathers, shouting *moggies oop, moggies oop*.

The feathers came from our traditional Easter Chicken Catching Party the night before. All the lasses of marriageable age would dress up in a sort of body stocking called a farckle (or, in Yorkshire, a pilch), then they would chase the chickens to see who could catch one and pluck it quickest.

When all the chickens were plucked, their bodies would be greased and they would be let loose again for the lads to have a try at catching them. It is amazing how much faster a chicken can run without its feathers.

Then the lads would race to see who could kill and clean his chicken first and lay it, oven-ready, on the lap of his favourite lass.

In Yorkshire, when the successful couple retired into the bushes, it was normal for the lads to imitate the noise a hen makes after it has laid an egg. This was called pilgering.

May 20, 1984

ONE MIGHT have thought that for someone who was once billed as the cleverest man in Britain, Peter Jay would have been clever enough to have bought himself a packet of French letters before investigating the charms of his former nanny, Ms Jane Fustian.

Now Fustian complains about the settlement which Jay has proposed, saying it is "miserly" and "not enough to live on". Poor Jay. Like Parkinson he should have learned that as we all become richer and more famous there are literally thousands of hellish women waiting to entrap us in this sort of way. Uganda is a dangerous country these days for the likes of us.

Personally, I feel he is going too far with his white man act. I simply do not see why chaps should have to pay for babies produced by women after a casual and brief affair of this sort.

In fact there is a strong case to be made for saying that Fustian should give Jay some money. I am prepared to bet she has a handsomer and more intelligent baby than she would have done from her other boyfriend, the embassy chauffeur. If she had gone to the Genius Sperm Bank Inc. in California she would have had to pay a fortune for the same service.

June 1, 1984

A TERRIBLE gloom falls over the West Country when we hear that David Frost's wife has given birth to an apparently healthy baby. It will be called Miles Paradine, to commemorate its blameless grandfather, the Duke of Norfolk, and Frostie's business interests, called Paradine Productions.

For many weeks the Duke – a brave and honourable man – has been rushing around like King Richard III on the field of Bosworth, bellowing for French letters, Dutch caps, Pills, intra-uterine devices, scissors, spermicidal sponges – anything to prevent this fair country of ours being invaded by a new brood of snivelling Frosties.

The Duke's behaviour is easy to understand when I reflect on my own anguish at the thought that this Miles Paradine Frost is in fact a distant cousin of my own.[1]

June 8, 1984

YORKSHIRE miners, Yorkshire miners! Dontcha hate them!!?! The Cabinet has decided to ignore my suggestion for solving the Yorkshire miner problem, which was for police stations to offer a £50 bounty for every Yorkshire miner's scalp brought in, as they used to do with squirrels' tails.

Instead they plan a national riot police, on the lines of the French CRS, which will be responsible for truncheoning and gassing Yorkshire miners as and when they appear above ground.

They think this idea comes from Mr Colin Sampson, Chief Constable of West Yorkshire, but in fact he cribbed it from me. My only worry is that this method will be more expensive than the squirrel tails idea. But any government always goes for the more expensive solution.

June 14, 1984

DAVID BAILEY, the trendy 60s hairdresser, has announced he will not be going to parties in London any more "because the class system is back in Britain with a vengeance".

I suppose he means that conceited East End hairdressers have gone out of fashion, so nobody is inviting him. This is very good news, although my friend Peter Tory[2] claims to have spotted the lout last night at a party with fellow crimper Patric Leischfeld,[3]

1 This is quite true. See Debrett's *Handbook of Distinguished People* for details of the Duke of Norfolk's claim to be connected with Waugh.
2 The *Daily Mirror* gossip writer.
3 Earl of Lichfield; not a hairdresser but a photographer.

ravishing 1940s crooner Bubbles Rothermere and all the usual crowd.

I hope the ban extends to Mick Jagger,[1] the 56-year-old "nouvelle cuisine" margarine artist. I think he is disgusting. Whenever I see him at a party – or even a photograph of him in the newspapers – I feel sick with the strange compulsion to go outdoors and kick a pigeon.

June 18, 1984

A RECORD post-bag of 14 invitations to speak in public, all unpaid. That good man Dennis Skinner, the Beast of Bolsover, has a novel way of answering these invitations. Asked to appear at one of the Inns of Court debating society, he replied:

"I am meeting some of my constituents on that date. I feel this would be more constructive than playing silly games with a bunch of claret-swilling snobs."

So instead he will spend his time over cups of tea listening to the whines and moans of these greedy, self-pitying, lower-class morons. I don't know. Whichever way one turns, life is nothing but a veil of tears.

June 25, 1984

ALTHOUGH IT is four months to St Crispin's Day on October 25th, I always begin to feel restless at this time of year when the seal culling season starts in Alaska. Should we not be there to fight the good fight? Those in England now abed shall hold their manhood cheap they were not there to keep the brutal, yapping hordes of seal pups at bay.

Over 22,000 of these treacherous creatures are poised to launch themselves into the ocean as part of a campaign to take over the world. Foolish women in Britain have been taking them to bed and breeding this hideous new race of Modern Britons, half human, half seal pup, which grins at us weekly from the Modern Living pages of the *Sunday Times*.

July 5, 1984

I PUT ON shorts and a green Wolf Cub's jersey to go to the *New Spectator* party in Doughty Street, wondering what fate holds in store for me.[2] Perhaps I will fall in love. Perhaps I will just be invited to squeeze an elderly High Church Cambridge don sometime.

Instead I meet my old friend Murray Sayle, the Australian journalist whom I last saw in Tokyo at a Japanese PT exhibition. Murray is desperately anxious to meet Jan Morris, the travel writer and former mountaineer who caused a sensation about 20 years ago by changing sex. She is among the guests and he asks if I can describe her to him.

I say she is quite tall, about 56 or 57, with greying hair and an agreeably convivial manner.

"Does she look like a man?" he asks.

"No, not really," I say. "Perhaps a little bit. Not much."

Murray wanders off on his quest. A little later I see him with an odd look in his eyes, locked in fascinated conversation with George Gale. Oh dear. Life is full of misunderstandings.

July 6, 1984

TO WESTMINSTER Abbey for John Betjeman's memorial. It is conducted with as much decorum as the age can muster. None of the priests is obviously suffering from AIDS, and none dies in the course of the service.

A minor diversion is caused by the entry of Lord Gowrie, Mrs Thatcher's swarthy, panther-like Minister for the "Arts". Goodness knows what he is doing here. A curious buzzing sound comes out of his wild bush of tightly-curled hair.

Perhaps a swarm of bees has made its home there. It is most distracting. But when I scowl at him he gives me a most piteous look and I relent. No doubt he is just thinking. He has had this unpleasant idea of charging people a sum of money – to be called Gowrie's Groat – whenever they visit a museum, and obviously finds it very exciting.

1 A popular singer.
2 The new editor, who succeeded Chancellor (see above) was a young man of 23.

But it will make him terribly unpopular. Perhaps the kindest thing he could do would be to have his head cut off and present it, free, to the Natural History Museum.

July 20, 1984

"CAPTAIN" Mark Phillips, the speechless grinning husband of Princess Anne, has made only two public pronouncements in his life.

The first, just before his wedding to the Princess, was to announce that he had no intention of marrying her. The second, today, is to announce that there is no question of a divorce. Oh dear. Things do not look too good.

August 8, 1984

Aude, France

A RUNNER from the *Spectator* brings the unwelcome news that my friend Taki Theodoracopoulos has been sentenced to 16 weeks in prison for allegedly trying to smuggle cocaine at Heathrow.

At his trial, the defence lawyer said that Taki "moved in social circles where cocaine was used at dinner parties in much the same way as the ordinary person would take wine". At the end of it, the same lawyer said he had made a mistake: Taki's social circle was not as he had described. I should think not.

The moral of this story is that one should never allow lawyers to present one's case in court. I certainly intend to conduct my own defence during the Tomalin-Murdoch ordeal.[1] Goodness knows what the wretched man would say about my social circles.

August 9, 1984

A BRAZILIAN lady I meet at Eugénie-les-Bains[2] – we are both trifling with some quails' wings in a delicate truffle sauce – tells me an amusing story about my friend Geoffrey Wheatcroft. It may not be true but I jot it down since it is a story of high moral content.

Wheatcroft, she claims, employed an attractive cleaning woman in his North London establishment. One day, when she had finished her work, he offered her a glass of wine. One thing led to another, and they ended up in bed. Next day she did not turn up for work, and has never been back since.

The moral of this story is obvious: do not go to bed with your cleaning lady. Attractive young women are two a penny in London, but a good cleaning woman is worth her weight in gold.

August 11, 1984

IN MY NURSERY, I was told the reason pound notes are green is that the Jews always pick them before they are ripe, but I caused enormous offence when I repeated that joke in the *New Statesman* many years later. A tremendously unfunny cartoonist called Calman said it was proof of anti-Semitism and cancelled his subscription.

Oddly enough, it is widely believed in Rome that Pope Paul Montini, the man who presided over the disintegration of the Catholic Church, was, like the founder of the Christian religion Himself, of Jewish parentage. I do not know whether this is true or not.

In any case, sandwiched between these two Jews in the history of the Christian religion there is the massive presence of Thomas Aquinas, who collected together all the strands of the Platonic and Aristotelian traditions with such parts of the Jewish and Christian Bibles as would form a coherent philosophy to inspire the whole of European history until about ten years ago.

Kneeling at the tomb of this wise and saintly man, I light a candle for Claire Tomalin that no ill may befall her; another for Michael Frayn, the millionaire jokesmith who is her lover and protector, that he may remain vigorous and true; and a third for Rupert Murdoch, that he may be spared the torments of Hell when he dies.

1 Claire Tomalin, literary editor of the *Sunday Times*, was suing Waugh for alleged libel. Her expenses were being paid by Times Newspapers, R. Murdoch proprietor.
2 A slimming resort and 3-star restaurant in South-west France.

September 1, 1984

ALL THE big news comes from the north of England these days. This is where Thatcherism is beginning to bite, where the bodies of miners' children litter the streets like so many broken dolls after every charge of the mounted police; and miners' wives, half crazed by hunger themselves, cannot sleep at night for the noise of their husbands' tummy-rumbles.

"Husband buys his wife a bigger bust," screams the *Daily Mirror*. Mr Andy Hunter, a Doncaster builder, has spent £1,500 to give his wife a bigger bust for beauty contests. "It was worth every penny . . . her boobs were very nice but a bit on the small side," he explained.

"I've always wanted bigger boobs," said Sharon, 24, at her home in Doncaster, Yorkshire. Now Andy is saving up a further £1,600 to send Sharon back to the clinic for a nose job.

What few people may realise is the reason for Sharon's small boobs: malnutrition – the direct result of Thatcherist anti-working class policies. No doubt Sharon's nose was injured when she was desperately looking into an empty tin of Kit-e-Kat for food. Greetings to Comrade Hunter for his high political and class vigilance in frustrating the efforts of Thatcherite militarists. The workers, uneeted, have never been defeated.

September 8, 1984

THE QUEEN's hatred of Margaret Thatcher is becoming so obsessive that I look forward to the times when the Royal Family is at Balmoral. She keeps urging me to attack Mrs Thatcher mercilessly in *Private Eye*, but I have to tell her the *Eye* is not that sort of magazine.

Mrs Thatcher may be bossy and irritating, as well as profoundly ignorant on most of the subjects that matter, but one can scarcely expect anything very different in her job. She does not strike me as nearly so dangerous as the sinister Mrs Glenys Kinnock. In any case, we on the *Eye* are not interested in politics. If Ma'am has any good stories to tell us about Bishops and actresses or homosexual clergymen, she will be paid at the usual rates. . .

But if she really wishes to humiliate Mrs Thatcher she has a golden opportunity. The death of J. B. Priestley has left a vacancy in the Order of Merit. This Order, the highest in the land, is in the gift of the Sovereign. An obvious candidate is that wisest of political philosophers, greatest of patriots and kindest of men Sir Perishing Worthless, or "Nig Nog" Worsthorne, as he was affectionately known at Stowe, where I was proud to serve as his fag.[1]

Thatcher takes a perverted delight in refusing to honour this saintly man. If the Queen gives St Peregrine the Order of Merit I imagine Mrs Thatcher will feel bound to resign or die of mortification.

September 10, 1984

AN EXCELLENT reshuffle of the Cabinet which, with the addition of David Young and Lord Gowrie, now includes four Jews and a Negro. At last we seem to be moving into the 20th century.

September 13, 1984

IN A PRIVATE conversation which I shall certainly not reveal, Lord Whitelaw tells me he is worried that he may catch fleas if he attends many Cabinet meetings with Lord Gowrie present.

This may seem an unreasonable anxiety, as the table in the Cabinet Office is huge and Ministers usually sit some distance apart. But in fact I learn from Dr Glyn Evans of the British Association (an expert on the subject) that fleas have been known to jump enormous distances.

Nobody knows why they do this, since for most purposes a jump of 5 or 10 centimeters would be quite enough. One reason may be naked terror when they are confronted with something or other – unknown, unexpected, and plainly of unspeakable horror – in those bizarre regions where most of us would never explore, like Lord Gowrie's head.

1 Waugh usually claims to have been to Eton, sometimes to Downside. This is the first time he has suggested he was at Stowe.

I tell William he will simply have to be brave. Think of the war. Flea bites do not hurt as much as all that. There must be room on this planet for a few terrified fleas, as well as for ourselves.

September 20, 1984

A USEFUL centre-page spread in the *Daily Mirror* helps us identify the Militant maggots in our midst. These maggots are usually working class and young, it says, and neatly dressed: they are collar and tie men with short hair who don't drink or smoke and never take drugs.

"When Militants make a speech, they emphasise what they are saying with extraordinary chopping hand movements. These are copied from Mr Peter Taafe, the Militant newspaper's editor and movement's organiser," it says.

So they should be quite easy to recognise. If in doubt, offer them some drugs. The problem is what to do with them when identified. This is how we manage in Somerset:

(1) Make space in bath by removing all newts, coal etc.
(2) Fill bath with water
(3) Place Militant in bath and hold there until drowned
(4) Let water out of bath
(5) Replace coal etc.

If every household in Britain could account for at least one Militant in this practical and humane manner, we might be half way towards solving the problem.

September 21, 1984

WITH A heavy heart I decide to cancel my *Daily Mirror* after 55 years as a faithful subscriber. It is not that I suspect Captain Robert Maxwell of being a Soviet agent. I am quite convinced he is no such thing. It is simply that I waste ten minutes every morning checking my Bingo number in a stew of mad optimism and greed; at last I have grown ashamed and disgusted with myself.

I do not want or need another million pounds. I am already extremely rich. If I had it, I would just eat and drink more than I already do. The same is true of the poor, most of whom already eat and drink far too much.

The rest of today's newspaper is devoted to telling us how to solve Britain's unemployment problem. This is typical of Captain Maxwell's growing impertinence. It is none of my business to solve the country's unemployment problem, and I do not really see that it is any of his business, either. Few Britons like working, and even fewer are any good at it. It is time this impertinent Czech went back to Bulgaria.

September 29, 1984

THE FIRST of ten Janet Street-Porter Late Night Shows which I have been hired to attend. I agree partly for the joy of meeting Janet again and partly because it is good for the soul to humiliate oneself before the multitude from time to time, to let ordinary people sneer at one's attempts to keep them amused.

One guest on the programme is a prostitute called Lindi St Clare, specialising in various abnormal tastes. She has to do worse things than this as part of her daily routine. Another guest is Martin Amis, the gifted young novelist. He does not yet seem to have understood about this idea of self-abasement before the multitude.

October 1, 1984

WHEN ONE of the most distinguished physicians in the land expresses concern about the health of the Prince of Wales one might suppose that the rest of the country would pay attention. There seems to be a conspiracy of silence in the media, determined to ignore Sir Nigel Dempster's revelation, as the Prince wastes away before our eyes.

His clothes are hanging about him, his face is haggard, and he has cancelled most of his public engagements for the next three months. Sometimes, when he tries to smile through his cracked and emaciated lips, one or other of his ears falls off.

October 17, 1984

TO THE Wembley Conference Centre where 10,000 jobs are being offered at a huge jobs fair by firms which had been unable to fill them through the local Jobs Centres.

It seems a forlorn hope. As I never tire of explaining, the English don't really like working and are not much good at it anyway.

The saddest of all the stalls is the one offering jobs in the Roman Catholic priesthood. One feature of this job is that successful applicants will not be able to marry or have anything to do with sex, but most people nowadays reckon that an advantage.

The snag is that they will have to go around smiling and looking joyful, clapping their hands and telling everyone that Jesus loves them. The money's not much good, either.

November 9, 1984

> "Lord, a healthy sexual relationship is so important in marriage that we want to thank You for ours. . . Please help us not to forget that the sign of our Sacrament, the sexual expression of our love, makes You present in our homes."

Thus the new Roman Catholic prayer-book *The Treasury of the Holy Spirit* compiled by Monsignor Michael Buckley (Hodder & Stoughton £9.95) in the section devoted to Prayers for a Good Sex Life. It has introductions by Cardinal Basil Vass, as well as by the Roman Catholic Archbishops of Edinburgh and Armagh, by "Killer" Runcie and, to his eternal shame, by the Bishop of London.

In the week this ludicrous document appeared, Pope Ringo made a passionate plea for sexual abstinence in marriage. Speaking in St Peter's Basilica, he said it was the only way of freeing oneself from inner tensions:

"Not only is continence possible and morally correct, it also corresponds to the personal dignity of the couple as parents and to the truth of the conjugal act."

It seems to me that the Catholic Church in England, as it wheezily tries to catch up with the sex-obsessed sixties, is set on a break-away course from the zoom-ahead Pope.

The latest 1960s idea in Somerset is that as sexual intercourse is a Sacrament it should be joined by the whole Congregation rather than seen as a private act, as if there was something dirty about it.

Whenever a couple in the Parish feels the urge coming upon them, they go to church and ring a bell. Then they buckle down on the High Altar; priest and people dance around the altar, clapping their hands and making joyful noises.

November 14, 1984

THE GLC GAYS and Lesbians Committee has sensibly suggested that all plaques in future should state whether the person commemorated was homosexual or not.

This does not solve the problem of what to do about distinguished persons who may or may not have been that way inclined: Shakespeare, Tennyson, Cardinal Spellman, Cecil Beaton, Noël Coward and Lord Mountbatten of Burma, the much-loved and deeply missed Soviet undercover agent, to name but a few.

And what about those like Mr Jeremy Thorpe, the former Liberal statesman, who had homosexual inclinations in his early thirties but later resolutely put all such temptations aside for the delights of the female sex?

I thank God I am not the sort of person who has to make decisions about these things.

November 30, 1984

LYING AWAKE in the small hours, I thought that if one could breed bald hedgehogs successfully they might solve the whole world's nutritional problem.

A main problem with the hedgehog, as everyone knows, is its prickles. I ate one once, as a boy Scout, by baking it in clay, which took the prickles with it when removed. But it was still rather messy, and such culinary refinements are hopelessly beyond the scope of the modern British housewife, let alone the poor African peasant.

I think we should all worry about the world's food problems. The trouble with pigs and beef cattle is that they are too big. Somebody has to cut them up, which always involves middlemen, health inspectors and government intervention. I once tried breeding four-legged chickens (also bald) since most people seem to prefer the legs, and nobody likes plucking them, but it came to nothing.

A hedgehog, on the other hand, is just the right size for an individual meal. If one could train them to prepare themselves on the baking tin, surrounded by onions and potatoes, all our problems might be solved and our womenfolk could go out into the world to realise their potentials, discover themselves etc.

At daybreak, I see that it probably wouldn't work. We would be left with a bald hedgehog mountain in Europe, while the Third World continued to starve. But I suppose it might provide employment in Merseyside, sticking the prickles back on them.

December 1, 1984

THE MOST interesting thing in today's *Daily Mirror* is the naked teenage girl on page 5. It is not just that only the most cursory attempt has been made to air-brush her pubic hair.

Her story is that she was a typical teenager standing in the dole queue in Bristol when she was spotted by a "printing firm's boss" and persuaded to pose for his com-

pany's 1985 calendar. Now she has a career in nude modelling.

She looks rather a fright, it is true. But it is a wonderful idea of Captain Maxwell's to get these teenage girls out of the dole queues and into nude modelling or similar occupations. Perhaps next time Jon Pilger goes north to describe the mass starvation etc he could bring back a coachload of them. He might make the point that they are naked because they cannot afford any clothes in Thatcher's Britain.

December 9, 1984

ON THE Lord's Day, our thoughts naturally turn to Prince Andrew's sex life. I would never have believed he was having it off with fun-loving West End club hostess Vicki Macdonald if Prince Andrew had not denied it so vehemently.[1]

One believes nothing one reads in the Sunday newspapers, of course, but one disbelieves Royal denials even more. Now I suppose the two are very much in love, and will be announcing their engagement soon.

At least it means that no delicate, blushing daughter of the old English nobility will have to sacrifice herself to this young man's unpleasant desires. At Foyle's Literary Luncheon for Arthur Marshall in the Dorchester last week I sat next to Russell Harty, who kept telling me he wanted to marry Princess Margaret. I advised him against it.

December 15, 1984

MY ENEMIES are putting it around that I have sent death threats through the post to Mrs Mollie Jenkins, wife of the controversial Bishop of Durham.

Needless to say, there is no truth in these accusations. I may have made the occasional suggestive telephone call to Rosalind Runcie, fun-loving wife of the Archbishop of Canterbury, but that is the full extent of my crimes in this field.

In the interests of truth, I must also admit that Mrs Runcie has never given me the slightest encouragement, even when her husband was away for long periods in his mysterious exploration of the Dark Continent. But I live in hope.

December 25, 1984

OFTEN THE gloomiest day of the year for fathers of large families, this Christmas is made much happier by two very nice oranges from Israel which I am able to produce as a surprise.[2]

1 It later transpired that the young lady had never met Prince Andrew, but was trying to publicise her nightclub.

2 Lord Gnome presented his employees with two oranges each to celebrate W.H. Smith's decision to sell *Private Eye* after 23 years.

To cheer ourselves up we try to think of all the people who are worse off than ourselves: those who will be killed or atrociously hurt on the roads, as Mrs Lynda Chalker keeps reminding us; the suffering masses in the north of England, many of whom have no shoes; all the foxes which have been killed, sometimes most unhygienically, to make Christmas fun-furs; the turkeys who will never see another dawn, or hear the little birds sing.

Saddest of all, we think of poor Taki Theodoracopoulos clanking his chains among all the Negroes and Yorkshiremen in Pentonville Prison.

With all the dreadful things happening around us, it is no wonder that so many families have decided to stay home this Christmas and sniff glue.

1985

As 1985 dawns, Mrs Thatcher seems to be in serious trouble. Oxford dons, infuriated by her heartless treatment of Mr Peregrine Worsthorne, the Conservative philosopher, vote to refuse her the honorary degree at Oxford University which she covets more than any other honour.

Mr James Cameron, the venerable left-wing thinker, dies, and so does K. Chernenko, the Soviet leader – possibly of AIDS, the new killer disease affecting many people at this time. The great debate on Lord Mountbatten's sexual proclivities continues, with important new evidence adduced.

A great boom in jobs is revealed, with Honours Degrees graduates finding useful employment as chalet maids, bus conductors and washers-up in many of the better hotels. Youth Unemployment is exposed as a myth.

Saddest news is the retirement of Mr Nigel Dempster, often described as the Greatest Living Englishman, from direction of *Private Eye*. Fears are expressed for the health of Lord Gnome. All Waugh's novels are republished by a Middle Eastern philanthropist. He meets Miss Selina Scott, but we leave him with his insane ambition to meet the Princess of Wales unrealized.

January 5, 1985

"IF SOMEONE rings me up and calls me Booker, I know it is one of the half-dozen people I call my real friends," writes Christopher Booker in the *Mail*, complaining about the premature use of Christian names among young people.

Booker, I should explain, is the man who single-handedly invented and endowed the notorious Booker Prize for second-rate pseudish novels. It is his money which keeps the whole rotten show on the road, ensuring that the English novel, once the pride of our culture, remains in a permanent state of thraldom to a small group of London voluptuaries, literary lesbians and poodle-fakers.

January 6, 1985

THERE ARE startling similarities, as Kenneth Rose has pointed out in the *Sunday Telegraph*, between Noël Coward's kiss and Lord Gowrie's handshake. As Official handshaker for the government, this swarthy nobleman first shook hands with President Pompidou, who promptly died.

Then he pressed flesh with Prime Minister Bhutto of Pakistan, who was hanged immediately after; President Nixon who resigned in disgrace; the King of Afghanistan, who lost his throne on the plane back; and the Shah of Persia who was immediately deposed by born-again Muslims and died of mortification soon after in Egypt.

January 7, 1985

EVERY DAY I open the new 200-year-old tit'n'bum *Times* in a state of dread in case Murdoch has bought an album of private photographs stolen from my Scottish home three weeks ago. One picture shows the Queen dancing the hokey-Cokey in a paper hat; another shows Princess Margaret trying to demonstrate a Cossack dance – and there is even one of me looking rather silly with a whistle.

None is very shocking, but I feel the Royal Family may take it hard in its present delicate state.

Worst of all, letters from old age pensioners to the *Daily Mirror* about a power struggle between the Princess of Wales and Princess Anne, Dame Anne Phillips, suggest the country may be on the brink of another War of the Roses. For my own part, I am quite happy to fight and die under the banner of the Princess of Wales. I think she is lovely, even if I make her nervous.

January 9, 1985

IF MI5 REALLY murdered Miss Hilda Murrell, the 78-year-old Shropshire rose-growing spinster, as Tam Dalyell MP claims, I can only suppose that she must have had an affair with Noël Coward, the bisexual entertainer.

A mysterious and distasteful pattern begins to emerge in these MI5 killings. First they murdered the late Duke of Kent by sabotaging his aeroplane in 1942 when he

was in the middle of a passionate affair with Coward. Their only motive appears to have been to make Coward cry, which he did.

Then they murdered General Sikorski, the Polish leader, by the same means in 1943, although his acquaintance with Coward was extremely slight, if it existed at all. Next came Lord Mountbatten, the much-loved Soviet agent, whose affair with Coward had been over for a quarter of a century – in fact Coward had died in the meantime. But MI5 blew him up just the same.

Now poor Miss Hilda Murrell pays the penalty for some youthful indiscretion, probably 50 years old, which she might never even have committed. Coward's kiss seems to have been the kiss of death for too many people for it to be treated as coincidence.

January 10, 1985

EVERY NEWSPAPER is full of adulatory drivel about this hard-faced adventuress, the Czech-born daughter of an Australian hairdresser whose first marriage to poor old Tom Troubridge had all his friends shaking their heads.

When she married the goofy, bearded Freemason Prince Michael of Kent, whom nobody had ever heard of until that moment, we all breathed a sigh of relief. At least she would be removed from circulation and spare old Tom any further embarrassment, we thought.

Princess Michael greets her fortieth birthday with the sort of statement which many women are making nowadays:

"I'm beginning to feel grown-up. I can begin to do what I think is right for me, what is right for my own and I don't terribly care any more about asking anyone's opinion. . . I must be allowed to develop that artistic side of me that is bursting to get out. It may not be good but it has got to be allowed to happen."

In my experience, the best treatment for this sort of condition is to lock the sufferer in a cupboard until all those sides which are bursting to get out have done so. But I doubt whether her goofy, bearded husband is up to it. People often sneer at Freemasonry, but I feel it has a useful function in allowing husbands to get away from their wives from time to time. Husbands who are really keen on getting away from their wives can sometimes rise very high indeed in the Order.

January 11, 1985

TO RANGOON where the temperature is 94 degrees in the shade. There is no wine to be bought in the entire Socialist Republic of Burma, so for the first time in nearly twenty years I find myself drinking water.

It is a strangely unnerving experience. What put me off it in the first place was when I discovered the human body is composed of 98% water. This means you have only to add 2% – perhaps a few tablespoonfuls – of Hattersley Essence (for

instance) to a bathful of water and out will climb the repulsive, farting Opposition Spokesman on Economic Affairs, ready to make a conceited speech describing himself as a Dream Ticket.

A similarly minute quantity of some other extract and you have Mrs Thatcher or Mrs Shirley Williams; add a touch of black treacle or soot to the mixture and you have Lord Gowrie. The only thing these people have in common is that they are all made of water. Nothing will convince me it is a healthy substance to drink.

February 1, 1985

DOWN TO Oxford to lobby for the election of Mrs Thatcher to an honorary degree.

All the dons flatly refuse to vote for Mrs Thatcher. They are still seething with fury and disgust at her refusal to honour Sir Peregrine Worsthorne. Of course, Oxford has always been the home of lost causes. New evidence suggests that Mrs Thatcher may have been quite right to leave this wise and good man well alone. His reward will be in the hereafter.

February 4, 1985

"THREE CHEERS because Biggles is back," trills lovely, broad-bottomed Glenda Lee-Potter. "Squadron Leader James Bigglesworth DSO DFC is being reincarnated on our screens to enchant small boys," she shrieks.

Poor Glenda is possibly not *au fait* with the latest research in the English Literature Department of Strathclyde University. It seems to prove conclusively that Biggles was not only an alcoholic but also a raving pooftah.

A few years ago one might not have objected to the idea of this drunken Nancy boy being put on television to tempt small boys. If they wanted to be buggered, that was their own affair. It was still a free country.

But since the arrival of the disease called AIDS, which destroys the body's natural immunities, it seems rather irresponsible to encourage small boys to take up a hobby of this sort. They might infect the rest of us by bleeding over our toes or peeing on our mosquito bites. I think I had better write to the Chairman of the IBA pointing out the dangers.

February 8, 1985

SAD TO HEAR of the death of James Cameron, doyen of left-wing journalists. Lunchtime O'Boccaccio's Decameron, as he was affectionately known to generations of hacks in the Street of Shame, was one of the journalists sent by Lord Beaverbrook to be exposed to the British nuclear tests at Bikini Atoll in 1946.

Some of them lost all their hair, others went mad and took to the bush, living the life of aborigines and drinking brake fluid. On Jimmy it had an entirely different effect: from that moment he *never changed his opinions*. Instead he stuck to his boyish left-

wing enthusiasms until the day he died, and thus became the Street's only Man of Principle.

The secret of survival in journalism is to think of one thing to say and go on saying it. Jimmy was a great man.

March 1, 1985

PHILIP ZIEGLER, Lord Mountbatten's new biographer, casts serious doubts on claims that the old Soviet agent was ever a pooftah, saying he has seen no proof of this. Nor have I. Mountbatten never made indecent approaches to me, and I never saw him in a compromising situation with anyone else.

Evidence in support is entirely inferential. As the late Senator Dodds of Connecticut used to say about Communists: "If it looks like a duck, walks like a duck, quacks like a duck and consorts with other ducks, I say sure as hell it is a duck."

If Mountbatten were not that way inclined, then I feel the burden is on Mr Ziegler to explain exactly how Mr Chernenko got AIDS. I rest my case.

March 6, 1985

WHAT DO graduates do? An exciting new survey from the Association of Graduate Careers Advisory Services reveals that graduates in art and design generally become chalet girls, croupiers or bus conductors. Those who have graduated in English generally prefer pop group management.

Job opportunities are now better for graduates than at any time in the last four years. There are vacancies for people with a good Honours degree in Classics or Theology washing up in some of our most prestigious hotels. Geography students are needed to make beds or work as au pairs to Arab families; strip clubs are crying out for anyone with a diploma in Environmental Studies, while even those with a degree in Government Statistics or Peace Studies can sometimes find seasonal employment cleaning lavatories.

Youth unemployment is one of the Big Lies being put around by the media. The truth is that the new race of young Britons are so stupid, so boring and so unattractive in their manners that we would all much sooner they stayed in bed all day until it is time for *Dynasty*.

March 18, 1985

A FURIOUS stranger on the telephone demands to know what was my proof that Mr. K. Chernenko has AIDS. I reply that I have no proof, but it seems a reasonable assumption from his close association with the late Lord Mountbatten of Burma, the much-loved sailor. The stranger starts quoting from what has now gone down in history as Parkinson's Law:[1] *Where there is no proof of sexual activity, none has occurred* – when my other telephone rings with the news that K. Chernenko is dead. I rest my case.

March 25, 1985

VERY SAD news at Gnome House. It seems that my old and dear friend, Sir Nigel Dempster, has decided to retire from further association with *Private Eye* after a disagreement with the Proprietor.

Man and boy, Dempster and I have known each other for many years and shared countless adventures which neither of us will reveal until the other is dead. Living, we could hang each other on any day of the week. I do not hesitate to judge that Dempster is in the right over this unfortunate squabble, and Lord Gnome is in the wrong.

It seems that "Lord Gnome" was displeased with an interview which Dempster granted to a hack from the *Sunday Times* and doubted the truth of some of the remarks attributed to Dempster. What Gnome does not realise, being a man of comparatively humble origins, is that any member of the English upper classes who is interviewed by the newspapers – and especially by the *Sunday Times* – feels honour bound to tell them nothing but whoppers.

The rationale behind this is that by the time the hacks have misunderstood and

1 Cecil Parkinson was suing *Private Eye* over allegations of sexual impropriety.

misquoted your remarks, taken them out of context and turned them upside-down in the process of sub-editing, they might just about have arrived at the Truth.

On this occasion the system does not appear to have worked. But that was no reason for Gnome to denounce Lord Dempster as a supplier of scurrilous gossip to his own tatty organ. It is a very serious charge to make and one of which my friend is entirely innocent, as I should know. In fact it was I who invented the story about Parkinson and I who advised *Private Eye* not to use it. Come back, Nigel.

March 26, 1985

AFTER HER appearance with Terri Wogan everybody now agrees that Princess Anne is a Super Star: "She looked relaxed, happy, and glamorous," drools Sandra Barwick in the *Daily Mail*. "The Princess revealed an engaging sense of humour and a razor-sharp wit."

Must I then admit defeat and retire to Somerset gnashing my teeth? I think there is still some hope of rallying the forces of the anti-Anneites under the banner of the Princess of Wales. This lovely lady, who has become more famous and more loved than Terri Wogan himself since her brilliant appearance on *Spitting Image*, often denies that she is at loggerheads with her sister-in-law. "It has all been got up by the Press," she told Peter Hillmore of the *Observer*.

I feel the Press could do a little better than this. Nobody is interested in conservatives and socialists any more and even the class war has lost its edge now that the lower or "working" class is so helplessly outnumbered. I think the country should divide into those who support Princess Anne and those who support the Princess of Wales. Then we can fight a civil war on that basis.

April 1, 1985

I HAVE never been tempted to mutilate a corpse and can't see the fun in it, but it seems a fairly harmless pastime for those who enjoy it. The Welsh Presbyterian Minister who took it up as a hobby has been sent to prison for four years amid a chorus of execration from the Press.

This seems most unfair to the Rev. Emyr Owen. His practices did not hurt anyone. In any case, what he did was less radical and considerably less disgusting than a standard post-mortem examination which may be ordered on any corpse by any doctor, whether relatives want it or not.

What horrifies people is that Rev. Owen should enjoy doing it, but other people's pleasures are usually pretty disgusting: pot noodles, Blue Peter, Frankie Goes To Hollywood. I would send them all to prison, if there was room.

But there isn't. The only reason Reverend Owen has been sent to prison is that people imagine his tastes are peculiar to himself. I suspect they are much more widespread than we realise. In any case there simply isn't room in our prisons for people whose only crime is to have odd habits.

April 3, 1985

MY PAPERBACK publisher who mysteriously calls himself Robin Clark (his real name is Rebecca Fraser) has decided to reissue five novels I wrote in my youth. They have names like *Buttercups and Daisies*, *Hypodermic Syringa* and *Cowslips Over The Moon*.[1] In order to publicise them I summon a hack from the *Grauniad* and ply him with champagne in my penthouse suite at Gnome House.

Unfortunately, he becomes overexcited by this treatment. In a confused account of his experiences, he omits to mention the name of the publisher (Robin Clark) or the books (*Buttercups and Daisies* etc). I have decided to ask Naim Attallah, the Christian philanthropist who owns Robin Clark, Rebecca Fraser, Harrods stores etc if he will give a party to celebrate the books.

April 4, 1985

NAIM HAS many talents – he can sing all the arias from Verdi's *Ernani* while accompanying himself on the french horn, he is a yachtsman, no mean shot, and very good

1 They are: *The Foxglove Saga*, *Path of Dalliance*, *Who Are the Violets Now?*, *Consider the Lilies*, *Bed of Flowers*.

at balancing lumps of sugar on his nose. But above all, he is the greatest party giver of our time.

Among the 500 guests who flock to the Arts Club in Dover Street are about 100 of the most beautiful young women in England, most of them called Emma or Sophia. They are not only beautiful to look at but shapely, well-mannered, cheerful, intelligent, and juicy. Some of them even wear black stockings.

I find myself gasping that so many delicious creatures should have emerged from the last decade of comprehensive education, fluoride in the water and watching filth like Roy Hattersley on television. Then it occurs to me that these lovely ladies are all that is left in England.

Consider the less lovely ladies who go to parties given by Lord Weidenfeld, the plain women who seem to be creeping into *Spectator* parties, the frankly hideous old slags to be seen at *New Statesman* dos. Then reflect on all the embittered females who never get asked to any parties at all. The country is a dung-heap. This is just the glorious foliage on top of it.

April 5, 1985

TO THE BBC's Lime Grove studio for a Breakfast TV programme to publicise my books, where I meet the golden Selina Scott, lovelier and sweeter than ever at 6 o'clock in the morning.

As we nibble our haddock kedgeree and sip some rather good champagne, Selina tells me she has always been a tremendous fan and has read all my novels, some of which first appeared before she was born. They are as true to life today as they ever were, she swears.

I swoon with happiness. Now the only ambition I have left in the world is to meet the Princess of Wales. I'm afraid her crazy warbling husband will never introduce us at this late stage. I think I will dress in an orange sheet and try to smuggle myself into her home disguised as a Buddhist monk.

April 15, 1985

THE BEST place to spend Easter is in the Philippines where people take the liturgy of the Passion much more seriously than they do in England. This year about 10 Filipinos have decided to celebrate the traditional Bank Holiday weekend by being crucified before cheering crowds.

Normally one would not approve of such practices, but these dear little Filipinos enjoy it all so much that the heart quite melts. It is a more impressive way of showing religious fervour than the English habit of jumping up and down and saying "Jesus loves me!"

This year I must spend Easter in the soggy English countryside where the Passion and Resurrection of Our Lord are celebrated by an occasional, desultory traffic jam. The newspapers try to whip up enthusiasm over the fate of some murdered schoolboys, but I can't be excited by it.

Two months ago – on February 24 to be exact – the *Mail on Sunday* carried a very interesting story about a 17-year-old cookery student called Jacqueline Fitzsimons who was walking down the corridor of her Technical College in Widnes, Cheshire one day, talking to some friends, when she suddenly burst into flames for no apparent reason. She died soon afterwards.

A terrible and tragic story, we must all agree, but also very interesting. Yet no other national newspaper followed it up, and the whole event remains a mystery. Poor Jacqueline should be seen as a martyr to English politeness. On the rare occasions when someone in England does something really interesting, nobody pays any attention.

April 16, 1985

TO COWCROSS Street, near Smithfield Market, where lovely, high-spirited Ms Valerie Wise, chairman of the GLC's Wimmin's Committee, opens a new £10 million Lesbian and Gay Centre. I do not understand why she supposes that lesbian women and male homosexualists get on particularly well together, or wish to belong to the same club. Is it not a trifle heterosexist to lump them together in this way? Why, for that matter does she not open the Centre to necrophiliacs and animal sodomists? Can it be she feels that these unfortunates are somehow not *normal*?

Perhaps a grain of common sense tells her that if the Centre is open to animal sodomists, people will want to bring their seal pups along.

April 28, 1985

SOME WEEKS ago Lord Gnome told me that if I honestly thought I was going to be made an earl before I died, then he would have to decide I had gone mad. I do not agree. I am extremely rich and live in a huge house. Most of my relations are earls. And I have never been to prison. But perhaps one has to work for charities, too.

This evening I go to judge the Conversationalist of the Year at something called a Chatathon in Glaziers Hall, London. It is sponsored by Taylors Port in aid of Spina Bifida and Hydrocephalus, two charitable diseases. First prize, which I award to a pleasant middle-aged author called William Hall, is an appearance on the Terri Wogan Show.

I never knew the guests on Wogan were chosen in this way. Perhaps Terri hopes to be made an earl too. Nobody present seems to be suffering from either of these two terrible diseases. I suppose they all hope to be made earls eventually.

If so they are mad. Half of them do not even begin to qualify, although I suppose there is no harm in their being encouraged to live in hope. One day people will wake up to the fact that earldoms are nowadays given only to politicians and mass-murderers. Then all hell will break loose.

April 30, 1985

OF COURSE I have known all along about Princess Michael of Kent's parentage,[1] just as everyone at the Palace knew. We also knew that if we let it out, the great soft-hearted British public would make a heroine of this Australian adventuress with her disagreeable habit of squashing cats every time she sits down.

This is exactly what has happened. Wherever she goes she is cheered to the echo, children present her with flowers and old age pensioners offer her their cats to sit on. It is a most unpleasant development. I have decided not to go to Badminton this year where she will be stealing the show. Instead I will go to Rome and see if by disguising myself as a Priest, I can put myself in the way of hearing the Prince of Wales's Confession.

1 It had just been revealed that the Princess's father had been a member of Hitler's SS.

May 1, 1985

THE BEST magazine in Italy – its equivalent of *Private Eye* for fearless investigations etc – is called *2000*. It has discovered that the Prince of Wales has arranged for his bedrooms to be sound-proofed during his stay in Italy:

"Lady Di has decided – I want from Charles a baby made in Italy," it announces, revealing that the Princess has taken some black shortie nighties with her. It hazards that the Prince will not make much use of the two pairs of silk pyjamas he has packed. "Charles loves to sleep naked," the Princess is alleged to have remarked. Sound-proofing has been ordered, it says, "To avoid even the most delicate whimper being heard by indiscreet ears."

The truth, I'm afraid, is somewhat different. The Prince of Wales's new passion is for singing. He has to practise every night and is understandably embarrassed that anyone may overhear his terrible warblings. What the Princess of Wales thinks about all this is not known. I am not in her confidence.